HISTORY OF THE FRASCH SULPHUR INDUSTRY
PRODUCTION FROM MINES BY COMPANIES
IN CHRONOLOGICAL ORDER
1895 THRU 1957

MILLIONS OF LONG TONS (To nearest 1,000)

Starting Order & Map Ref. No.	DOME	Co.	Began / End	Tons
1	SULPHUR ⌖	(U)	12-28-95 / 12-23-24	9,400,000
2	BRYAN MOUND ⌖	(F)	11-12-12 / 9-30-35	5,001,000
3	GULF (BIG HILL) ⌖	(TG)	3-19-19 / 8-10-36	12,346,000
4	HOSKINS ⌖	(F)	3- 3-23 / 5-26-55	10,865,000
5	BIG CREEK ⌖	(U)	3- 6-25 / 2-24-26	2,000
6	PALANGANA ⌖	(D)	10-27-28 / 3-10-35	238,000
7	BOLING ⌖	(U)	11-14-28 / 8-30-29	8,000
	BOLING ●	(TG)	3-20-29	49,993,000
	BOLING ⌖	(D)	3-23-35 / 4-25-40	571,000
	BOLING ⌖	(BW)	6- 2-35 / 12- -35	2,000
8	LONG POINT ●	(TG)	3-19-30	1,600,000
	LONG POINT ●	(JL)	6- 7-46	1,198,000
9	LAKE PEIGNEUR ⌖	(JL)	10-20-32 / 2- -36	431,000
10	GRANDE ECAILLE ●	(F)	12- 8-33	19,791,000
11	CLEMENS ●	(JL)	5- 3-37	1,988,000
	CLEMENS ⌖	(TG)	5- 3-37 / 4-18-49	746,000
12	ORCHARD ●	(D)	1-29-38	3,735,000
13	MOSS BLUFF ●	(TG)	6-24-48	2,604,000
14	STARKS ●	(JL)	6-15-51	586,000
15	SPINDLETOP ●	(TG)	5-12-52	2,111,000
16	BAY STE. ELAINE ●	(F)	11-19-52	817,000
17	DAMON MOUND ⌖	(Std)	11-11-53 / 4-20-57	140,000
18	GARDEN ISLAND BAY ●	(F)	11-19-53	2,318,000
19	NASH ⌖	(F)	2- 5-54 / 11-21-56	149,000
20	CHACAHOULA ●	(F)	2-25-55	291,000
21	SAN CRISTOBAL ⌖	(MG)	3- -54 / 5- -57	152,000
22	JALTIPAN ●	(PA)	9-26-54	1,767,000
23	AMEZQUITE ●	(G)	5- -56	275,000
24	NOPALAPA ●	(TG)	2- 8-57	90,000

TOTAL FRASCH SULPHUR UP TO JANUARY 1, 1958		
(TG) TEXAS GULF	69,490,000	53.7%
(F) FREEPORT	39,232,000	30.4%
(U) UNION	9,410,000	7.3%
(D) DUVAL	4,544,000	3.5%
(JL) JEFFERSON LAKE	4,203,000	3.3%
(PA) PAN AMERICAN	1,767,000	1.4%
(G) GULF	275,000	0.2%
(MG) MEXICAN GULF	152,000	0.1%
(Std) STANDARD	140,000	0.1%
(BW) BAKER-WILLIAMS	2,000	
	129,215,000	

BRIMSTONE
The Stone That Burns

HERMAN FRASCH: 1851-1914
Inventor of the Hot-water Sulphur-mining Process

BRIMSTONE
The Stone That Burns

The Story of the Frasch Sulphur Industry

by

WILLIAMS HAYNES

D. VAN NOSTRAND COMPANY, INC.
PRINCETON, NEW JERSEY
TORONTO · · · LONDON

NEW YORK

D. VAN NOSTRAND COMPANY, INC.
120 Alexander St., Princeton, New Jersey (*Principal office*)
257 Fourth Avenue, New York 10, New York

D. VAN NOSTRAND COMPANY, LTD.
358, Kensington High Street, London, W.14, England

D. VAN NOSTRAND COMPANY (Canada), LTD.
25 Hollinger Road, Toronto 16, Canada

Published simultaneously in Canada by
D. VAN NOSTRAND COMPANY (Canada), LTD.

Library of Congress Catalogue Card No. 59-13851

This book is based on an earlier work entitled *The Stone That
Burns,* by Williams Haynes, copyright 1942 by D. Van Nostrand
Company, Inc.

PRINTED IN THE UNITED STATES OF AMERICA

To three old friends
Frank G. Breyer
Charles Owen Brown
Charles Raymond Downs

A Note to the Reader—

AT THE CHEMISTS' CLUB in New York, early in December 1955, a friend, just returned from Mexico, told me that second-hand copies of "The Stone That Burns" were selling there for the fabulous price of twenty-five dollars. You recognize, I am sure, that this was a hint that no author could ignore.

A third printing of the first edition had been exhausted and the book had been officially out of print for several years. I must go to the Isthmus of Tehuantepec. During the early Spring of 1956 I made the first of three trips to the Mexican sulphur operations.

In November 1958, after the manuscript of this revised edition had been written, I was in France, partly on vacation and partly hunting down the landmarks of the Du Pont family as background material for a biography of E. I. du Pont. I made a side-trip to the sour gas sulphur recovery plant at Lacq. What I saw there made it plain that I must see the similar developments in Northwestern Canada and also that the two final chapters of this book must be rewritten. The story of the sulphur industry has thus been brought up to date from 1942 until this day when it goes to the publisher.

To hold this book to reasonable length, the early history, as recounted in the original edition, has been condensed. Material on the Sicilian industry and details of the controls and allocations of World War I, as least pertinent today, have been rather drastically cut. At that, this edition contains a third more words than did its predecessor.

You will get more out of this book, I believe, if I direct your attention to two of its features: the illustrations and the Appendix.

Based upon priceless old photographs of the original Frasch operations of the pioneering Union Company, collected by Dr. F. C. Fogarty of Texas Gulf, the pictures have been grouped to depict graphically what might be called the Ancient, the Medieval, and the Modern Eras of the industry. In this way, the illustrations become a vivid, and I believe, a unique pictorial history of the production and distribution of one of our civilization's most essential commodities.

Less glamorous, but extraordinarily valuable, are the facts and figures set forth in the Appendix. This is the work, almost wholly, of the Statistical Departments of the Texas Gulf and Freeport companies. Revised and brought down to the latest available data, these tables represent years of painstaking, expert compilation and critical comparison, based often upon confidential information.

In writing a book of this sort, one incurs a great debt to many collaborators. My gratitude to them is expressed in the "Acknowledgments," but the measure of my indebtedness is pinpointed in the "Notes and References." In conclusion, I can only repeat what I wrote in the earlier Preface, acknowledging with sincere thanks the frank and cordial cooperation I have had from the entire industry.

Stonecrop Farm,   WILLIAMS HAYNES
Stonington, Connecticut.
10 February, 1959

Preface to the First Edition (1942)

"Salt, lime, and sulphur—and
the greatest of these is sulphur."

Thus did James Muspratt, the famous British chemical manufacturer, once summarize the chief raw materials of his business. This yellow brimstone, the stone that burns, was no doubt the very first chemical element found and used by the caveman. Today we use it in some form in all our industries. In some way it enters into all our wares and mechanisms. Sold for less than a cent a pound for the 99.5 per cent grade, sulphur is the cheapest chemical element now available in such purity, and we have ready to hand the largest stockpile—over three million tons—ever amassed of an elemental material. These are important chemical assets.

Here in the United States we consume each year close to two million tons of sulphur; thirty pounds plus for every man, woman, and child; twice as much as we use of copper; three times as much as of rubber; five times as of tobacco; thirty times as of nickel [written in 1942]. Hardly a pound of that vast tonnage is imported. Indeed, we supply most of the rest of the world with most of their sulphur supplies. Like coal and iron and petroleum, sulphur is one of the essential materials of our modern civilization, which we may be thankful is not in the United States a critical material.

Yet most Americans know little about this vital mineral. They know even less about the ingenious American process that melts sulphur a thousand feet underground and pumps it to the surface; a process that broke an ancient, world-wide monopoly quite as important, though less publicized, than Chile's monopoly of nitrates or Japan's of camphor; a proc-

ix

ess that gave us new industries, that is vital to our chemical independence, that has created nearly a billion dollars of new wealth for the American people and brought to our use more than fifty million tons of sulphur which, save for this clever invention, would have been locked, useless, deep in the earth.

Eight years ago [that is, in 1934] I sat one evening in the comfortable guest house at the world's largest sulphur mine. I had just come from the newest sulphur operation in the floating swamps of the Mississippi delta. On the way across to Texas I had nosed about the relics of the exhausted, abandoned, pioneer American sulphur mine in Calcasieu Parish, Louisiana. Late into the night I sat there listening eagerly while three brimstone veterans talked of the old Union, of the Brazos Syndicate, of the Mound Company; of "shoestrings" and "blow-outs," of hurricanes that piled derricks and piping into heaps like jackstraws. But most of their talk was of men: of Frasch, the clever, persistent inventor; of the forceful Swenson; the persuasive Pemberton; the quiet-spoken Seeley Mudd; of smart traders in mineral rights, of rugged financiers who backed sulphur against long odds; of dogged, resourceful engineers who built plants in a sea of sticky gumbo miles from town or railway. And as I listened, fascinated, I resolved someday to write that thrilling story of struggle and achievement, the story of the American sulphur industry.

It is a capital story; and if you do not find it highly interesting I have missed my chance, for I have had exceptional opportunities to get its facts and figures first-hand. For more than two decades I have lived daily in contact with the chemical industry. I have visited all but two of the American sulphur operations on the Gulf Coast. I have known many of the sulphur pioneers and they have talked with me freely and frankly. Every sulphur-mining company, big and little, has put its records at my disposal and assisted me in every possible way to make this story complete and accurate. In thus acknowledging this assistance (which I do most grate-fully), I do not want to bolster the following pages with any false claims of official authenticity nor to bestow on them, even by implication, the endorsement of the men who have helped me with information. In my endeavor to write a full, true, carefully documented history, I received the sin-cere and cordial co-operation of the entire industry, a fact that seems to me significant and certainly worthy to be re-corded.

WILLIAMS HAYNES

Stonecrop Farm,
Stonington, Connecticut.
16 March, 1942.

Acknowledgments

MY GREAT INDEBTEDNESS is to the men of the Frasch sulphur industry: from top executives to plant operatives. In the most frank and friendly fashion, they have helped me in writing this book. Every sulphur company, large and small, American and Mexican, has cooperated cordially, making it possible for me to visit their mining operations and giving me access to their records.

Relying heavily, as I have done in both editions, upon the first-hand testimony of the men who have made—and are today making—the history of this distinctively American industry, there are so many individuals to whom I am indebted that the long catalog of their names would be but a summary, perfunctory expression of my gratitude. My debt to each is specifically recognized in the references. To make the record clearer, their names are indexed.

However, in each company a few good friends have earned, as mentor or guide far beyond the line of duty, thanks that cannot be expressed in a footnote: C. F. Fogarty, Emile Vanderstucken, W. W. Duecker, E. Orrin Mason, and Elgin D. Bell of Texas Gulf; John C. Carrington, Peter Lowry, Robert H. Johnson, and Marshall B. Sheldon of Freeport; Charles J. Ferry, H. W. Manley, and Mark J. Roy of Jefferson Lake, George Zoffman and X. T. Stoddard of Duval; Harry C. Webb, Harold Jaquet, and Stephen M. Richards of Pan American; Stuart C. Dorman, Gerard R. Marlow, and V. V. Jacomini of Gulf Sulphur; J. T. Claiborne, William P. Barnard, and Paul Nachtman of the now-suspended Mexican Gulf Sulphur. In the Preface I called attention to the value of the Appendix, and here I have every reason to be most grateful to L. B. Gittinger of Freeport and E. Wick

Eddy of Texas Gulf and their associates in the Statistical Departments.

Outside of the industry I want especially to thank two distinguished geologists, J. H. Pollard and Paul Weaver; in Mexico, the Brady brothers, General Alfredo Breceda, Joseph Sperling, R. B. Roberson, José Camillo of Mining Chamber of Commerce, and David Segura of the Fomento Minera; in France, General André Blanchard, Claude Bienvenu, and Jean Roubaud; in Canada, A. D. Insley, in charge of the Oil & Gas Department of the Royal Bank of Canada and Carl O. Nickle, editor of the *Daily Oil Bulletin*. General G. E. Wildman-Lushington and John M. Lancaster of the British Sulphur Corporation, whose *Quarterly Bulletin* is a uniquely valuable periodical, have been cordial and important collaborators.

Acknowledgments are due also to the Editors of *The Reader's Digest, Science,* and *Chemical Week* in whose pages portions of this book have previously appeared.

WILLIAMS HAYNES

Contents

List of Illustrations

Between pages 204 and 205.

Offshore sulphur: construction of the mile-long, $30,000,000 Grand Isle plant.

Mexican sulphur—the Brady brothers' historic rig and Pan American's Jáltipan plant, leading Mexican producer.

Frasch plants in Mexico—Texas Gulf at Nopalapa and Gulf Sulphur Corp. at Salinas.

Sulphur in France, new and old—housing development for employees of new plants using Lacq sulphur and the historic refinery built by Frasch at Marseilles.

Recovered sulphur; the sour gas plants at Lacq in France and Poza Rico in Mexico.

Sulphur from H_2S—plants of Jefferson Lake Petrochemicals in British Columbia and of Texas Gulf at Worland, Wyo.

Employees homes on Main St. Sulphur Mine, La. in the Gay Nineties and at Port Sulphur, La., Freeport's townsite built over a swamp.

The search goes on for more domes in the cedar swamps and offshore.

Maps, Charts and Diagrams

1

Prelude to a New Era

AT DAYBREAK on April Fool's Day, 1944, a dozen wiry Mexicans, ankle deep in the muddy banks of the Coachapan River, were unloading an oil-drilling rig. Straining and sweating they inched the top-heavy machine over makeshift skids from a barge to the dry land.

Beyond them four others had begun hacking a road through the jungle of the Isthmus of Tehuantepec. They were reopening a forsaken path from their village of San Cristóbal to a foot-length of iron pipe standing hidden in a snarl of vines and creepers.

Led by their headman, Julio Blanco, and an American geologist, Ashton Brady, they were a band of treasure hunters, guided by an old map and cryptic directions that read:

"Sandstone, encountered salt water, 167 M . . . Shale and sand, 213 M . . . Limestone with sulphur, 224 M."

These treasure hunters were on the trail of Cortéz. In nearby Tabasco he had won his first battle on Mexican soil, and the most valuable of the spoils of this victory had been his beautiful Indian slave girl. Marina Malinche became his mistress and interpreter, strategist and diplomat. She was born at Jáltipan, scarcely 20 miles away, and is buried there under a great mound, so the Indians devoutly believe, in a golden crown and silver slippers.[1] However, the Brady party was not seeking yellow Aztec gold but a yellow mineral, more precious to us today than all the wealth of Montezuma —sulphur.

Without sulphur there could be no modern industries, no jobs, not even enough bread and beef to feed us. For sulphur is the key ingredient in making sulphuric acid, the King of Chemicals that enters somewhere into the manufacture of every article we touch from cotton diapers to bronze caskets.

If Ashton Brady could find sulphur on the doorstep of Mexico, next door to industry-awakening South America, he and his two brothers would uncover new riches beyond the dreams of Cortéz—a conquest, not of Mexico, but for the Mexican people. The Brady brothers, Lawrence, William, and Ashton, were playing for high stakes against long odds. Their treasure hunt was to prove once more that correct timing is as important in launching a new industry as in boiling an egg.

Back in 1902 sulphur had been found in the Isthmus of Tehuantepec.[2] Here Mexico narrows to a mere 150 miles and twists across the map so that the Gulf of Mexico lies due north of the Pacific Ocean. Across the Isthmus, at the turn of the century, an English company had built the shortest transcontinental railway in the Western Hemisphere. Revamped by Sir Weetman Pearson, a thrusting English enterpriser who was then hip-deep in Mexican engineering projects, the Tehuantepec Railroad did a booming business. Twenty freight trains a day, each way, transshipped cargoes between his big concrete docks at Coatzacoalcos and Salinas Cruz, the Atlantic and Pacific ports. He wanted very badly a cheaper fuel for his locomotives than the coal he imported from Newcastle, England. Pearson, later Lord Cowdray, had paved the streets of Veracruz with tar obtained, it is said, from petroleum collected by Indians along the banks of the Coatzacoalcos River, and along the right of way of the railroad similar seepages had been observed. He had little trouble getting a petroleum concession for the whole Gulf Coast region of the Isthmus from his good friend Porfirio Diaz.[3]

Pearson's company, Cia. Mexicana de Petroleo el Aguila,

S.A. (Mexican Eagle Petroleum Company, Inc.) brought down a drilling rig and an experienced crew from Texas. They began boring into a rise of ground known as Potrerillos, close to the railway, some 20 miles from Coatzacoalcos. They drilled three dry holes. However, signs of oil were obvious, so they moved up to the highest ground. In Well No. 4 at 709 feet their drill ran into limestone whose cracks and crevices were filled with pure sulphur.[4]

The drillers were jubilant. Nobody gave a hoot for the sulphur. But everyone recognized they had struck what they thought was the sulphur-bearing caprock of a saltdome. No doubt, in accord with the immemorial custom of all wildcatters, they celebrated that night with a tequila party of heroic dimensions. Every man of them knew that the year before, 1901, near Beaumont, Texas, the incredible Spindletop oil gusher had been struck along the edges of a saltdome.[5]

From the delta of the Mississippi to the Rio Grande and again in the Isthmus of Tehuantepec, the coastal region lies over a thick bed of salt evaporated out of a vast sea in the hot and humid days of the dinosaurs. During the past 115 million years this salt has been buried under 20,000 feet of sedimentary deposits; clays, sands and shales, and less frequently, gravel and volcanic ash.

Under the static pressure of the weight of these overlying sediments the salt becomes plastic and fluid. This phenomenon has been actually observed in Persia.[6] From the base of salt-cored mountains a veritable salt glacier flows down into the valley.

Throughout the Gulf Coast this dynamic pressure, upthrusting the salt from the mother bed beneath, and the static pressure of the overlying materials have combined to create the distinctive saltdomes of this region.[7] Friction and gravity compress the salt rising through the sediments into the form of gigantic pillars topped with a caprock of limestone. De Golyer has graphically pictured these strange structures as billiard cues of salt tipped with limestone.[8]

Although similar in origin and form, the saltdomes differ greatly in detail. Their tops vary in area from 60 acres to twelve square miles. Some have risen to be actual outcrops; others have been located by geophysical methods at depths

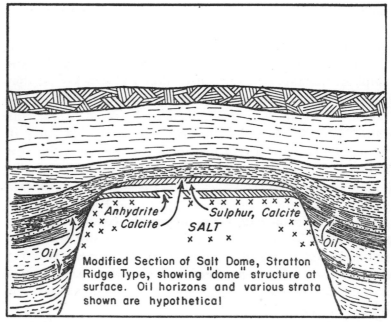

Fig. 1.   Cross section of typical Gulf Coast sulphur dome.

greater than 2000 feet. As they approach the surface the domes have pushed up conspicuous mounds, distinguishing and characteristic landmarks of the flat coastal plains.

Like the domes, their caprocks display great variety. They differ in size and shape, in depth and internal structure. Again the general pattern is well fixed. First comes a layer of limestone, barren of sulphur but usually containing anhydrite (anhydrous calcium sulphate) and gypsum (hydrous calcium sulphate). Beneath this lies a stratum of limestone of varied thickness and continuity whose fissures, cracks, and seams may be—or may not be—impregnated with pure native sulphur. Beneath this sulphur-bearing stratum is a layer of anhydrite covering the salt core of the dome itself. (Figures 1 and 2.)

Similar saltdomes, formed by the same geologic forces, have been found in Colorado and Utah, Germany, Roumania, and Persia. But only those in the coastal plain bordering on the Gulf of Mexico are topped with a limestone caprock containing sulphur.

It was in such a sulphur-bearing saltdome—located in a Louisiana swamp 35 miles north of the Gulf of Mexico, 20 miles east of the Texas line—that Herman Frasch, in De-

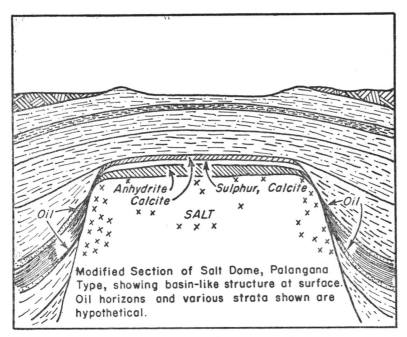

FIG. 2. Cross section of crater type dome.

cember 1894, had conducted a gigantic gambling experiment. To melt the yellow crystals of sulphur out of the limestone, he pumped down superheated water, believing that he could then pump the molten mineral to the surface.

This novel method of mining worked in theory. It did bring to the surface a molasses-colored liquid that solidified in minutes into sparkling bright brimstone, better than 99.5 per cent pure elemental sulphur. In practice, however, the Frasch process kicked and balked like an evil-tempered mule. It took the courageous and persistent Dr. Frasch six years to achieve consistent operation.

Frasch having learned how to bring up sulphur efficiently, his Union Sulphur Company now found that they could not sell it profitably. In hot-water mining, the prime necessity is millions of gallons of water: the prime cost factor, the cost of fuel. In the early Union operations it required more than 4000 gallons of water heated to 320°F. to raise a ton of sulphur. The cheapest fuel, soft coal from Alabama delivered in Louisiana at $4.05 a ton, did not enable the Union Sulphur Company to compete on a cost basis with sulphur from Sicily.[9] Since the days of Imperial Rome, Sicilian sulphur, dug with pick and shovel and crudely refined in kiln-like furnaces, had been the world's chief source of supply.[10] By a lucky coincidence, in 1901, when the kinks had all been ironed out of the Frasch process, the Spindletop gusher was struck only 30 miles away. Cheap fuel oil from nearby Spindletop made the Union Sulphur Company a fabulous financial success.

The ingenious Frasch process has brought up over 130 million tons of sulphur which otherwise would have remained buried underground, useless. It has reduced the cost of this vital chemical element by 40 per cent. Today it produces over 80 per cent of the world's brimstone. It has created a distinctively U. S. industry which for 30 years has been supreme in the international market. (Figure 3.)

The supremacy enjoyed by the four American sulphur companies operating in Texas and Louisiana has not been based upon patents, cartel agreements, or a trust. Sulphur can only be mined by the Frasch process from the caprock of saltdomes, such as are found in the coastal regions of the

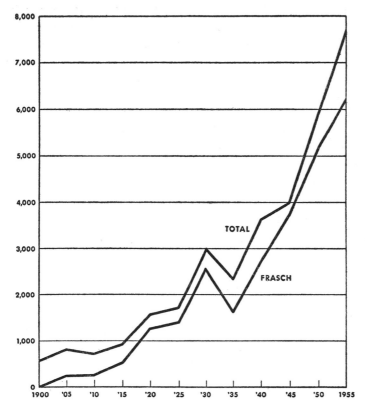

FIG. 3. World production of elemental sulphur (1000 long tons).

Gulf of Mexico. Since the Rio Grande River is, geologically speaking, but a scratch upon the plains of the Gulf Coast, no geologist was surprised when similar deposits were found in the Isthmus of Tehuantepec.

By the same token, no oil man was interested in these sulphur discoveries. Spindletop's fountain of oil, which drove the drilling rig through the derrick and roared 200 feet into the sky, had been stunning proof that these great plugs of salt are sometimes a sign of an adjacent oil pool. The discoverer of Spindletop, Capt. Anthony Lucas, an ex-Austrian naval officer turned American geologist, and a score of others

rushed off to drill into every saltdome from the Mississippi
to the Rio Grande. As Lucas picturesquely said, "I am going
to punch a hole in every pimple on the Gulf Coast."

Guided by the same obvious, tempting analogy, the Eagle's
oil scouts struggled through tropical underbrush to locate
every mound in the Isthmus. Following them, drilling crews
slashed roadways through creepers as brutally barbed as our
bull briers and dragged in the rigs. Seeking petroleum, they
found and roughly outlined seven large domes and spotted
more than 30 others whose caprocks showed more or less
sulphur. The Eagle people were oil men to the core and
naturally they considered sulphur important only as a promise of petroleum. They dreamed of striking a second Spindletop: they never thought of founding a second Union Sulphur
Company. The great gusher was a miraculous reality: at that
time the Frasch process was still a highly dubious gamble.

Thirty years later, in 1937, after the Frasch process was a
proven success, Ing. Frederico Deschamps, in an address[11]
before the Mexican Geological Society, berated the oil companies for having neglected the commercial possibilities in
the Isthmus sulphur deposits:

> In practice and in experience, the exploitation of sulphur
> has proved to be much more remunerative than of oil itself.
> Unexplicably industrialists have overlooked the existence of
> this mineral in the saltdomes and they have not considered
> the benefits, both to the investor as well as for the nation,
> which would result from the exploitation of this mineral.
> Although the saltdomes in the Isthmus of Tehuantepec have
> been carefully examined, I have noticed that all these studies
> previously made have invariably omitted to mention the
> economic importance of the sulphur deposits.

Deschamps was flogging a dead horse. As a matter of plain
fact, in 1937 the Mexican sulphur deposits were of no
"economic importance" whatsoever.

From the domes in Texas and Louisiana more than enough pure sulphur was being pumped to supply the world's demands. Production that year totaled 2,734,545 long tons: shipments were 2,466,512 tons.[12] This production came from four efficient, independent American companies, Texas Gulf, Freeport, Jefferson Lake, and Duval. At their plants loomed large blocks of yellow brimstone, 3.4 million tons of it, a stockpile sufficient for 16 months' supply.[13] What sane industrialist would plunge into the jungles of Tehuantepec in order to invest some $5 million to produce sulphur for sale in a market already oversupplied by established competitors?

Furthermore, at that time, everybody believed that the sulphur reserves of the American Gulf Coast were ample for many, many years. Nobody could foresee a sulphur shortage. Nevertheless, a claim had been staked, fair notice had been posted: Mexico had a store of saltdome sulphur presumably capable of being extracted by the Frasch process. Still nobody was interested in Mexican sulphur. The time was not yet ripe.

A year after Deschamps pointed out the neglected sulphur, Mexico expropriated the oil industry. At the time, the three Brady brothers were wildcatting just south of the border and they thus found themselves with a drilling rig and no place to drill. They liked Mexico and the Mexicans: accordingly they began looking for other opportunities in the Republic. They investigated several mining ventures and even considered custom drilling of water wells, a good, steady business that suited their temperaments about as well as ploughing would a thoroughbred race horse.

When the Brady brothers learned of the saltdome sulphur in the Isthmus, they were captivated by this adventurous prospect. Accordingly, Ashton, the geologist of the trio, went scouting in the library of the Mexican Geological Institute. In old technical and trade journals he found news stories of the Tehuantepec explorations, reports from prospectors, scientific papers by geologists, even maps and geological data.

In the spring of 1944 the Bradys freighted down their drilling rig and barged it up the Coachapan River to San Cristóbal. Nearby, alongside a sulphur-bearing formation, was the "discovery well" of all Mexico. Here, in 1902, the Eagle company had brought in the first commercial oil well. They also developed the nearby pools at Jáltipan, Capacan, Tecuanapa, and Soledad, and in 1908 built the first oil refinery in Mexico at Minatitlán. These Isthmus developments were soon to be eclipsed by the spectacular Portrero del Llano field in the Tampico-Tuxpan region. The Isthmus field had been thoroughly exploited, but when the Eagle drillers had struck sulphur, but no oil, they economically pulled their pipe and moved on. Accordingly, although many logs recorded brimstone, the location of these holes was unmarked.

Ashton Brady found an invaluable guide, Julio Blanco, and the night before April Fool's Day they huddled in the village schoolhouse, a bamboo hut. On the dirt floor, between them, lay a faded map of the San Cristóbal property and copies of some drilling logs. The soft spoken geologist, as lean and bronzed as his Indian companion, was interpreting the oil map's hieroglyphics—"Limestone with sulphur, 224 M."

"See, they hit sulphur at 224 meters. That's about 745 feet down in Well No. 13. Look, Don Julio, Well No. 13 must be right there, about 1000 feet southwest of Well No. 8 where they struck oil. You're sure they capped No. 8? They left the pipe in when it ran dry? Do you know where it is?" and Brady's finger jabbed the map excitedly.

"*Si, si, Senor*"—Of course, Don Julio could go straight to the capped iron pipe that marked the first commercial oil well in all Mexico. Hadn't he been spokesman for the workers when the great President Diaz had come down to the opening? He would guide them. All would be well.

Amid a tangle of vines, Don Julio unhesitatingly found

the capped iron pipe of historic Well No. 8. Brady paced off to a point where he calculated he stood 745 feet above a rich sulphur deposit.

To that fateful spot they must move the cumbersome drilling rig a mile and a half over a fresh-cut jungle pathway. And it was the rainy season.

Their truck's wheels churned down to the hubcaps in the midst of the village. Sopping wet, slathered with mud, they cut trees to pry up the axles, rocked the engine, pulled and shoved. If they inched forward a couple of hundred yards it was a big day. Even with the help of a tractor borrowed from a neighborly lumber camp, it was two weeks before the drill was mounted on location and spudded in.

It thrumped merrily for an hour. Then it suddenly stopped dead. The oil strainer was clogged and a bearing had burned out. That meant a 20-mile trip down the river in a mahogany canoe to Coatzacoalcos for a new part that could not be found in that little city's only machine shop. Time and money were running out.

After a frustrating series of breakdowns and delays they reached the caprock in mid-September—five months for a job they estimated would take six weeks and which under normal conditions could now be done in five days. The showing of sulphur was microscopic. Brady pulled his drill and dragged the rig another 1000 feet through a Slough of Despond to another likely location. Two months later he hit an even more barren spot in the caprock.[14]

Half the friends who had joined the Bradys in financing this sulphur gamble withdrew at the first dry hole: the others now abandoned the venture. However, Ashton Brady was now certain that he knew just where sulphur had been found and his brothers scratched together the money for a final try. He reached a rich showing of sulphur.

Eugene L. Norton, former Baltimore banker and past chairman of the Freeport Sulphur Company, became interested in San Cristóbal and visited the property. He and three friends, Edwin D. Belknap, Edwin S. Gardner, and Cyrus M. Lerner, organized the Mexican Gulf Sulphur Company and through it negotiated with the Bradys' American Sulphur Company for the purchase of half of its interest in these concessions for 355,000 shares of Mexsul's common stock (par value 10 cents a share); $75,000 in cash, and a royalty of $1 per long ton of sulphur produced.[15] They also obtained an option on a further quarter interest for an additional $75,000 and the same royalty agreement. To finance this purchase, April 3, 1946, Newkirk & Company, Inc., as underwriters, offered 99,300 shares of Mexican Gulf Sulphur stock at $3 a share, most of which was bought in the Metropolitan area. A second offering to raise additional capital was largely bought in Houston and Dallas, where naturally interest was keenly aroused in these sulphur developments below the border. Here, too, six alert, wealthy oil men, led by J. R. Parten, became interested in Mexican sulphur. In exchange for an option on the Bradys' concession at Jáltipan they sent down a modern drilling rig and underwrote the preliminary exploration of this property.

At Jáltipan Ashton Brady was again fortunate in finding some veterans of the old oil days, and with a twisted rusty piece of cable and a broken length of pipe for clues, he struck sulphur in the first well. The Parten group took over, and after drilling over 100 wells to outline the structure and estimate the reserves, they organized the Pan American Sulphur Company.[16]

At this critical junction, when it appeared that the Mexican sulphur industry might be stillborn for lack of financial nourishment, an unexpected sulphur shortage focused attention on this possible new source of supply. Frasch sulphur had filled the war's extraordinary demands, but these imperative needs had cut down our prewar stockpile of 4.4 million tons to 3.5 million in 1945. Instead of the expected postwar slump, a great worldwide expansion of chemical activity further reduced that stockpile to 2.5 million tons by 1950.[17]

Despite a 38 per cent increase above the World War II peak output, American producers were unable to catch up with the growing world demands increased by the Korean conflict. The chemical community suddenly realized that our American reserves of saltdome sulphur are not unlimited.

The entire Gulf Coast region has been punched like a pincushion: except offshore, there is little prospect of finding important new domes. Overnight Mexican sulphur became exceedingly interesting. Concerned over our domestic reserves of this essential chemical commodity, the Export-Import Bank made loans to complete the plants at San Cristóbal and Jáltipan. The time was now ripe for the development of the Mexican industry. Or as Shakespeare[18] aptly phrases it:

> *There is a tide in the affairs of men*
> *Which, taken at its flood, leads on to fortune.*

Brimstone, "the stone that burns," had entered upon a new epoch, Part Two of the significant story of Frasch sulphur.

2

"The Workhorse of Chemistry"

SULPHUR—or as chemists and geologists, following the old English spelling of Chaucer, now like to write it, *sulfur*—
In Spanish it is *azufre*—
In French, *soufre*—
In Dutch, *solfer*—
The Greeks, too, had a name for it, *apyron*.

But in whatever language, sulphur "plays a more important part in chemical industry than any other chemical element." [1]

Over a century ago James Muspratt, father of the British chemical industry, speaking of the raw materials of his business, declared: "Salt, lime, and sulphur; and the greatest of these is sulphur." That declaration of dependence upon sulphur is more true now than it was then.

Luckily for us, sulphur is one of the most abundant chemical elements in the make-up of this planet. It stands eighteenth, behind chlorine.[2] The sulphides are among the commonest minerals: pyrites, iron and copper sulphides; galena, lead sulphide; zinc blende, zinc sulphide; and cinnabar, mercury sulphide. Vast beds of gypsum, calcium sulphate, are found all over the world, and barite, barium sulphate, is widely mined in the United States and Canada, Mexico and Brazil, England and Germany, many other countries.[3] Sulphur also occurs in native form imbedded in limestone, in the craters of volcanoes, and encrusting the edges of hot sulphur springs.

14

Erupting volcanoes and spouting geysers were much more common half a million years ago when man first began examining the world in which he found himself. They terrified him, no doubt, but they also roused his insatiable curiosity. This bright yellow, sparkling substance must have arrested his notice. He must have soon learned that it burned with a strange, sputtering, blue flame, pouring forth evil-smelling, choking vapors. Along with carbon in the form of charcoal and the free metals, gold, silver, and copper, sulphur must have been among the first true chemical elements recognized and used by our ancient ancestors.

The priests and witchdoctors of many a primitive people burned sulphur as a sort of inverted incense. The sweet-smelling smoke of aromatic gums and resins was, so they believed, pleasing to the good spirits. According to their thinking, the disagreeable fumes of burning sulphur, which made their eyes water, their noses burn, and their throats gag, would surely drive away the bad spirits. Early man must also have discovered that sulphur fumes kill insects and take the color out of feathers, wool, fur. Thus he learned unwittingly the value of sulphur in fumigation and its bleaching action.

Homer praises "pest-averting sulphur," and after the slaughter of Penelope's suitors, Ulysses called out, "Quickly, Dame, bring fire that I may burn sulphur, the cure of all ills." [4] It was a ritual that lasted many centuries. Right down to grandmother's day the burning of a sulphur candle was a regular part of the housecleaning that followed every case of scarlet fever, measles, and other contagious diseases.

The fame of sulphur's medicinal virtues was won early (somewhere between 4000 and 3000 B.C.) and it spread widely. A prescription for sulphur salve to treat granulated eyelids is set forth in the Ebers Papyrus.[5] This famous Egyptian formulary has been dated about 1550 B.C. Moses was then tending the flocks of his father-in-law on Mount Horeb where God spoke to him from the burning bush, ordering him to

Egypt to deliver the Hebrews from Pharaoh's bondage.[6] Some nine centuries later this same prescription, somewhat simplified, was incised on a baked brick that was unearthed in the royal library at Nineveh. Seven centuries later, still further condenses, it is repeated in Pliny's *Natural History,* together with other information about sulphur, its occurrence, refining, and employment in various arts and industries.[7]

The realistic Romans put sulphur to work for all its known uses and found a new application in warfare. By mixing brimstone with tar, rosin, bitumen, and similar combustible materials, they invented the first incendiary weapon. They also found the rich sulphur deposits of Sicily, for many years the principal European source of supply.

In truth, the demand for sulphur was trifling until gunpowder arrived on the medieval scene. This mixture of 70-75 per cent saltpeter (sodium nitrate), 14-16 per cent charcoal, and 10-15 per cent sulphur was discovered by the Chinese about 1200 A.D.[8] and introduced into Europe independently by Roger Bacon and Berthold Swartz. This new weapon was used with stunning effect at the Battle of Crécy (1346). Like cheap steel, the first coal-tar dye, and penicilin, it was a revolutionary chemical substance. It literally blasted the strongly entrenched Feudal System, with its divine kings and robber barons, its mitered bishops and armored knights, out of history. Until the Boer War (1899-1902) gunpowder remained the sole propellent ammunition.

Even this new need for sulphur in gunpowder was met by stripping of the outcroppings of underground Sicilian deposits, eked out by scrapings from volcanoes and sulphur springs. Cortéz, you recall, replenished his dwindling stock of gunpowder by the daring exploit of one of his lieutenants who was let down in a basket into Popocatepetl's sulphur-lined crater to collect this important ingredient.[9] Not until the middle of the 18th century did the birth of the modern chemical industry and the fast-growing manufacture of sulphuric acid make sulphur an important commodity of world commerce.

The alchemists, like the cavemen, were intrigued by this yellow stone that burns, and in their efforts to transmute base metals into gold, they experimented with it in many ways. Impressed by its distinctive properties, they elevated it to one of the three primary elements: sulphur or heat, mercury or liquidity, and salt or solidity.[10] These weird notions misled the early chemists and for a century obscured from them what really happens in the simplest chemical reactions. Without this basic knowledge there could be no true science of chemistry. Without chemistry, the manufacture of chemicals, as we know it, was not possible.

For the past 150 years the principal use of brimstone has been in the production of sulphuric acid. Back in the 12th century the alchemists prepared this acid and christened it "oil of vitriol." They made it by heating either green vitriol (ferrous sulphate) or pyrites in a retort, collecting the fumes in water. They also put brimstone in a dish, supported by an iron tripod over a bowl of water, firing the sulphur by means of a red-hot horseshoe and immediately clapping over the whole a large glass bell. By this method they prepared sulphurous acid,[11] which they called "spirits of sulphur," distinguishing it from sulphuric acid, but, of course, not suspecting that the "ic" acid came from sulphur trioxide (SO_3) and "ous" form from sulphur dioxide (SO_2).

Sometime early in the 17th century, Johann Glauber, a German alchemist who was almost a chemist, had a brilliant idea. It did not work out at all as he planned. But he discovered a process destined to become the cornerstone of the chemical industry. Irked because under the glass bell brimstone did not burn freely, but frequently went out, Glauber added to it a bit of niter, the highly combustible ingredient in gunpowder. This worked beautifully, but now the bell process produced, not sulphurous acid, but sulphuric. Glauber was surprised and puzzled: he had no idea what had happened or why.

Now we know that the oxides of nitrogen, evolved from the niter, act upon the oxygen in the air so that it combines with the sulphur dioxide (SO_2) from the burning sulphur, converting it into SO_3. Sulphur trioxide in water becomes sulphuric acid ($SO_3 + H_2O = H_2SO_4$).

While the oxides of nitrogen promote this reaction, they do not enter into it but escape into the air. In other words, they serve as a catalyst, which has been likened to a clergyman performing a wedding ceremony. Johann Glauber innocently scored a double triumph. He stumbled not only on the reaction upon which the manufacture of the most important industrial acid is still based, but also on the first catalytic reaction, today one of the most versatile and valuable of all chemical processes.

In Glauber's time, sulphuric acid was confidently prescribed for many human ills. Especially, it was recommended to cure "melancolic distempers" and to remove tartar from the teeth, two cases in which one suspects its therapeutic action would be violent, if not beneficial. To meet these medicinal demands other alchemical chemists on the Continent began adding niter to the bell process, so that we do not know whom to credit with the first practical use of Glauber's chance discovery. But it was undoubtedly introduced into England by a quack doctor.

Joshua Ward, for sundry crimes and misdemeanors, including bribery, was expelled from England in 1717. He went to France where he lived at St. Germain, the aristocratic suburb of Paris. Pardoned in 1733, he returned to London and began to exploit a marvelous cure-all, his "Drop and Pill." It was a splendid success—at least financially—and Ward began making oil of vitriol by the bell with niter to supply his own needs. On June 23, 1749, this rascally character was granted British Patent No. 644 covering this ancient and well-known process. Typically, he used his patent to blackmail other acid manufacturers, for by this time the acid was becoming an important industrial chemical.[12]

Even after the glass bell was replaced by a larger, wide-mouthed glass globe, output by this process was limited by the glassblower's inability to make a globe much larger than 18 inches high and one foot in diameter. Even when batteries of such globes were set up, production was low and breakage of the fragile vessels high; the price exorbitant and the acid weak. All of this was probably fortunate for the patients of the physicians who prescribed it so freely.

Sulphuric acid is the great commercial acid, "the workhorse of chemistry," because it is the cheapest acid available in quantity in every industrialized country.[13] The man who made this possible was another physician, John Roebuck (1718-1794) who studied chemistry and medicine at Edinburgh and won an M.D. at Leyden. He practiced in Birmingham, England, and in this nursery of the Industrial Revolution became keenly interested in technical chemistry. In partnership with Samuel Garbett, Roebuck opened a chemical laboratory where they made sulphuric and nitric acids, corrosive sublimate (mercuric chloride) and hartshorn (ammonia) besides recovering and refining gold and silver and serving as consulting chemists, the first of this profession.

That lead resists sulphuric acid was well known, and Dr. Roebuck simply replaced the glass globe with a big lead-lined box. Within three years the partners established a second acid works at Prestonpans, near Edinburgh. Their lead box now grew to a lead chamber 10 feet square.

Roebuck did not patent his new apparatus and within an amazingly short time similar acid manufactories appeared. By 1820 there were 23 such plants in England alone, seven in or near London. The price of the acid came down from 2s6d to 33/4d a pound.[14]

Until this time the "chemicals" used by the dyers and bleachers, the soap and glassmakers, the tanners and apothe-

caries, were all natural substances. The favorite acids were
vinegar (acetic) and sour milk (lactic). The chief alkali was
pot-ashes, crude potassium carbonate, leached out of wood-
ashes in big iron pots. But now the application of power to
tools, transforming them into machines—the Industrial Revolution—greatly increased the output of all sorts of goods,
creating new chemical demands. The old natural products,
weak and reeking with impurities, would no longer do:
stronger, purer chemical reagents were needed in greater
quantities. By now too, the first principles of chemistry were
sufficiently clear so that the manufacture of true chemicals
had become practical.

Sulphuric acid soon replaced buttermilk in bleaching, but
its first big use was in making soda alkali by the Leblanc
process. This consists of three stages: (1) decomposition of
common salt by sulphuric acid; (2) furnacing the sodium
sulphate so formed with limestone and coal; (3) washing out
the sodium carbonate which was known as soda ash. It
quickly replaced pot-ashes. The first English soda alkali plant
was built near Liverpool by James Muspratt in 1823, the
birthday of the modern chemical industry.

Sulphuric acid was one of the first chemicals made in
America. Easy to produce, this highly corrosive liquid has
always been difficult and expensive to transport. A century
and a half ago the captain of a wooden sailing vessel found
that no matter how carefully they might be packed with straw
in wicker or iron baskets, big glass demijohns filled with this
acid were a troublesome, dangerous cargo. It raised the cost
of insurance, so the ocean freight was increased correspond-
ingly. On this side of the Atlantic, all these extra importing
costs added up to a protective bonus for an American manufacturer.

So reasoned John Harrison, a young Philadelphian who
had studied chemistry in England and acquainted himself
with the latest manufacturing methods. Accordingly, on

his return in 1793 he set up the first lead chamber and produced the first sulphuric acid in America. His output was 45,000 pounds a year and his initial price, 40¢ a pound.[15] Harrison soon had competitors in Baltimore, Boston, New York, and at his own doorstep in Philadelphia.

What was happening in England and the United States was duplicated in France, Germany, and Holland. The demand for sulphur zoomed. From haphazard hand-picking, the underground mining of the Sicilian deposits became one of the most profitable mining operations in the world.

From the beginning the Sicilian sulphur industry was built upon a shaky foundation. The deposits lay under the land of large estates owned by Italian noblemen or, as time went on, by an increasing number of bankers and merchants who bought them as an investment. All were absentee owners. Enterprising local men worked the deposits under a variety of farm-out and royalty contracts. Since the owners were most interested in regular income, these agreements commonly specified a minimum yearly output. There was no local demand for sulphur, so the mine operators sold to commission houses and brokers who had contracts with consumers abroad. This sharp division of the functions of ownership, production, and sales among groups that had no common interests—except to make as much money out of sulphur as quickly as possible—prompted overproduction and speculation. These disjointed elements have never been able to set up and maintain balanced production or an effective marketing machinery.[16]

The sulphur market was—and still is—fundamentally controlled by the chemical industry's demand for the element. This grew rapidly: it continues to grow today. However, as is also characteristic of this dynamic industry, its favored source of sulphur has frequently shifted in response to advances in chemical technology. The uses of sulphur are also being continually revised by new consumers. In this whirligig of changing technical and commercial conditions the pivotal point, the key factor in sulphur economics, is always sulphuric acid.

After the introduction of the Leblanc soda process at the close of the 18th century, the demand for sulphur increased more rapidly than Sicilian production. Prices advanced and a frenzy of speculation, similar to the California gold rush of 1849, gripped the whole Island of Sicily. By 1831 exports passed 44,000 short tons. The price advanced from $20 to $70 a ton. The next year, output jumped to almost 80,000 tons and the price edged up to $80 a ton.

Then the bubble burst. The world around, sulphur buyers, frightened at the prospect of a runaway market, had been accumulating stocks. In 1833 exports dropped to 35,000 tons and the price broke to $15 a ton. The sulphur market became utterly demoralized; owners were ruined; miners and teamsters were destitute. To rescue his distressed subjects (and incidentally his personal tax interest in sulphur sales) Ferdinand II, the Bourbon king of the Sicilies and Naples, in 1838 ordered the entire Sicilian production sold through Taix, Aycard et Cie. The French firm promptly restored the $70-a-ton price.

This government-backed attempt to stabilize the market failed for four reasons:

1—The price greedily set by the French syndicate was exorbitant, thoroughly uneconomic.

2—There was no control over production and sulphur began slipping out into the market surreptitiously at cut prices.

3—The British Government, through diplomatic channels backed by a display of naval force in the Mediterranean, compelled King Ferdinand to cancel his contract Taix-Aycard.

4—The chemical industry found a new source of sulphur in pyrites which served, and still does, as an unofficial, but effective check upon the price of brimstone.

The whole episode is a pretty example of the powerful economic and technical forces set in motion to break any chemical monopoly. The same story is told of potash and nitrates, of indigo, vanilla, camphor, and a score of less prominent chemical products.

The chemical industry is vitally concerned with a free, abundant supply of its basic raw materials. For good reasons it abhors fluctuating prices. Even more than a hundred years ago sulphuric acid had become so essential to the industrial economy of the entire world that an international chemical industry could not tolerate the chaotic Sicilian sulphur market ruled by speculation and politics. Naturally, they sought a chemical solution to this chemical problem.

Scores of chemists began hunting for new sources of sulphur. Liebig, the great German chemist, tells us that during this period nearly 150 patents were taken out in Germany alone for the production of sulphur or sulphuric acid from gypsum. Although in England William Gossage did for several years produce acid from this abundant raw material,[17] nevertheless the solution was found, not in gypsum, but in pyrites.

In 1833 a French chemist, Michel Perrett, found a practical, reasonably economical method of obtaining sulphur dioxide by roasting pyrites in his patented furnace. He himself improved his invention, and the development of the rotary furnace in 1870 made pyrites not only a satisfactory but a profitable raw material for the acid. By 1880, with the single exception of the United States, the sulphuric acid industries of the world had gone to a pyrites basis.

American sulphuric manufacturers were not ignorant of this change: they ignored it because it did not fit into the situation in the United States at that time. In 1830 demand for the acid was small and specialized. Accordingly, it was possible to absorb higher raw materials costs. By the time a big market developed in the superphosphate and oil industries, the price of sulphur had again become reasonable. The incentive to switch to pyrites were therefore weak and there were several positive deterrents. After 1871 there was no import duty on brimstone, but a tariff of 20 per cent on the iron and of 3¢ a pound on the copper in pyrites was in effect until 1890 and 1894, respectively.[18] At current prices this then amounted to a tax of about $7 a ton on the sulphur content of pyrites.

Furthermore, the use of pyrites involved more than writing off a perfectly good plant and making a substantial investment in new apparatus. Pyrites requires the physical handling of twice as much material and a longer operating-time cycle. It also creates a dust nuisance and the problem of disposal of by-product cinders.

But sulphur supply and demand never remain static. Having lost their European acid customers, the Sicilian industry was much curtailed. It was revived by new uses of sulphur which pyrites could not serve.

Suddenly, in 1845 in England, a strange disease appeared on the grapevines of a wealthy fruit fancier named Tucker. It was caused by a parasite which multiplied so rapidly and spread so widely that within five years it threatened to destroy all the wine industries of Europe. Frantically remedies were sought for this powdery mildew disease, and its discoverer, Tucker, himself, found a wash made by boiling sulphur in lime (the original lime-sulphur spray) which was notably successful.[19] Shortly, it was discovered that dusting the vines with finely pulverized sulphur was an effective preventative. This soon became standard vineyard practice.

In the United States another new use for sulphur was created by the rubber vulcanization process. In its natural state rubber has two grievous faults: in hot weather it becomes sticky as flypaper; in winter, as brittle as glass. During the 19th century many chemists tried to cure these undesirable characteristics. Charles Goodyear himself experimented many years before he discovered by chance that if rubber is heated with sulphur, it retains its highly desirable properties of moisture-resistance, elasticity, and resiliency regardless of weather or temperature.[20] After 1873 the consumption of sulphur was further increased by its use in the lime-sulphite paper pulp process, discovered by the Swedish chemist, C. D. Ekmann.

Meanwhile there had been even greater growth in the use of sulphuric acid. Upon the foundation of Liebig's researches in plant foods, the chemical fertilizer industry was founded, and the treatment, first of bones, later of phosphate rock, with sulphuric acid to produce superphosphate, became the chief consumer of this acid. To acidulate a ton of rock requires a ton of 50 per cent acid,[21] and around the world the fertilizer industry remains today the largest sulphur consumer. In the United States the first great fertilizer demand was for cotton in the Southern states. Since the deposits of phosphate rock were in the Carolinas, Tennessee, and Florida, and because sulphuric acid has never been a commodity that stands a high freight rate, a great number of sulphuric acid plants were established south of the Mason-Dixon Line. Baltimore, Savannah, and later Jacksonville and Tampa, became great centers of this new and growing industry. Most of these acid plants were owned by fertilizer manufacturers.[22]

In the northern states following the Civil War, another great typically American industry grew up and soon became an enormous consumer of acid. At this time the petroleum industry's chief product was kerosene for illuminating purposes, and sulphuric acid played an important part in its production. One pound of acid was used in refining eight gallons of kerosene; that is, seven pounds of acid per barrel.[23] Acid plants sprang up in the centers of petroleum refining, then chiefly in Cleveland and western Pennsylvania, somewhat later in New York and Philadelphia.

Until the close of the last century American sulphuric acid makers continued to use brimstone as their source material. They were the largest customers of the Sicilian industry, which taking advantage of the tariff on copper in pyrites held the market against pyrites on a sulphur-cost basis. However, the Sicilians were chronically in trouble. Many small producers promoted overproduction which was followed by closing down of the least profitable mines and a consequent reduction of stocks in hand. Prices fluctuated widely; deliveries were uncertain.

After 1894, when the tariff on copper was removed, the American acid makers turned to pyrites and Rio Tinto, the largest producer of Spanish pyrites, built a plant in Delaware to extract copper from the pyrites cinders returned by its customers after they had burned out the sulphur content. The switch from Sicilian brimstone to pyrites came swiftly. In 1885, 85 per cent of the sulphuric acid made in the United States came from sulphur; in 1909, it supplied only 2 per cent, the balance coming 84 per cent from pyrites (domestic, 20; imported, 64) and 12 per cent from a new process for recovery of sulphur as by-product acid from zinc and copper smelters.[24]

At this juncture a new, revolutionary acid-making process was injected into the constantly changing sulphur situation. Until the 1880's, when the manufacture of coal-tar dyes became an important chemical enterprise, there had been little need for extra-high strength sulphuric acid. World demand had been supplied by a single firm in Nordhausen, Bohemia, which made the so-called fuming acid or oleum by distilling ferrous sulphate. Output had been modest, about 1000 tons, sold for about $100 a ton. Responding to the greater demand, production was shoved up to over 4000 tons in 1884, and the price rose to a fantastic $220 per ton.[25]

Again the chemists went to work. Several variations of the contact acid process were devised. By this method the conversion of sulphur dioxide into trioxide is accomplished directly by means of a catalyst, resulting in a high-strength, exceedingly pure product. The starting material is SO_2 obtained either by roasting pyrites or burning sulphur. However, brimstone enjoys certain distinct advantages. Less material need be handled and there is no by-product to dispose of. Pyrites commonly contains various contaminants, notably arsenic, and the demand was now for an extra-pure acid.

Compared with the chamber process, the new contact method also has advantages. It calls for less initial investment and maintenance costs are lower. Though the chemistry involved is complex, the contact process lends itself admirably to automatic control and continuous operation. Accordingly, its labor costs are lower.

The scales had tipped in the opposite direction. Back in the 1830's one technological advance, the invention of a pyrites-roasting furnace, had ousted brimstone from its exclusive position as a starting material for acid manufacture. In the early 1900's another advance in technique restored it to the position of the most economically favorable material for this same use. Thus, a double-switch was promoted in the production of the most important industrial acid: from chamber to contact process; from pyrites to sulphur. And these drastic changes came almost simultaneously with the advent of the new synthetic chemicals, coal-tar dyes, rayon, and plastics, which tremendously stimulated and expanded the chemical industry's activities.

To cap the climax, sulphur from an unexpected source appeared suddenly. Within a few years it was destined to change completely the international market for brimstone.

3

Sulphur in a Swamp

THE UNFORSEEN COMPETITOR of Sicilian brimstone came from an island in a swamp in Louisiana, U.S.A. It was "mined" by a hitherto undreamed of method—the Frasch hot-water process—at a cost below the traditional procedures of pick-and-shovel. Its bright yellow color and better than 99.5 per cent purity quite equaled the finest, hand-picked, specially refined, "yellow superior" grade of Sicilian brimstone. Again a radical sulphur revolution was in the making.

This newcomer had not reached the world's chemical market by a short and easy path: it had struggled through forty years of failure after failure. It had collected a toll of hundreds of thousands of dollars. It had cost the professional reputations of several highly respected geologists and mining engineers. It had tragically taken the lives of five honest workmen. The price of progress was indeed heavy: the ultimate rewards have been great and each of us has shared in them.

In Calcasieu Parish in southwestern Louisiana, thirty miles inland from the Gulf of Mexico, and roughly halfway between Lake Charles and the Texas state line, fifty acres of rolling land rise gently from the hyacinth-choked Bayou Choupique. It is an oasis of dry ground surrounded by swamps; an open clearing amid a jungle of bottleneck cypress festooned with Spanish moss.

So conspicuous a landmark could not escape attention. It had been owned for several generations by a prominent local

28

family, the Perkins, but they had not done much about it. However, there were plenty of trespassers, for in those days the snowy egret was fair game and his beautiful crest brought a big price in the millinery shops of New York, London, and Paris. Many a sharp eye must have observed that oil seeped from the island's shore, coating the water in the stagnant pools with an iridescent purpleblue film.

In 1859 a railway conductor, E. L. Drake, struck oil in a drilled well in western Pennsylvania. The first petroleum boom flourished wildly and the speculative fever quickly penetrated even into the Louisiana bayou country. The very next year the Perkins brothers, Eli and William, in partnership with their family physician, Dr. Kirkman, rigged up a long-pine tree trunk in a swivel, a simple, homemade contraption such as the water-well drillers used, and they drilled a test hole. They made a small showing of oil, but the Civil War interrupted their trials. The Perkins sold out to Hilaire Escoubas and Truston Lowell who brought their families to the island and began growing cotton.[1]

In 1867 an experienced oil driller named Mudd arrived on the scene. His employers were the Louisiana Petroleum & Coal Oil Company, recently organized by Gen. Jules Brady of New Orleans, and for them he made the first truly exploratory boring. He drilled some 400 feet through successive strata of clays and gravels to a layer of quicksand, where he met a heavy flow of sulphurous water. Beneath the quicksand he drilled into a thick bed of limestone and under that 100 feet of porous limestone impregnated with pure sulphur. Below this 100-foot deposit he found gypsum which he drilled for 600 feet. He quit at 1230 feet without leaving the gypsum or striking oil.[2] Mudd was puzzled: quicksand, sulphur, and gypsum were unlike anything encountered in his past drilling experience in Pennsylvania.

To his relief an experienced geologist, Prof. Eugene W. Hilgard arrived in Calcasieu. He was making a survey for Louisiana of the state's oil and mineral resources. Hilgard carefully studied Mudd's single set of cores and wrote a technical article[3] which is truly remarkable for its accuracy and foresight. Hundreds of subsequent borings into this formation have only confirmed his description of the structure and his conclusions that the prospects for petroleum were poor but its sulphur possibilities were great.

Hilgard made the definite suggestion that a shaft be sunk to the sulphur bed which could then be mined by conventional methods and the brimstone recovered by the kiln process in vogue in Sicily. He foresaw difficulties and urged that the enterprise be adequately financed and placed in the hands of a competent mining engineer.

Acting upon this advice, the Louisiana Petroleum Company attempted to switch operations from oil to sulphur. The landowners protested that the lease made no provision for mining brimstone and they sued to annul this contract. When the Louisiana court decided in their favor,[4] the Calcasieu Sulphur Mining Company was organized in 1870 specifically to lease the sulphur rights and work the deposit.

Organized in New Orleans and financed largely by wealthy Creoles, this company had French connections. They engaged as manager, Capt. Ino A. Grant, recommended by the French Government, and they imported a well-known French engineer, Antoine Granet, as consultant. Unwilling to accept previous exploratory work, Granet drilled a new well of his own halfway between the Perkins and Mudd borings. He examined with great care the quicksands and the underlying bed of limestone. Though a flow of 150 gallons of sulphurous water a minute was encountered in the quicksands, nevertheless he concluded that the limestone strata 25 feet thick resting directly above the sulphur "protects it, as it were, from the contact of the sulphurous water." [5]

This was an important conclusion. It was the first identification of the typical caprock of a sulphur-bearing salt-dome. It became the basis of all future efforts to mine the sulphur through a shaft. Finally it contained the germ of

Herman Frasch's idea that the sulphur might be melted and pumped to the surface.[6]

To overcome the difficulties bound to be met in the quicksand stratum with its big flow of water, Granet proposed to line the shaft with 87 castiron rings, each 5 feet high and 10 feet in diameter, weighing 941,600 pounds. While setting these rings he planned to keep the shaft full of water, the hydrostatic pressure of which he estimated would overcome the tendency of the sand to flow up from the bottom of the well. By these means he expected to prevent the influx of water and quicksand into the shaft. The lower end of the rings was to be set in the limestone overlying the sulphur deposit and the upper end cemented to the dry stratum above the quicksand. Then the water was to be pumped out and mining would be carried on by men descending the dry shaft, digging down to the sulphur and working out in lateral galleries. He recommended the purchase of castiron rings in Belgium and pumps and boilers in France, estimating the entire job at $114,000.[7]

Granet's recommendations and specifications were adopted in toto by the Calcasieu Sulphur directors and work began digging the shaft and lining it with the imported iron rings. Little is now known of how long they persevered and how far they were able to penetrate, but they abandoned the project in 1879, selling the rings, engines, and buildings which they had erected, all their tangible property and their land leases to a newly organized Louisiana Sulphur Company.[8]

This company also failed and during the next ten years was followed by half a dozen other abortive attempts to drive the shaft down to the caprock. However, it accomplished one thing that had a direct favorable bearing upon subsequent operations. Doubtless because of the failure of previous attempts, the Louisiana Sulphur Company was able to buy the sulphur island from its owners at a reasonable price. Title to the land in fee simple was passed to several unfortunate successors and ten years later became a valuable advantage to Frasch and his associates.

Throughout the 1880's similar efforts continued to fail. "The deposit seemed to bring misfortune to everyone connected with it," wrote Herman Frasch,[9] "and I have heard many stories and met many people who have told me of having lost money in the various schemes that marked the progress of the sulphur mine. Progress there seemed to mean failure. An Austrian company, a French company, and numerous American companies, everybody failed and not a ton of sulphur was produced." [10]

Some of these ventures must have been get-rich-quick schemes, for Frasch continued ". . . in 1891 I obtained a core from the sulphur deposit and many pamphlets from the various companies who had tried to operate it, each one telling the prospective purchaser that his fortune was made if he but owned a few shares of the stock of that particular company. I became interested, and, having had a great deal of experience in drilling and mining petroleum and salt, I thought the problem might be solved if all the facts concerning the deposit were known. Unfortunately, all the drilling records have been colored by the people who expected to float companies."

In 1890 the last attempt was made to drive a shaft down to the sulphur-impregnated limestone. It was a serious, adequately financed effort, backed by three seasoned mining men, and conducted by expert mining engineers. The American Sulphur Company, which took over the land and buildings, the iron rings and the imported boilers and pumps, was a personal venture of Abram S. Hewitt, his partner and brother-in-law, Edward Cooper, and Hamilton McKay Twombly.[11] The trio had been associated in other mining enterprises and they put this obviously baffling job into the hands of a noted mining authority, Rossiter W. Raymond, who for twenty-odd years had served as confidential consultant to the well-known engineering firm of Cooper, Hewitt &

Company. They reinforced him by engaging the services of the distinguished editor of the *Engineering & Mining Journal*, Richard P. Rothwell.

These experts decided to start with a fresh set of cores and extraordinary care was taken to arrive at an honest appraisal. To take advantage of their experience with this peculiar formation, the Chicago contract drilling firm, which two years before had bored a test hole here, was called back. Realizing that since it is an exceedingly friable, crumbly material, sulphur is ground by the drills into a creamy liquid easily carried off in the drilling water, Rothwell used a larger core drill, two inches in diameter. H. H. Hall, the drilling superintendent, kept a scrupulous log by constantly watching the pressure on the drill to note any differences in the hardness of the ground being bored. At the same time he noted the color of the cuttings carried up by the water flow. His record gave by far the most exact knowledge of the deposit yet available. While the drill was penetrating the sulphur-bearing formation, Hall stayed on the job day and night.

As soon as the underlying gypsum bed was reached, he carried to New York all the cores of the brimstone-impregnated stratum. Analysis indicated an average sulphur content throughout the stratum of 80 per cent sulphur. This seemed to be an incredible figure. Accordingly, the whole scrupulous core-drilling procedure was repeated. A second analysis confirmed the first. What nobody then realized was that the core drills gave unintentional, but definitely optimistic cuttings.

Their experience is significant. It shows how hard it is, even with the most sincere, conservative intentions, to make an accurate determination of the sulphur content of any dome formation. Even with the greatly improved core-drilling bits of today and with the more exact mathematical formulas for estimating the sulphur content, this uncertainty continues to plague anyone seeking an honest appraisal of the reserves in a saltdome deposit. Variations in the structure and depth of the limestone matrix make it necessary to plot its contours scrupulously, if the richness of the formation is to be estimated with any accuracy. Experience with the San Cristóbal dome in Mexico shows how misleading the results of spotty exploration can be.

With some adaptations of his own, Rothwell borrowed both Granet's plan and his castiron rings. He cleared the accumulated debris out of old Shaft No. 1; pumped it dry and cut the edges smooth to an even 12-foot width. At the bottom he set a large iron ring, 10 feet in diameter, 8 feet high, with a sharp cutting edge—similar to that used in digging tunnels. On this he piled, one on top of the other, Granet's old castiron rings until they reached the surface of the ground. These rings were furnished with internal flanges, and for the important task of bolting them together and packing the joints watertight, he brought down from a mine in Canada, an old trusted employee, Jacques Toniette.

When this modified caisson was all set the pumps were started; a bucket hoist rigged to the engine; and a digging crew sent down the shaft. As the clay and gravel were removed from the bottom, the weight of the iron rings forced the shield lower and lower. All went well until at about 250 feet down, they struck the quicksand. A mixture of sand and water surged up, carrying the pump platform and the workmen 40 feet up through the shaft.

Rothwell was determined and resourceful. With a clamshell bucket, he scooped out quicksand until he had lowered his caisson the depth of four more iron rings, that is, about 20 feet. Not an inch further would it budge.

To get better information on the quicksand and the flow of sulphurous water, six more exploratory wells were driven and another outside consultant, E. J. Schmitz, was called in. He studied the cores and the flow of water at various levels and made a discouraging report.[12]

"While I have only small hopes that the property of your company can ever be mined by common methods (shafts, etc.)

on account of the porous and cavy structure of the formation and the water masses present in the sulphur deposits and formation, I think it but proper that the directors of your company shall take no decisive step as to the abandonment of the property until they have fully satisfied themselves that the waters of the sulphur horizon below the big flows are too large to be controlled, and as well, that there exist no other practical methods of extracting the sulphur than by the common shaft methods." [13]

Frustration was climaxed by tragedy. While the further test wells were being drilled and Schmitz was carrying on his investigations, work on the shaft was suspended. The pipe in Well No. 6, which was Rothwell's first test hole, had broken off about 25 feet below the surface and was sealed with a wooden plug. To salvage this pipe, a shaft with a square curbing of pine planks was dug down to it. When all was clear, two men were sent down to draw the plug.

Out rushed a flood of water and gas. The two men at the bottom of the shaft collapsed. Thinking that they were drowning, three men ran over from the foundry and started down the ladder to rescue them. Halfway down, their grips on the rungs slipped, they crumbled and dropped with a splash into the water which was rising rapidly.

Choking fumes poured forth and C. C. Lovejoy, superintendent of Schmitz' drilling operations, recognized deadly hydrogen sulphide. Realizing that the victims below had been asphyxiated, not drowned, he pulled two other volunteers away from the ladder. The gas now poured forth in such quantities that burning eyes and gagging throats drove all from the edge of the curbing. It was several hours before the five limp bodies could be dragged with grappling irons from the shaft.

This fatal accident sealed the last attempt to mine this deposit by a shaft dug down to the mineral. The backers of the American Sulphur Company agreed to forego this unpromising, dangerous gamble. They had risked venture capital: they would not risk human lives. The engineers were recalled to New York; the workmen dismissed. The drilling contractors dismantled their rigs and departed. Only Jacques Toniette and two helpers remained as caretakers of all the relics of 40 years of successive failures. They smeared the machinery with grease; made shipshape the machine shop, the foundry, the blacksmith shop; boarded up the little office, the bunkhouse, and the kitchen. Toniette settled down to the lazy job of watchman.

While Jacques Toniette lolled in the warm Louisiana sun, only a couple of miles away the energetic Dr. Herman Frasch was wildcatting for sulphur. The idea that brimstone could be melted underground and pumped to the surface in molten form had germinated in his fertile brain in 1890, and he was hunting for a likely underground deposit where he might put it into operation.

Frasch had learned all that an outsider could about the frustrating mine on the little island in the Bayou Choupique. The thick layer of limestone impregnated with sulphur appeared to be quite similar to the famous deposits in Sicily, and he realized that, like these, the formation spread out over several miles. Accordingly he picked up a likely piece of land in the neighborhood and drove a test well down 2000 feet. He struck no petroleum, no limestone, no gypsum, no sulphur—nothing but the alluvial deposits of clays, gravels, and sands. He drilled three other dry holes. Technical articles in some geological journals gave him the hint and he concluded that all the sulphur in Calcasieu Parish must be in a dome structure, buried beneath the 50-acre island owned by the American Sulphur Company.[14]

With painstaking care Frasch had worked out all the details of his novel idea. He calculated all the physical data of temperatures, pressures, and time, and he designed his two concentric pipes to conform with these conditions. He drew upon all his practical experience with drilling oil wells and pumping salt brine to the surface. He studied the Sicilian industry, paying particular attention to its costs, its marketing organization, and the world demand for sulphur. He convinced himself that sulphur could be mined by his process at a cost that was competitive with either brimstone or pyrites. Then, on October 20, 1890, he took out three patents.[15]

Two of his associates in the Standard Oil Company, Frank Rockefeller, brother of John D. Rockefeller, and F. B. Squires, secretary of the corporation, had been in close touch with Frasch during the first installation of his desulphurizing process,[16] and they became interested in the sulphur-mining project. After his applications were filed, Frasch assigned to each of them a three-tenths interest in these and all future sulphur patents. The three agreed to share proportionately to their respective patent interest in the expenses of developing and exploring. This preliminary work was to be carried on as a majority of the partners directed and continue so long as two of the trio believed it promised success and profit. If this project materialized, it was further agreed that a corporation should be organized to work the patents and to take over any property that had been acquired by the group.

With the approval of his partners, Frasch went to New York to work out some sort of a deal whereby he might try out his hot-water process on the property of the Amerian Sulphur Company. He had a free hand in these negotiations. Hewitt was also in a position to speak for his associates, Cooper and Twombly, since he was not only the largest stockholder in their Louisiana sulphur venture, but long association had established a close, mutual understanding among them. Furthermore, Frasch and Hewitt were both trained engineers—they spoke the same language—and, at the first meeting, they established a rapport based upon mutual respect and admiration.

Both these shrewd negotiators recognized exactly what the situation was. The Frasch process without sulphur was useless: sulphur 600 feet underground was valueless. To join forces seemed logical and might well prove a heaven-sent business opportunity for both. It was a situation, however, full of the possibilities of a deadlock.

So far as Hewitt was concerned, the sulphur mine was a closed book. Shocked by the fatal accident, he had shut down the operation, taken his losses—some $350,000[17]—and made no effort whatever to salvage the property. Naturally he would be glad to recover his losses and, having pioneered several new methods in the iron and steel industry, he was interested in this new process. He comprehended immediately Frasch's concise technical description of how he proposed to bring up the sulphur beneath the treacherous bed of quicksand and he was inclined to believe that it would work.

"It appears to me," said Frasch, after he had explained his process, "that a consolidation of our interests is inevitable. You have the only considerable sulphur deposit suitable to the operation of my process that I know of anywhere in the United States. I have the only means by which your sulphur can be brought through that bed of quicksand."

"What do you propose?"

"Fifty-fifty, Mr. Hewitt—my process for your property," and Frasch smiled in his beguiling manner.

Abram Hewitt smiled back, "You are very persuasive Mr. Frasch, very indeed, but," and he became serious, "my sulphur property is known to exist. We have pretty accurate estimates as to its extent. Your process is unproved, utterly unproved. It may not be able to bring up an ounce of sulphur. Known against unknown hardly seems to me to be fifty-fifty."

"Wouldn't it be a good idea," said Frasch still smiling, "if you got to know my process? Investigate it thoroughly yourself or have anyone else you wish look into it. Don't forget to check up on our patents. I am quite sure that once you know all about it, then—."

So the negotiations opened. Hewitt and his partner, Edward Cooper, pored over the blueprints and specifications of the Frasch process. They appraised it favorably and then called in the Coleman brothers, James and Michael, who had long been consulting engineers for the firm. Their report, too, was favorable. All agreed that here was a process that might extract the sulphur from this defeating location.[18]

The conception of the Frasch process was strikingly original. But its elements were all familiar. That sulphur could be melted by water at 240°F. was an established fact. That it could be pumped to the surface in the fluid state as readily as brine or petroleum appeared reasonable. All the equipment Frasch proposed to use was thoroughly standard in these established practices. And the inventor's *pro forma* balance sheets of estimated plant and operating costs, of prospective sales and profits, seemed to be completely realistic—and tempting.

With but little wrangling it was agreed that as soon as Frasch was able to "demonstrate the possibility of success" a new corporation would be organized. Fifty-fifty, its $400,-000 capital stock was to be divided between Frasch and his associates and the shareholders of the American Sulphur Company. Appropriately, it was to be named the Union Sulphur Company.

It was now up to Herman Frasch to prove his process. He hurried back to Cleveland to buy equipment and collect personnel for his crucial demonstration.

4

Frasch and His Process

ON CHRISTMAS EVE, 1894, Herman Frasch carried out his daring experiment in a 10-inch test tube 623 feet long. Its failure had been flatly foretold by a number of experts. It could not possibly be tested in laboratory or pilot plant. At his desk Frasch had worked out temperatures and pressures, thermal efficiencies and specific gravities. In no way could he check these figures experimentally. He was perforce compelled to jump from paper calculations to field operation. The whole thing had to be a gigantic gamble.

It seemed a fantastic idea anyway to pour superheated water down hundreds of feet underground to a stratum of porous limestone impregnated with sulphur; melt the yellow mineral; then pump it to the surface in molten form. And Frasch himself did not appear to be the man for such a job. He was a stubby little chemist with a Vandyke beard and beribboned eyeglasses who spoke with a German accent— the perfect TV picture of an ivory-tower scientist.

But Dr. Frasch was an exceedingly exceptional man. He was at once calculating and venturesome and persistent: a sound chemist, a resourceful engineer, a shrewd businessman. His technical knowledge was expert. In both chemistry and engineering he displayed a bold, creative imagination that made several first-class discoveries and valuable inventions. He was an excellent salesman, both of ideas and tangible goods. He was realistic, aggressive, and foresighted, hence a tough bargainer and dangerous competitor. His astounding

40

versatility was indeed based solidly upon an equally amazing combination of talents. He had his faults. He was impatient of stupidity or delay, inclined to be dictatorial. He was conceited, or perhaps more accurately, overconfident. Like most of the executives of his time, he held the reins tightly clenched. Because he did not delegate authority, he failed to train a group of associates among whom a fitting successor might have been found after his death.

Everyone who knew Herman Frasch remembers him as a vivid personality. He had radiant vitality, extraordinary powers of concentration, a conspicuous capacity for hard work, whether mental or physical. Off duty, he was a friendly man, full of fun, a great storyteller and practical joker. He enjoyed the theater and the opera and relished good food and good wines.

Son of Johannes Frasch, burgomaster of Gaildorf, Württemberg, Germany, he was born in that town on Christmas Day, 1851.[1] When 19 years old he came to the United States and became laboratory assistant to Prof. John M. Maisch in the Philadelphia College of Pharmacy. Arriving during the first burst of industrial expansion that followed the Civil War, young Frasch sensed the important part that chemicals were to play in this economic growth. Deliberately he set himself to work at chemistry. The petroleum boom was in full blast, and with a clear eye on the main chance, the aspiring young chemist concentrated upon this "liquid gold."

In 1876 Frasch perfected an improved process for refining paraffin wax. He sold his patent to the Standard Oil Company, and John D. Rockefeller sold him the idea of moving to Cleveland and setting himself up as a consulting chemist specializing in petroleum and its products.[2] No one knew more about the chemistry of this complex mixture of hydrocarbons than he, so Frasch soon built up a profitable practice.

In 1885 Frasch bought the Empire Oil Company which had wells and a small refinery near Petrolia, Ontario. The company was then the sole Canadian producer, but although protected by a Canadian import tax of 9¢ a gallon, the little Ontario refinery seemed headed for bankruptcy. Its main product, kerosene, had a bad smell. Furthermore it burned with a smoky flame that deposited so much soot on the lamp chimney that its light was soon almost blacked out. Frasch was not buying a corpse. Both bad smell and excessive smoke, he was convinced, were caused by sulphur contamination, and within a year he had perfected a desulphurization process which "sweetened" his sour crude oil into a salable product.

The sour crudes of Ohio and Indiana had the same faults. Possibly John D. Rockefeller knew of Frasch's Canadian experiments. At all events, he was so sure that a technical solution to this chemical problem would be found that he was buying up hundreds of acres of oil rights in the Lima, Ohio, field. He promptly bought outright the Frasch patents and his Canadian company.

Frasch also secured a lifetime job for himself as the first director of research of the Standard Oil Company with a good salary plus royalties on future inventions in the petroleum field. His contract further stipulated that he was to have two months of his own choosing every year free for his own work. For his patents and the Empire Company Frasch received Standard Oil stock. It was then selling at $168 a share and paying 7 per cent dividends. Although certainly not the sole factor in Standard Oil's sensational success, his desulphurization process did raise the value of Midwestern oil from 14¢ to $1.00 a barrel. Standard Oil dividends increased to 40 per cent and he sold half of his stock for $820 a share. Frasch now had a secure position and was independently wealthy.

As a member of Rockefeller's team of specialists, Frasch made many contributions to early petroleum-refining technology. He also made good use of his sabbatical two months. Back in 1875 he had invented a recovery process for tin scrap and soon afterwards a method for the manufacture of white lead from galena. He held other important patents: for making elements in thermal-electrical generators, for a paraffin waxed paper, for electric light carbons, for poducing sodium carbonate from salt, a process he himself operated for several years in Detroit. He was the first to suggest revivifying worn-out oil wells by means of hydrochloric acid. Up to the time of his death in 1914, he had taken out 64 U. S. patents. Most of them were commercial successes: many of them involved huge operations. His discoveries in petroleum and sulphur, two of our most important chemical raw materials, have added billions to the world's wealth.

Just how Herman Frasch first became interested in the curious sulphur deposit down in Louisiana is not known. He was already interested in sulphur. The many articles published at this time about this deposit and the various unsuccessful efforts to mine it could hardly have escaped his alert attention. Nor is it hard to guess how his familiarity with drilling techniques, which were being rapidly improved at this time, planted the seed of the idea that eventually matured into his hot-water mining process.

Frasch was an original thinker and certainly this idea was startingly novel. But he was not one to go off half-cocked. He reasoned logically from sound premises and always with a nice appreciation of economic values. He was therefore at pains to study his prospective competition, the Sicilian industry, and he had reached a conclusion, obvious enough, but one that all those who had previously failed in this sulphur venture had either overlooked or deliberately ignored. Even if the difficulties and expense of reaching the sulphur through the quicksands and of controlling the big flow of poisonous sulphurous water were overcome, the mineral-impregnated limestone could not be profitably mined with pick and shovel. At that time, American miners were being paid $5 a day; Sicilians, 60¢. It was a plain dollars-and-cents axiom that, if the Louisiana mine were to be profitable, some entirely new and radically cheaper method was needed. This simple economic fact, and the cost figures Frasch had to support it, clinched his arguments with Hewitt and Cooper and induced them to take his untried process on a 50-50 basis with their land, mining rights, and tangible property.[3]

Back in Cleveland, having set up the Union Sulphur Company upon an if-and-when-proved basis, Frasch approached a sober-minded, industrious young German-American, Jacob C. Hoffman, who was assistant to the Standard Oil treasurer.

"Jacob," he said, "could you possibly be spared for a couple of months to go down to Louisiana for me and take charge of a well I am drilling?"

Hoffman had been brought into the office from field work and this move appealed to him, so he had his regular summer vacation extended to two months. That two months was later stretched to four years. Hoffman became the first superintendent of the Union Sulphur Company, the first field-operating man in this new industry.

On his arrival at that strange barren island in the midst of the lush swamp, Hoffman was greeted by Jacques Toniette. Despite the difficulties each had in understanding the other's use of the English language, the two hit it off admirably, and Hoffman boarded with the Toniette family all the time he was in Louisiana. Together they explored the property: the two deserted shafts, one lined with iron rings, the other with timbers where the fatal accident had occurred. Together they checked the thirteen test wells that punctured the mound.

Frasch had sent down a driller, E. T. Wurth, with instructions to start a new 10-inch well, No. 14. At 200 feet, the drill struck the quicksand and bogged down. Wurth forthwith resigned and left the day after Hoffman arrived.

The shifting sand gripped the driving pipe as in a vise. In order to force the pipe down a single inch, a stem weighing nearly a ton was rigged up and struck the driving cap on the top 200 times. By spudding and pumping the sand out, the pipe could be started again. The sand would move up suddenly through the pipe with speed enough to float

Sulphur, like gold, is where you find it—along the marshy shores of Louisiana's Gulf Coast is Bay Ste. Elaine, the first Frasch plant to use sea water, and in the wide open spaces of Texas, Boling Dome holds the industry's record for total production, over 50,000,000 tons.

In the Mexican jungle, at Gulf Sulphur's Salinas plant they do not mow the lawn, macheté-men cut back invading vines and creepers, and there are unique problems in laying a transmission line in the Delta of the Mississippi.

Freeport Sulphur Co.

Photo by Author

Freeport Sulphur Co.

In the Gulf of Mexico, seven miles from land, the $30,000,000 Grand Isle plant is the first offshore sulphur mine, and in the shadow of the Canadian Rockies stands British-American Oil's pioneer sour gas sulphur recovery plant at Pincher Creek, Alberta.

British-American Oil Co.

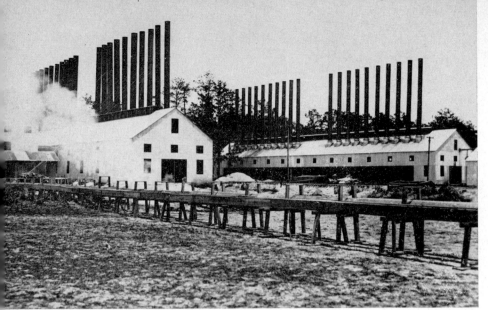

Union Sulphur Co.

Texas Gulf Sulphur Co.

The power plant is the heart of a Frasch operation —daddy of them all at the Union plant about 1900 and the original installation at Newgulf in 1929.

Texas Gulf Sulphur Co.

The modern look—power plants at Spindletop (*above*) 4,000,000 gals./day water capacity; Jefferson Lake's Clemens (*right*) 160,000 lbs. steam per hr.; and Bay Ste. Elaine, four boilers, 1·75 million gals./ 24 hr. of sea water treated and heated.

Photo by Author

Jefferson Lake Sulphur Co.

Boilers show vividly the improvement in apparatus over the years—
the Frasch plant at Sulphur Mine, La. after conversion from coal to
fuel oil and the ten, 1500 h.p. Sterling-type boilers at Newgulf, designed
for gas or oil, equipped with economizers which recover practically all
the waste heat from the stack gases.

Water pumps at the Union plant (*above*); at Grande Ecaille (*below*) centrifugal-type, steam turbine driven, capacity 6,470,000 gals./ day; at Salinas, showing open-air construction in Mexico.

Air compressors deliver air at 500-600 lbs. pressure to lift the melted sulphur to the surface—at the old Union plant (*above*) and at New-gulf (*below*) where the efficiency of up-to-date machine design is quite obvious even to the layman's eye.

the driving tools. There was a wild scramble to get them out before the sand again engulfed them. By immediately putting on driving clamps, the pipe could sometimes be forced down as much as four feet before the sand settled. It took three months to finish a job that modern drilling tools could do in less than a day.

When the 10-inch pipe reached the caprock above the sulphur deposit, it was set firmly in place. Hoffman now reduced his drilling bit from 10 to 8 inches and continued boring to the bottom of the sulphur bed. Here, when the bit first ground into the porous limestone, a great rush of sulphur water suddenly flowed like a fountain from the top of the drive pipe. The drillers were forced from the derrick floor by the choking, smarting gas which accompanied the water. They were compelled to raise the drilling tools eight feet into the air on a platform so as to be clear of this poisonous menace. The drillers worked on what the men, with good reason, called "the headache post." It was early December before the 8-inch bore reached the bottom of the sulphur deposit.[4]

Hoffman fitted the boring through the sulphur deposit with a 6-inch casing at the bottom of which was a perforated pipe to act as a strainer. Above the strainer, inside the 6-inch pipe was an iron ring, bored to allow a 2½ inch nipple to pass through. Above this ring were a series of larger holes, which were to provide for the hot water outlet. A 3-inch pipe was now lowered through the 6-inch casing and set upon the iron ring above the strainer.

At 175 feet below the surface, an ordinary sucker-rod pump was placed inside the 3-inch pipe. On the top of this pipe was a tee from which a line fitted with a safety valve extended horizontally beyond the wellhead. The first Frasch process sulphur mine was now rigged for action.

The original power plant consisted of four secondhand Erie ironwork boilers of 100 hp each. The steam from all of these ran into a manifold provided with valves so that it might be sent to the heater from any boiler. In a little wooden building between the boilers and the wellhead was set up a cylindrical steel heater, 20 feet high, 30 inches in diameter. It was raised sufficiently above the ground so that the water would flow to the mine by gravity. In this heater were staggered perforated castiron pans. Flowing slowly from pan to pan the water was thoroughly heated by the steam.

The water supply came from the surrounding swamp. It was pumped to the heater through a 4-inch pipe. A 6-inch outlet led directly from the heater to the 6-inch casing of the well. In order that the water temperature might be constantly checked, a thermometer was inserted in this 6-inch pipe close to the heater. For insulation the heater was wrapped outside with old drilling cable covered with Portland cement. The steam lines were laid in a box filled with Spanish moss plucked from the neighboring trees. The tops of the boilers were covered with clay into which this moss had been worked as a reinforcement.

It was the middle of December before Hoffman could notify Frasch that they were ready for the first test. He suggested Christmas Day. The better the day, the better the deed; besides, December 25th was Frasch's birthday. But there were unexpected delays.

Frasch came down from Cleveland before Christmas, and he and Hoffman tested the steam and water lines to check that they were all clear and the connections tight. They sent cold water down the 6-inch casing in order to be certain that the strainer at the bottom had not become clogged. Everything seemed shipshape. The time had come for the big experiment.

One after another, Hoffman turned steam from the four boilers into the heater. This was a tricky job since the hot steam must be admitted into the cold water cautiously to prevent pounding in the lines. It was a task the superintendent always reserved for himself.

For 24 hours the superheated water poured into the well.

Had the sulphur melted? Had it formed a pool at the lower end of the two concentric pipes?

Frasch himself opened the safety valve of the inner 3-inch pipe at the top of the well. A jet of steam hissed from the pipe. In a few moments the white spurts began to subside. Frasch smiled and nodded at Hoffman. The angry hiss sank to a whistle and suddenly stopped.

"She's sealed over!" exclaimed Hoffman. That should mean that a pool of sulphur had formed at the end of the pipe and extended upwards at least as far as the topmost holes in the outer pipe through which the hot water was pouring into the mine. But no one could be sure.

Frasch said nothing but he beckoned to Toniette who removed the valves from the top of the 3-inch pipe and began feeding down into it the plunger and the long sucker rod of the pump. With trembling hands Hoffman fixed the stuffing box on top of the 3-inch pipe through which the polished sucker rod operated. They connected the rod and started the pumping engine. The crucial moment had arrived.

Gripped with excitement, thirteen men clustered around the wellhead. Some knelt; some squatted on their haunches. Toniette was on all fours, his head thrust forward, his ear cocked, listening for the gurgle that would tell that the valve on the end of the sucker rod was beginning to draw. Hoffman straddled over the pump, watching for the first sign of suction. Frasch stood outside the circle tugging at his little beard. His keen gray eyes, darting from pump to walking beam to engine to stuffing box, were watching every detail.

The up-and-down swing of the walking beam began to slow down ever so little. A real and increasing strain began to exert itself against the engine. More steam was applied. Suddenly the man at the throttle shouted at the top of his voice, "She's pumping!"

Quickly Herman Frasch stepped over and touched his finger to the polished rod which had begun to film over with some liquid. He held up his hand for all to see. His finger was smeared with yellow—sulphur—melted sulphur pumped up from the deposit 600 feet below ground.

Amid a chorus of Oh's and Ah's Jacob Hoffman reached over and grasped the pump's outlet valve. At a nod from Frasch he twisted it open. Out poured a beautiful golden-brown stream. A gasp of startled astonishment was followed by a loud shout of triumph from the little circle of drillers and laborers. The Frasch process worked.

Within 15 minutes the 40 barrels on hand to receive the sulphur were seen obviously to be utterly inadequate. A space of ground just beyond the floor of the drilling rig was quickly cleared and bounded by a miniature levee lined with planks. Into this first of all sulphur vats poured the molasses-like stream, solidifying almost immediately into a great yellow block.

Four hours later the big walking beam operating the sucker rod began to falter and jerk. Something was obviously wrong with the pump valve. The early winter sun was already setting so the operation was shut down. The pump was stopped and in order to prepare a place for the next day's output, the sulphur was cleaned out of the vat into a big heap.

In his acceptance speech of the Perkin Medal, the chief actor himself wrote the perfect epilogue to the opening act of this drama of the American sulphur industry:

When everything had been finished, the sulphur all piled up in one heap, and the men had departed, I enjoyed all by myself this demonstration of success. I mounted the sulphur pile and seated myself on the very top. It pleased me to hear the slight noise caused by the contraction of the warm sulphur, which was like a greeting from below—proof that my object had been accomplished. Many days and many years intervened before financial success was assured, but the first step towards the ultimate goal had been achieved. We had melted the mineral in the ground and brought it to the surface as liquid. We had demonstrated that it could be done.

This was especially gratifying, as the criticisms I had received from technical papers and people who had heard of what I was attempting to do had been very adverse. Everyone who expressed an opinion seemed to be convinced that this thing could not be done, one prominent man offering to eat every ounce of sulphur I ever pumped. A fair illustration of public opinion is the remark of the mail boy who drove me over to the railroad the morning after our first pumping. He said, "Well, you pumped sulphur sure, but nobody believed it but the old carpenter, and they say he's half crazy.[5]

5

Double Trouble

NEXT MORNING they learned that the steel sucker rod, corroded down to a matchstick, had snapped. Frasch determined to return to Cleveland at once and hurry down a set of aluminum rods.[1] Throwing his clothes into a bag, he instructed Hoffman:

"Keep the hot water flowing. Let's accumulate a big pool of sulphur at the bottom of the well."

As he climbed into the buckboard to be driven to the train by John Henning, he shouted back, "I'll have the new rods here as quick as I can. Don't let the sulphur freeze in the pipes."

Frasch was hardly out of sight when Toniette came running to Hoffman at the boiler house crying, "The heater! The heater! The top, she all bulge: maybe she blow."

Together they scrambled up the platform surrounding the heater and discovered that the iron head had given way under the steam pressure and was swelling like a mushroom. Fearing an explosion they shut off the steam. Hoffman hurried over to the nearest town, Lake Charles, to buy a heavy castiron top which they bolted down fast to the top of the heater. Again they started the flow of the water. It began to back up. The sulphur had frozen hard in the 6-inch pipe.

What was wrong was plain enough and not serious, but the remedy was tedious. It was chip, chip, with the drilling tools, and then, when a section of pipe had been cleared, pull it to the surface. All spring, during the long, hot summer, well into the fall, they hacked and yanked to clean out the 6-inch pipe, reset it, and fit it with the pump.

Frasch came down from Cleveland. Again the lines were tested to be sure all connections were tight and the new water outlets at the bottom clear. Again Hoffman carefully turned on the steam in the heater units. For a second time the mine was steamed for 24 hours. As in the first pumping, the new sucker rod was lowered and connected.

Close by the wellhead, three new sulphur vats had been built. They were shallow tanks, 12 × 20 feet, only a foot deep. The new pump worked perfectly; the first of these vats was soon full and the flowing yellow stream was turned into the second. As soon as the sulphur had solidified in the first vat it was dug out and shoveled to a floor of loose boards laid on the ground. The second vat was also quickly filled; then the third. Everything was working as smooth as wax.

The Negro pick-and-shovel men sweated to keep ahead of the flow of sulphur. Toniette and the drillers scoured the island for more planks to raise the vat walls. Frasch was jubilant. Even the quiet Hoffman bubbled over with delighted excitement. Then suddenly the flow of sulphur stopped.

Up and down swung the walking beam. Up and down the polished sucker rod slipped through the stuffing box. But down below, the pump was not drawing. Had the valve clogged? Or had it become disconnected? Or had the aluminum rod broken under the strain of lifting the heavy column of sulphur? Puzzled and worried, the men drew the rod. It had snapped off.

By this time 500 tons of pure sulphur lay in the pile beside the wellhead.[2] The failure of the pump stopped the operation, but everyone from Frasch to the water boy now knew that the process really worked. The breaking of the rod was an accident. It did not affect the principles of the process.

Furthermore, Dr. Frasch had learned a valuable, practical lesson: the first requirement of hot-water sulphur mining is plenty of hot water. If the operation were to be carried on continuously on a commercial scale, greater boiler capacity must be available and the water pumps to the heaters must never run dry. Swamp water, collected through ditches into small reservoirs beside the edge of the mound, was not enough to supply the millions of gallons needed.

Accordingly, before he returned to his Cleveland laboratory to work out the pump problem, Frasch promised Hoffman additional boilers and instructed him to dig a canal to bring water to the mine eight miles from the Houston River. At the riverbank they built a small pumping station. Throughout the operation at Sulphur Mine this portable boiler with two little pumps furnished water, eked out by what could be drained away from the adjacent marshes. In due course four new 150-horsepower boilers arrived. Erecting them, building a new heater house and installing two new heaters, together with digging the eight-mile canal and building the pumping station kept Hoffman and his men very busy during the summer and fall of 1896.

Returning to Cleveland by way of New York, Frasch conferred with Abram Hewitt and Edward Cooper. They agreed that 500 tons of pure sulphur proved the Frasch process was practical. Accordingly, on January 23, 1896, the Union Sulphur Company was incorporated in New Jersey to acquire title to the land and the mineral rights at Sulphur Mine and to take over the Frasch patents. The original issue was $200,000 of 8 per cent preferred stock, half to the shareholders of the American Sulphur Company and half to Frasch, Squires, and Frank Rockefeller. Later, $200,000 of additional common stock was issued and sold at par to the original group to provide working capital.[3]

Meanwhile, back in Cleveland, Frasch tackled the problem of raising the liquid sulphur to the surface. Typically, his solution was daring and radical: why not eliminate the troublesome pump entirely? Again he was compelled to calculate theoretically and design his equipment on paper with no possibility of testing it except in the mine itself. Knowing that liquid sulphur has a density of 1.811 grams per cubic centimeter,[4] Frasch concluded that he could lift this liquid by means of compressed air.

In principle, this air-lift is quite simple, but it becomes rather involved in practice. Since water is about half as heavy as sulphur, the sulphur normally rises in the pipe about halfway to the surface. The air fills the sulphur in the 3-inch pipe with bubbles, making its density less than the density of the ground water outside of the pipe. The result is that the outside, heavier liquid raises the aerated column of sulphur by means of the excess hydrostatic pressure on the outside of the pipe. To work effectively, the air must therefore be delivered into the column at from 50 to 200 feet and for efficient operation the level of the sulphur in the pipe must stand fairly constant. This requires a steady, almost unlimited supply of sulphur to replace itself in the column as fast as it is being pumped.[5] Frasch comprehended this problem. The depth of Well No. 14 was 545 feet, 3½ inches, and the column of melted sulphur stood 274 feet, 10 inches below the surface.[6]

Sulphur melts at 114°C. into a thin, light yellow liquid. At 150°C. it becomes a thick brown liquid, about the consistency of cool molasses. If the temperature is raised to 220°C., the sulphur becomes almost plastic and dark brown in color.[7] It is critical that the mining temperature be rather exactly controlled and continuously maintained. Deep underground this is not so simple, especially as the limerock structure continually differs and varying quantities of cold water are encountered.[8]

In his third setup, Frasch connected the hot-water lines from the heaters to the 6-inch pipe, and also to the 10-inch outside casing, making it possible to get a flow of hot water both at the top and the bottom of the sulphur deposit. This

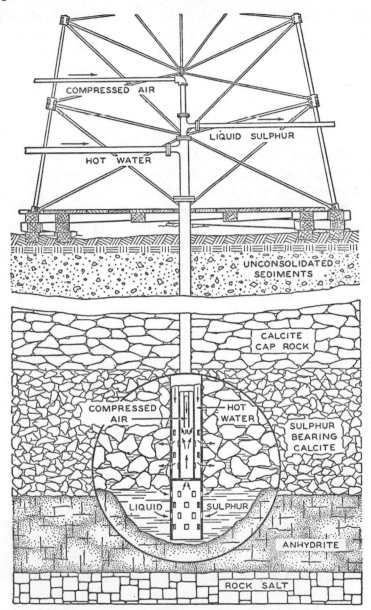

Fɪɢ. 4. Diagrammatic sketch of Frasch sulphur mine piping in relation to the dome structure.

gave better control of the temperature and speeded up melting of the sulphur. (Figure 4.)

At the same time, Frasch added one more improvement. He shortened the strainer at the bottom as a precaution against the sulphur line freezing. Above it, for a distance of 20 feet, he placed a smooth casing with outside couplings to hold the pipe at the joints. Should it again become necessary to cool the well, it was possible, before shutting off the hot water, to disconnect and pull the 6-inch pipe high up into the derrick before the sulphur could congeal.

All was ready for another trial on April 19, when Hoffman for the third time tested the steam and water lines and began steaming Well No. 14. Early next morning, Frasch opened the safety valve at the head of the 3-inch pipe. Steam rushed forth but soon subsided, indicating that the bottom of the well had sealed over with melted sulphur. Slowly he opened the valve of the air line. Breathlessly, everyone peered over the wooden wall, watching the discharge pipe hanging in the center of the empty bin. Seconds dragged into a full minute.

Hoffman glanced across at Frasch: he was frowning at the outlet pipe, tugging his Vandyke beard. Toniette clasped his head between his hands, eyes and mouth wide open. The other men began to fidget, shifting from one foot to another.

The flow of sulphur came suddenly with a great gush that splattered big yellow splashes all over the wooden planks. Half a dozen jerky spurts and the flow steadied to a thick, slowly pulsating stream. That day they brought to the surface 50 tons of pure brimstone.

Frasch and many others have added refinements to the hot-water mining process, but in all essentials the apparatus and operating technique had now become thoroughly practical. In some formations the double discharge of hot water at the top and bottom of the sulphur deposit was an improvement. It aided in maintaining the proper temperature for if hot water is delivered only to the top of the mine cavity, being lighter than cold water present in the formation, it tends to stay on the top. The sulphur it melts, being twice as heavy as water, sinks to the bottom of the cavity, but in passing through the cold water below, it tends to congeal. On the other hand, hot water delivered at the bottom rises quickly and is usually the most economical method. But if there is much cold water present in the formation, the hot water rapidly loses its melting efficiency. By double delivery, the top water spreading out laterally over the deposit fills a comparatively large cavity with water above the melting point of sulphur. Simultaneously, the bottom water rising, maintains a warm channel for the melted sulphur to reach the pool around the strainers. This divided-delivery also helps keep the melted sulphur near the strainer at the proper temperature for pumping. Frasch undoubtedly pictured all this in his mind's eye. What happened below ground was exactly as he had figured it out on his drawing board.

It seemed natural to send the air down through the smallest, innermost of the three concentric pipes. For operating efficiency this was a most fortunate arrangement. It is likely too, that Frasch figured out theoretically that in raising the column of molten mineral by means of air pressure, as the melted sulphur mingled with air rises in the 3-inch pipe, the hydrostatic pressure becomes less and less as the surface is approached. Accordingly, the air bubbles expand and thus the density of the liquid sulphur at the top of the column is less than at the bottom.

Furthermore, this expansion of the air has a tremendous cooling effect. It has been estimated that compressed air at 500 pounds pressure delivered at the bottom of a 300-foot sulphur column at a temperature of 200°F. would, in its expansion during the process of raising the sulphur, lower its temperature to 225° below zero F., provided that it did not absorb any heat from its surrounding liquid. This great withdrawal of heat, due to air expansion, would be quite enough to freeze the sulphur in the inner tube, if that

3-inch sulphur pipe were not within the 6-inch hot-water pipe.[9] In actual practice the air comes from the tubes with the sulphur about the same temperature, that is, approximately 300°F.

Well No. 14 was pumped from April 20 to May 26, 1896. Including the 500 tons raised during the first two tests, total production was only 771 tons.[10] At this time the well began to "blow," that is to sputter and spurt, indicating that the flow of sulphur was inadequate to maintain a sufficient head of melted material in the sulphur line.

At full speed, Well No. 15 was driven, equipped, and operated in the same manner. It was steamed and pumped in December 1896, and it promptly developed an operating difficulty which has since become distressingly familiar, one for which the resourceful Frasch immediately devised a solution. It was plain that this well was taking an excessive quantity of hot water while the pool of molten sulphur at the end of the line was rather scanty. Obviously, the limestone structure was what operators recognize as "loose," too porous in structure, full of cracks and crevices through which the hot water was escaping. Frasch conceived the idea of pumping down some material which would seal these fissures and so maintain better heat efficiency. Mud was tried first; later he used cut straw from the nearby rice fields. These expediencies worked admirably. During December, No. 15 yielded 101 tons and later in February, 30 more were extracted.[11]

In drilling Well No. 17 through the quicksand, a cavein buried the drilling tools. They had to be abandoned and Well No. 18 was started. This also proved disappointing. Less than 50 tons had been produced when the 10-inch outside casing broke in the quicksand formation and this well was also abandoned.

The prospect was dismal indeed: the hot-water process was now practical, but the operation was not profitable. In fact, the September 1897 balance sheet of the Union Sulphur Company showed on the debit side a mortgage assumed on the acquisition of the land of $125,606.25; bills payable, $100,259.30; plus expenses of development work, $72,294.77; and interest on borrowed money, $21,145.59. Against this total investment and indebtedness of $319,305.90, the company had received from the sales of sulphur only $38,908.69.[12]

Two stumbling blocks prevented profitable operations: irregular production and the high cost of fuel. Originally they burned wood, but their demands soon exhausted all the slabs that could be collected from sawmills for miles around. It became necessary to import coal from the Pratt Mine in Alabama. The price was only 15¢ a ton at the mine, but delivered it cost $4.05.[13] Continuous operation of a single well consumed some 50 tons of coal a day to raise roughly 50 tons of sulphur. Fuel costs plus freight to Boston and New York, then the chief consuming centers, were prohibitive in competition with Sicilian sulphur. Furthermore, it was plain as a drilling derrick that successful commercial production could only be maintained by operating several wells simultaneously. Even had the prospects of profits been brighter, the Union Sulphur Company simply did not have resources to operate on such a scale.

In the field, Hoffman, who was in charge, was continually bedeviled by lack of funds, even by lack of cash to meet his payroll. On more than one occasion he overdrew the balance at the First National Bank of Lake Charles to pay freight bills. While these checks were always honored, thanks to his personal friend, A. L. Williams, cashier, the bank told him bluntly that they did not care for that kind of an account.

Desperate for money, Hoffman wrote to Capt. Anthony Lucas who was then running a salt mine operation 75 miles away in the Five Islands for the Myles Salt Company, offering him the old French castiron rings. They made a deal quite without authority from headquarters and in this way Hoffman raised $1000. With this check in his pocket he

went to Cleveland to beg from L. H. Severance, treasurer
of Standard Oil, who was acting as treasurer for the Frasch
group, enough money to drill another well.

The answer was grim: "Go back to Louisiana. Clean up
and get everything shipshape for an indefinite shutdown.
Then come back to Cleveland. Mr. Frash is in Italy and he
may want you to join him there to try out the process in the
Sicilian field."

Once again, the ill-fated Calcasieu operation was shut
down. Leaving Henning and Toniette to put the plant in
stand-by condition, Hoffman returned to the Standard Oil
offices where he received cable instructions from Frasch to
buy all the equipment used in operating a star drill and
come to Italy as quickly as possible. They met in Naples
early in September 1898.

They moved their drilling rig over to Porto Empedocle,
Sicily, and secured mining rights to land nearby between
two actively producing mines. Frasch went home while
Hoffman started drilling and promptly ran into all sorts of
difficulties. With a drilling crew that knew as little about
drilling as he did about the Italian language, he at last succeeded in getting down two 1000-foot holes, but did not
find even a trace of sulphur. Having contracted malaria in
Louisiana, Hoffman was half sick amid the terribly unsani-
tary conditions of the little Sicilian seaport where he could
get neither drinking or bathing water fit to use. He cabled
Frasch he was coming home at once. Going straight to
Cleveland and into Dr. Frasch's office he offered his resig-
nation.

"Too bad, Jacob. There's nothing for me to do but accept
it. There is no work for you and no money to pay you."

Experienced Capt. Lucas, who knew more about saltdome formations than any other geologist, had warned Hoffman, "Sure, the hot-water process works, but it will never
pay." Other experts had also doomed the Calcasieu mine to
failure.[14] These dire prophecies seemed to have come true.

Again quiet reigned over the bewitched island deep in the Louisiana swamp. Toniette again lolled in the sunlight guarding the relics of a deserted sulphur mine. Once more it seemed that all efforts—even this new, most ingenious method of exploiting this difficult sulphur deposit—had failed.

At this point, Hamilton McKay Twombly had a brilliant idea. This shrewd capitalist, director of more than forty big corporations, son-in-law of William K. Vanderbilt, and substantial partner in this unfortunate venture, was disgusted and convinced that its chances of success were nil. He had heard that Lucas was something of a fanatic on these salt-domes, so why not offer his Union Sulphur stock to Lucas at a bargain price? The Captain, to his later chagrin, politely refused to buy.[15] This incident points up the poor opinion even his own associates had of Frasch's enterprise at that time.

But persistent Herman Frasch was not dismayed. He went to his New York associates pleading, "If we could only get continuous production from two or three wells simultaneously, then we could operate profitably."

He sat down with Abram Hewitt, his brother-in-law, Edward Cooper, and Mrs. Hewitt, and laid before them a sheaf of cost figures. Hewitt was not at all enthusiastic. Already he held a mortgage on the patent rights of $51,150.00 for cash advanced.[16] Cooper was openly sceptical, but Mrs. Hewitt had a mind of her own. If her husband and brother would sell her their interest in the Union Sulphur Company for 50 cents on the dollar, she was prepared to go ahead with Frasch, dollar for dollar for whatever he and his Standard Oil associates were ready to advance. Her courageous and shrewd proposal shamed the whole group into authorizing an additional $100,000 worth of stock to be subscribed for, if and as needed.[17] It was agreed to proceed with drilling and pumping, but cautiously and economically.

Once more, Frasch went down to Sulphur Mine. He recalled the faithful Henning from a job in the telegraph office at Lake Charles to be general manager and Toniette was put in charge of drilling.[18] During 1899-1900, they drilled and steamed but a single well from which was pumped only 36 tons of sulphur. During 1901, two additional wells were drilled which between them produced 3078 tons.

Then, unexpectedly, January 10, 1901, came a discovery wholly unrelated to sulphur mining which made the Union Sulphur Company a fabulously profitable enterprise.[19] Capt. Anthony Lucas, the fanatic on saltdomes, struck the famous Spindletop gusher, one of the greatest oil producers of all petroleum history. This flood of over 100,000 barrels of oil a day poured from the earth only 60 miles from the sulphur mine.

This 200-foot fountain of oil was sensational justification of a theory that every responsible oil man in the country had pooh-poohed. No other man had accumulated so much salt-dome experience as Lucas now possessed. Several of his exploratory holes had shown signs of petroleum. Moreover, he had seen for himself the Frasch operation at Calcasieu. He was convinced that these strange structures were the outward and visible signs of important mineral resources—salt, sulphur, and particularly petroleum—and he became especially interested in the dome near Beaumont, Texas, then known as Big Hill, now famed as Spindletop.[20] Once his fabulous gusher had been brought under control, Lucas hurried off to sign up oil leases on domes throughout the entire Gulf Coast region. Seeking a quick strike, he bored a couple of test holes into a score of these, moving on if he did not immediately find petroleum. During these hasty explorations, as we shall see, Lucas tapped two domes that later were to make sulphur history.[21]

It was oil from Spindletop at 60¢ a barrel delivered at Sulphur Mine—cheap fuel in unlimited quantities—that solved the last of Herman Frasch's problems. Thereafter, the Union Sulphur Company burned fuel oil, bought in the open market in tankers, first from Spindletop and later from the Jennings, Sour Lake, Humble, Batson, and Saratoga fields.[22] Production leaped forward sensationally. The year of Spindletop's discovery, 1901, two wells produced 3078 long tons; two years later, twelve wells—23,715 tons; in 1905, nineteen wells—218,950 tons.[23]

6

Competition Abroad

LEADERS of the Sicilian sulphur industry paid little attention to the incredible stories of this fantastic mining operation in far-off Louisiana. They recalled vividly the flat failure Jacob Hoffman had scored in their midst only four years before: many had watched his drilling rig at work. The grandsons of the men who in the 1860's would not believe that sulphuric acid can be made from a rock like pyrite, could not believe that sulphur might be mined by hot water through a hole no bigger than the head of a mandolin. Besides they had other troubles: their illogical marketing system had once more broken down; they had a competitor much closer to home.

Ancient custom that separated the interests of landowners and mine operators and put the sale of sulphur into alien hands was the root of the crisis of 1893-96. The twofold urge to overproduce was strong as ever; the temptations to speculate still enticing and more easily satisfied. Heavy taxes, imposed unevenly by a hungry, shortsighted government, added to their difficulties. Besides local taxes there were land taxes, a tax on income from mining leases, and on top of these, the sulphur export tax, which under the Bourbon king had been Lire 8.50 per metric ton (about $1.70) rose gradually under the Italian Government to Lire 11 (roughly $2.20). It was cold comfort that even in Rome it was admitted that taxes were choking the industry, killing the goose that laid the golden egg.

63

Stocks of sulphur on hand went up: the price of sulphur dropped down. All Sicily was in an uproar. Many mines were closed. There was rioting and bloodshed among the workers. The bedeviled producers, unable to agree among themselves, called upon the Government for help.

The simplest solution would have been a compulsory cartel, giving producers control over output and enabling them to sell through a single agency. The Minister of Mines liked this plan; the Minister of Finance had a pet program of his own; and the deputies in the Chamber had their own ideas deeply colored by the interests of their constituents, who were mainlanders with little sympathy for Sicilian troubles. Amid this welter of disagreements, the Government dodged decisive action, and for the second time, the distressed Sicilian sulphur monopoly was rescued by a foreign company.[1]

By one of those quirks of chemical advance, British manufacturers of alkali by the original Leblanc process had become sulphur producers. Although the backbone of the chemical industry, they now faced a dangerous competitor created by another technological advance, production of alkali by the new Solvay ammonia-soda process. Eventually this replaced the Leblanc process, but temporarily the older method survived because of its by-products, chief among them, sulphur.[2] These alkali makers at that time were recovering some 30,000 tons of very pure, finely divided sulphur that was highly favored by farmers as a fungicidal dust.

Distressed by the falling price of sulphur, the British alkali makers approached the Sicilian firm of I. & V. Florio, which for generations had been interested in sulphur and which enjoyed the highest reputation in Italy and abroad. At its head was young, energetic Ignazio Florio who eagerly embraced their proposal to rescue the Sicilian industry. A £1,000,000 corporation was organized to acquire for five years the largest possible quantity of Sicilian sulphur and the entire production of the by-product sulphur in Great

Britain. The object was to stabilize the market through centralized selling.

Thanks to the Florio reputation and the hard work of its active head, the Anglo-Sicilian Sulphur Company was able to contract for some two-thirds of the Sicilian output and to persuade the Government to abolish all taxes save a one-Lire levy on every ton of sulphur that left Sicily. The contract with the sulphur producers was curiously reminiscent of the old Taix agreement. Its flaws were quite obvious. Control over production depended on a voluntary contract with producers, and this did not legally supersede existing contracts between landowners and leaseholders which often specifically were drawn to prevent reduction of output. Anglo-Sicilian had no control over producers who refused to market through the company nor over landowners paid in kind even by producers under contract to them. The whole program encouraged a mounting stockpile which had repeatedly wrecked the sulphur market. Though many foresaw these dangers, a majority of the operators signed up.

For the first five years the arrangement proved generally satisfactory. Demand for sulphur was growing, and although outsiders took up most of this increased consumption, still Anglo-Sicilian was always able to pay 6 per cent on its preferred stock and frequently declared handsome common stock dividends. Production grew, but fortunately so did the exports. Nevertheless stocks piled up from 245,233 tons in 1896 to 306,438 in 1901.[3]

At the end of the second five-year contract period, the situation was quite different. Sulphur consumption had slackened: Sicilian production continued to increase. Stocks accumulated to 557,588 tons—over 150,000 tons more than 1905 shipments—and American sulphur had appeared on the European market.

Sicilians still refused to recognize this new Louisiana competition. But the directors of Anglo-Sicilian were worried, if still unconvinced of its reality. They attempted to test the market by selling 20,000 tons in the United States at a price well below their quota figure and not far above actual costs.

Frasch confessed that this disturbed him.[4] With a stockpile larger than his bank account he was anxious to get all the business possible, so he went to London to confer with the directors. He laid before them Union production and stockpile figures; explained frankly that he needed the American market; told them he intended to keep it even if he had to sell below Sicilian costs. He met what he described as "great lack of enthusiasm for this American humbug," and was told plainly that Anglo-Sicilian would go its own way and he could go his. He did.

Frasch appointed sales agents in the leading European countries and before he was back in America the first cargo of American sulphur had been unloaded at Marseilles. Union Sulphur representatives were busily calling on the big buyers, offering attractive prices, and the Anglo-Sicilian directors decided they had best learn the facts firsthand. Accordingly, they sent one of their Italian members, L. Dompé, to investigate. He brought back a disquieting report.

Now thoroughly alarmed—their fears were unpleasantly confirmed by the loss of £285,000-worth of business—the directors hastily covered the last year of their Sicilian contracts (expiring July 1, 1906) by agreeing with Frasch to ship no more than 75,000 tons to the United States while he agreed to export no sulphur to Europe.[5] Although the Anglo-Sicilian management appears to have been unduly panicky, they were certainly in a poor position to meet this formidable, determined competitor. Furthermore, the Solvay process had become well established during the past ten years, so that the United Alkali Company, a merger of all firms operating the older process, now depended more on its bicarbonate and bleaching powder than upon by-product sulphur.

In anticipation of the expiration of the second 5-year contracts, the Anglo-Sicilian Company had optioned a considerable portion of Sicilian production during the third period. It might have forced the issue by throwing its year's supply on the market at drastically cut prices. Such ruthless tactics were repugnant to the conservative directors, who after weighing all the causes and consequences, decided to sacrifice their option payments; not to renew another 5-year agreement; and to dissolve the corporation.

The Sicilian producers appreciated keenly the complications of the local situation which justified winding up the Anglo-Sicilian Sulphur Company. But they failed to comprehend that, in the last analysis, it was American competition that led to this drastic step, nor did they appreciate the effect this competition would have on sulphur world trade. Some of them even accused Anglo-Sicilian of using American sulphur as an excuse to get out from under the increasing load of sulphur stocks.

The Italian Government stepped in to determine the facts. It sent an investigator to America. He wrote a full report[6] which reached the following conclusions:

1—Gulf Coast sulphur deposits are very great and might be expected to produce as much as 10,000,000 tons of pure brimstone.

2—The Frasch process is practical.

3—The cost of American sulphur landed at a European port is Lire 39.50, about one-fifth below the cost of extracting and purifying Sicilian sulphur at the mine.

Unimpressed by his detailed descriptions of the Calcasieu deposit and the Union plant, the Sicilians ridiculed these scrupulously estimated cost figures, and a great clamor was raised for government intervention and a compulsory sulphur syndicate.

The Anglo-Sicilian contracts were to expire the end of the month, but no arrangements had been made for taking

over the surplus stock of the English company. Some ex-
porters were making sales for delivery far beyond August.
Yet no definite steps had been taken; nobody knew where
they stood. Again Sicily was in an uproar. Serious rioting
took place in Caltanissetta. Prompt, vigorous action became
imperative. On July 15, 1906, the Italian Parliament passed
a law creating the Consorzio Obligatorio per L'Industrial
Solfifera Siciliana—the Compulsory Consortium for the Sicilian Sulphur Industry.

This third attempt to rescue the monopoly introduced
a new device into modern economics. It was the first effort,
since the coming of the Industrial Revolution, on the part
of a national government to valorize a domestic commodity
widely sold in world trade. Not until 1908 did Brazil take
official steps to stabilize the coffee market,[7] and it was 1910
before the voluntary potash syndicate was supplemented in
Germany by the official compulsory cartel.[8] The pioneering
efforts of the Sulphur Consortium have therefore a special
significance today. Separated from us by half a century and
involving issues we can consider quite dispassionately, they
illuminate the incompatibility of practical politics and
sound economics. However nobly such controls may be
undertaken to strengthen a nation's economy for the benefit
of all its people, they inevitably become a political issue and
create an official bureaucracy which, in the end, becomes the
chief beneficiary.[9]

In the debates over the Consortium in the Italian Parliament[10] all speakers avoided like the plague any criticism of
the Sicilian landowners or mine operators or workmen. All
the blame was heaped upon the Union Sulphur Company.
The politicians slurred over not only the fundamental problem of overproduction, but also the inefficient mining
methods, the antiquated leasing system, the faulty financial
structure, and the marketing evils. By making American
sulphur the scapegoat, any serious effort to strengthen the
foundations of the Sicilian industry was neatly avoided. As

an official statement aptly summarized it, "The Consortium is a central sales office which does not impose any restrictions on production and accepts any quantities of goods which the individual mines like to produce. . . ." [11]

As set up, the Consortium was quite incapable of coming to grips with the causes of the situation it was organized to correct. Strictly political considerations forced upon it a clumsy administrative framework and a dangerous financial policy. To reconcile sound economics with smart politics, it became necessary time after time to revise both organization and finances, both devised to appease rival interests, rather than to secure competent, responsible, executive management. The Consortium suffered even more severely from its financial setup than from an incompetent management based on political rivalry. To enable producers to obtain advances on sulphur delivered but unsold, it issued a warrant upon receipt of the sulphur. These warrants were legally negotiable paper at the Bank of Sicily. The price of sulphur in hand represented by these warrants was at first set optimistically too high. Within two years a "prudential price" was adopted which was naturally set low; so low that it wrung cries of anguish from the producers.

It would be unprofitable to trace out all the compromises and expediencies forced upon the Consortium by the pressures from landowners, producers, and workmen. Long before its allotted life, 12 years, its finances had become a very expensive muddle, a pleasant salve to the sulphur industry, but no cure for its ills.

In one area the Consortium did serve the Sicilian industry well. Because it controlled sales, it was able to present a united front to the attack of American sulphur.

In the meantime Frasch had not been idle. Back in 1902, when cheap fuel from Spindletop became first available, he had engaged William R. Keever, a driller with years of experience, who came straight from the famous Jennings Field, Louisiana.[12] After drilling four wells Keever left to do some contract work, but in January 1905 he returned to Sulphur Mine. Under his competent management standard practices for drilling and equipping the wells were worked out, and he became expert in the art of hot-water mining. The notably successful extraction of sulphur from this dome was due to his skill, patience, and good judgment. With Keever in the field and John Henning in the office, Frasch had a pair of devoted representatives in charge of the Union operations.

When Union Sulphur swung fairly into production, Sicilian sulphur, which was commonly sold on six months contracts, was quoted at $24 a ton, delivered in New York. Union's first price was $17 a ton at the mine.[13] In January 1904, however, Frasch announced $18 at the mine regardless of quantity or destination. When the newborn Consortium suggested that Union keep out of Europe and give the Sicilians a share of the American market, he dropped to $14 a ton at the mine. The Consortium countered with $12 a ton delivered in New York.

By cable Frasch and Dompé, now Director General agreed to keep out of each other's markets for one year. Thereafter the Sicilians proposed that the Americans continue to stay out of Europe and that they be given a third of the American market. Dompé knew very well the seriousness of American production. However, many of his members did not yet believe the Frasch process was practical and all were sure the Louisiana production was a flash-in-the-pan. The Consortium's proposal of a share in the American market was, therefore, more than a shrewd trading move: it was good psychology at home.

At this stage of the negotiations, the Union Sulphur Company was represented in Europe by Herman Hoeckel, a short, swarthy, bald-headed German, with a black beard and thick glasses, not a prepossessing or pleasant personality, but a strong, domineering man. He knew every weakness in the Consortium's position. Official figures of production and exports were published. It was common knowledge that the Consortium owed the Bank of Sicily and the National Mining Bank for cash advanced on the warrants, more than the 10,000,000 Lire which had been allotted it for working capital. This dangerous financial position, the complaints of producers, the demands of workmen—all the Consortium's many troubles were openly and loudly discussed. Hoeckel replied to their proposal with the ultimatum that the Consortium ship no sulphur to the United States and that the northern European market be divided equally.

"Accept this proposal," he said with brutal frankness, "or else—."

These terms would have cut away two-thirds of the Sicilian sales. The Italians railed and protested, but Hoeckel was adamant. To emphasize the full implications of this disagreeable alternative, he carried on a vigorous sales campaign throughout Europe.

Early in the autumn of 1908 Frasch met in Milan with Pietro Lauro, chairman of the Consortium, and negotiations immediately took on a new complexion. Frasch made it clear that far from desiring to ruin the Sicilian industry, he had a lively sympathy for the 250,000 Sicilians dependent upon the mines.[14] He withdrew Hoeckel's harsh terms.

Once a reasonable basis for a working agreement was reached, Frasch returned to America to determine the legal status of a contract between Union and the Consortium. The latter being an official organization, the contract was in effect with the Italian Government. Accordingly, he laid the matter before the Secretary of Commerce, and obtained an opinion that it was quite lawful for an American corporation to make such a contract allocating markets abroad, but that it would be contrary to our anti-trust laws to divide or limit in any way the American market.[15]

Back in Rome early in February 1908, Frasch came to an agreement with Lauro and representatives of the Italian Government, which was to last until the legal expiration of the Consortium, July 31, 1918. It stipulated that the world market, outside the U.S.A., was to be reviewed annually and allocated on the basis of two-thirds to the Consortium and one-third to the Union Sulphur Company. Any mention of the American market was scrupulously avoided, but minimum prices were agreed upon, equivalent to $22 per long ton, c.i.f. New York, and for domestic sales, $18 f.o.b. the mine. Any variations from these quotations were subject to mutual consent.

Year after year the Sicilian producers asked for higher prices, but it was evident that any price rise would not only promote further use of pyrites but also tempt overproduction in Sicily.[16] It was further agreed that the Consortium and Union would jointly support an office in Hamburg to promote the use of sulphur in industry and agriculture.

Both parties lived up to this agreement sincerely and honestly. It stabilized the markets, saved the Sicilian industry, and actually gave consumers the advantage of a known fixed price considerably lower than they had been paying. Nevertheless it did not cure the internal ills of the Consortium.

There was still much loose talk among Sicilians that Union production would not last long and European buyers were warned not to tie up with so uncertain a supply. Accordingly, Frasch decided to build a grinding plant at Marseilles, and he instructed Hoeckel to make an impressive demonstration, orders he executed to the letter. An enormous plant was built with foundations and walls so solid that during World War I the French accused Hoeckel of having built an embryo fortress for the Germans. It was a scare spy story, but Hoeckel, thoroughly frightened, slipped away and so far as the sulphur industry is concerned, vanished completely.

In 1912 an unexpected legal complication upset the marketing agreement. The Union Sulphur Company was incorporated in New Jersey and during the governorship of

Woodrow Wilson, the famous "Five Sisters Law" was passed, certain clauses of which appeared to make an international contract illegal for a New Jersey corporation. In his apartment at the Plaza Hotel in New York, Frasch sat down with the Company's attorney, Frederick W. Whitridge and John Henning to study this unforeseen problem.

Frasch, who was meticulous in fulfilling all his commitments, was loathe to repudiate a contract entered into in good faith and so scrupulously carried out. Moreover, he feared to disturb the stable price. Whitridge insisted, however, that no consideration weighed against the possibilities of involving the company in an illegal contract. Henning pointed out that the Sicilians must by now be convinced that Louisiana brimstone could successfully invade any market and would therefore not be apt to disrupt the price structure. Very reluctantly Frasch cabled over his own signature "All agreements must be abrogated: you go your way and I will go mine." [17]

Then Sicilian sulphur had to be purchased on two months' leeway on shipping date since the seller had the right to deliver any time within 60 days. There were no guarantees as to quality or weights. If a buyer secured a lower price, he was apt to receive material containing enough "thirds" to more than make up for the cost saving. The American buyer "took Sicilian sulphur as is and liked it." [19]

Since 1905 the position of the Union Sulphur Company had enormously strengthened. The output had risen from 220,000 long tons to 787,735 in 1912 and exports from 11,522 to 57,736 long tons.[18] Furthermore, the staff was loyal, experienced, and capable, and the company's financial position was exceedingly strong.

As salesman and executive, Herman Frasch was proving himself as able as he was as a chemist and engineer. His price policy showed his appreciation of the advantages to the consumer of a steady, open price, quoted alike to all. He believed that a reasonable price would help increase the sale of sulphur and as early as 1898 he supported research aimed at finding new uses for sulphur. He engaged Francis H. Pough, whose ten years' experience as manager of the sulphur refinery of T. & S. C. White at Bayonne, New Jersey, antedated the advent of Louisiana sulphur.

At the refinery Frasch built in Brooklyn, New York, Pough worked out a process to produce "ventilated sulphur," competitive with a very light, fluffy form of flowers of sulphur produced in Germany. Shortly afterward he introduced carbon dioxide gas into the grinders to prevent explosions. Pough also made contributions in the sales-service field. At the Barnes Bros. Nursery, Yalesville, Connecticut, he initiated experimental insecticide work. Later he co-operated with the U. S. Department of Agriculture and established fellowships at Cornell University. All this was pioneering work, quite comparable in chemical merchandising to Frasch's accomplishments in engineering.

7

Competition at Home

IF THE SUCCESS of the Union Sulphur Company were watched
from Sicily in a spirit of hopeful scepticism, in Texas it was
hailed with hearty optimism. The whirlwind exploration
of the salt domes had struck some oil, but there was no
second Spindletop. So interest in these mounds cooled off.
It was rekindled and given a new focus—sulphur. Stories of
the big money being made over in Louisiana lost nothing in
the telling.

One hot, sunny morning in June 1906, the senior partner
of the oil prospecting team of Staiti and Bright walked into
the Planters & Mechanics National Bank in Houston, carrying a battered tin water bucket. He went straight to the
desk of the cashier, George Hamman, and sitting down,
tucked the bucket between his legs. Its contents were hidden
by a newspaper.

Henry T. Staiti mopped his brow and leaning across the
desk asked, "What do you know about sulphur?"

Hamman had visited the sulphur mine and confessed he
knew more or less about the Union Sulphur Company and
the Frasch process.

"Well, what do you think of these?" asked Staiti removing
the newspaper and revealing a pailful of coarse, grayish-white
cylinders of rock, as thick as a man's wrist, four, six inches
long, all streaked and splashed with yellow.

Without waiting for a reply he continued. "They're cores
from Bryanmound which we have tied up with mineral

75

rights leases.[1] Would you be interested in exploring that dome for sulphur?" Hamman was very much interested.

Back in 1901, Lucas himself had drilled two wells at Bryanmound.[2] The first struck a big flow of hydrogen sulphide gas which could not be controlled, and when the second well struck no oil, Lucas moved on. Several other attempts were made to find petroleum in Bryanmound. In all seven wells, all dry holes, were drilled prior to 1905 when Staiti was attracted by the sulphur possibilities. No clear record exists of the discovery of sulphur here. Local tradition credits a well drilled in 1904 by a Dr. Reed, as the first to show the mineral.[3]

George Hamman's interest in this project took a practical form. He interested Edward F. Simms who in turn persuaded the Texas Company to advance $100,000 on a royalty basis to explore Bryanmound.[4] A number of wells were cored. No petroleum was found, but there were unmistakable indications of sulphur. The Texas Company management decided they were in the oil business, not sulphur. Simms and Hamman, however, were steadfast in sulphur's future, so they organized the Gulf Development Company. In 1908 they took up additional leases.

The principal landowners were the Bryan family who had given their name to this conspicuous historic landmark near the mouth of the Brazos River. On the west bank, between the Gulf of Mexico and the mound, had stood the Spanish town of Quintana,[5] the last vestiges of which were wiped out by the hurricane and tidal wave of 1900. On the east bank, a mile above the river mouth, was the town of Velasco. Here had been established the first free port of entry into Texas, then a Mexican province, and here, in 1823, Stephen F. Austin made his headquarters. He brought 300 colonists for which services the Mexican Government granted him thousands of acres.[6]

Austin had his pick of land and it is easy to see why he chose 177 acres on this mound. It rises some 20 feet above the level, treeless plain, all streaked with marshy swamps, the home of flocks of big gray herons, the wild range of the famous Texas longhorn cattle. In such a landscape this rise of land, like the island in the Calcasieu swamp, was an oasis.

Sometime between 1855 and 1861, 132½ acres of Austin's grant were sold by his heirs to W. J. Bryan. Besides the original Austin grant, three other large tracts of land on this dome, granted to their original owners by the State of Texas, eventually became the site of the sulphur-mining. It is interesting that the owners of one tract thought so little of it that in 1867 Texas took over 1000 acres for back taxes and sold them for $6.97. The buyer later sold 85 acres for $150 and the remaining for $2085. The Bryan family liked this mound that bore their name and they gradually acquired considerable acreage.[7]

While Staiti continued drilling, Simms and Hamman rounded up a group of wealthy Texans. Their plans to develop the dome fell through because the Frasch patents had not yet expired and there was no other known method of recovering the sulphur.[8] By this time at least 27 test wells had been cored. It was said that more or less sulphur had been found in all and that some 300 acres had now been proved up. Encouragement must have been substantial, for the Gulf Development Company, which had been operating under leases, now began to secure purchase options in the Bryanmound area.

During the winter of 1909 a colorful personality was injected by chance into the sulphur situation at Bryanmound. Francis R. Pemberton, son of General Pemberton, the Confederate defender of Vicksburg, came to Houston from St. Louis to make some timberland investigations. This charming gentleman of the Old School of the Old South had had a long and varied financial investment career and counted among his close friends many important political and financial figures of the day.[9] The Kirby Lumber Company assigned a young man named Brooks to guide this distinguished visitor and together they traveled about the country inspecting Kirby properties. One evening on the train going to New Orleans from Beaumont, Major Pemberton's attention was attracted by the red glare of the furnace fires at Sulphur Mine. This unexpected industrial activity roused his curiosity and from Brooks he learned the story of the Frasch operation.[10]

Keen as a bird dog for any business opportunity, the chance to visit the sulphur plant was too good to be missed, so he left the train at Lake Charles and spent the next three days at Sulphur Mine. Back in Houston he promptly negotiated an informal option on the leases and options of the Gulf Development Corporation. On his way north he stopped at Charleston, South Carolina, to discuss this new proposition with W. D. Chisolm, a fertilizer man.[11] Any fertilizer manufacturer would naturally be interested in a likely sulphur proposition, and Chisolm accompanied Pemberton to Richmond where they met H. A. M. Smith, and Sidell Tilghman of the Virginia-Carolina Chemical Company.

The Frasch patents were about to expire. It seemed possible to develop Bryanmound by some modification of the hot-water process without legal infringement. Accordingly, they organized the Brazos Syndicate to take over Pemberton's option on the Bryanmound property. The project needed big money so Tilghman and Pemberton went to New York and presented the sulphur idea to J. P. Morgan, the elder. He was interested, if the deposits were as good as they believed, and they invited him to investigate. Charles Steele of the Morgan firm asked Bernard M. Baruch, who had made a name for himself in the development of Western copper mining properties, to explore the sulphur proposal with the understanding that, if the prospect was worthy, Morgan would furnish the capital and Baruch would do the work on a 60-40 profit basis.[12] Flattered to be working with the most important financial house in the country, Baruch consulted the noted mining engineer, Seeley W. Mudd, and together they went to Houston. Pemberton was to whip his informal option into definite legal form, if possible upon better terms, and Mudd was to make a professional appraisal of the sulphur property. Mudd telegraphed a trusted assistant, Spencer C. Browne, and they all met in Houston, July 4, 1910, the day that Jack Johnson beat Jim Jeffries for the heavyweight championship at Reno, Nevada.

During the spirited contract negotiations, Browne, to familiarize himself with oil drilling methods made a tour of the Gulf Coast region with an eye open for other likely sulphur deposits. During this scouting trip he learned of a conspicuous showing of sulphur at Big Hill, another dome, near Matagorda some 60 miles southwest of Bryanmound close to the Gulf.[13] Simms and Pemberton having reached an agreement, Browne was recalled and began the first scrupulously controlled test of the sulphur deposit. He recognized the difficulty of securing satisfactory sulphur cores. The drillers naïvely assumed that any soft material penetrated was pure brimstone, but Browne tried several methods to get reliable samples and finally designed a reverse-flow system which brought the water and the cuttings out through the inside of the drill pipes. During the summer of 1910 until April 1911, eleven such test holes were drilled. Mudd and Browne reported: "The Bryan deposit is good but spotty: the chances of profitable mining are 50-50."

Baruch carried this report to J. P. Morgan, but in his presentation he made what he has himself confessed, was a costly error:

> Explaining that we could buy the whole property outright, including royalties, for $500,000, I added that I was willing to gamble half of this sum from my own funds. 'Gamble' was a poor choice of language. I should have said 'invest.'
>
> "I never gamble," replied Mr. Morgan with a gesture that signified the interview was over and the adventure closed as far as he was concerned.[14]

Houston was now buzzing with sulphur stories. The success of the Union operation; the imminent expiration of the Frasch patents; the interest in sulphur displayed by Wall Street; all incited gossip and reports of sulphur showings began coming in from domes all over the Gulf Coast. The prospects of keen competition seemed certain and the Mudd-Browne report was not too sanguine. Convinced there would soon be an overproduction of sulphur, the Virginia-Carolina group withdrew. Baruch came back to Texas to negotiate for the Brazos Syndicate, but he and Simms could not agree upon a price.[15] During the next couple of years Simms and Hamman tried to interest various people in the Bryanmound property. They called upon Frasch and offered it to the Union Sulphur Company. His reply was curt and final.

"We have all the sulphur that we need, and I do not believe that anyone else knows how to get sulphur out of a dome." [16]

Major Pemberton also continued to promote this sulphur project. In New York he called upon a National City Bank vice-president, and as a matter concerning Texas, he referred it to one of the directors, Eric P. Swenson. The organization of the Freeport Sulphur Company and the development of Bryanmound were chiefly due to the foresight and enthusiasm of this vigorous Texan. He was the son of the first Swede, S. M. Swenson, to come to the State. The elder Swenson, so the story goes, was wrecked off Sandy Hook in the ship that brought him to America and landed stark naked. He drifted down to Texas in 1838, and beginning as a peddler, became one of Texas' greatest landowners, the confidant and friend and banker of Sam Houston. His son, Eric, went north to college at Trinity in Connecticut and stayed on to enter the banking business, but he retained his love for Texas and for Texans. He was a man of keen mind and great energy. He made his decisions quickly and finally, and there was never any doubt who was the boss in any project with which he was connected. After his father's death he spent much time in Texas and there the formal decisive financier of New York became a hale-fellow-well-met comrade.[17]

Swenson decided to investigate sulphur firsthand. He visited Bryanmound and walked sunk in deep thought over the site of the old Spanish seaport at the mouth of the Brazos. He had promoted two townsites in his vast properties in West Texas and he envisioned a bustling city, a freeport (hence the name of the sulphur company) at the mouth of the biggest Texas river, a rival to Galveston and Corpus Christi, an ocean outlet for fast-growing Houston.

November 6, 1911, the Gulf Development Company gave a 30-day option to S. M. Swenson & Sons on some 10,000 acres on and adjacent to the Bryan dome. Only about 800 acres covered the caprock proper, but these included all the sulphur area except 15 acres.

The month of grace was to be employed by Simms in taking up the options which the Gulf Development group held to purchase land in this area, depositing the titles with George Hamman as trustee. Swenson was to arrange the financing of the purchase and check the patent situation.

In New York, E. P. Swenson set up the Vanderlip-Swenson-Tilghman Syndicate with a pooled capital of $700,000, $100,-000 of which was paid over on November 30 to the American Sulphur Royalty Company, representing the Simms-Hamman-Staiti interests. If the New York group took up this option, it agreed to pay an additional $300,000; erect a sulphur-extraction plant by June 1, 1913; pay $1.75 a ton royalty on the first 200,000 tons of sulphur extracted, and thereafter a royalty of 75¢ per ton.[18]

The Vanderlip-Swenson-Tilghman Syndicate was made up of two groups: fertilizer men in Richmond, members of the Brazos Syndicate, and financiers in New York, friends of Vanderlip and Swenson. Although the Virginia-Carolina Company had officially withdrawn, several of its directors were personally still interested. Sidell Tilghman was one of the largest and most active participants. Also heavily interested was John Skelton Williams, head of the investment house of John L. Williams & Sons, founded by his grandfather in Richmond shortly after the Civil War, and a prominent factor in the Virginia-Carolina fertilizer merger.

The previous March, Frank A. Vanderlip, returning with Mrs. Vanderlip from Palm Beach, had stopped off in his private car at Sulphur Mine to visit the Union operation. It so impressed him that he headed up the new sulphur project, and interested the financiers James Stillman, Samuel Mac-Roberts, John S. Steele, and John Hayes Hammond in it.

It was proposed to extract the sulphur at Bryanmound by the Frasch process on the expiration of the patents. Subsequently, the Union Sulphur Company brought suit on the grounds that the Frasch process was impractical without the use of subsequent supplementary patents issued to Frasch and still unexpired. This contention was upheld in the U. S. District Court, but the U. S. Circuit Court of Appeals unanimously reversed this decision because the claims of the supplementary patents were invalid as not revealing true invention.[19] The Supreme Court refused to review this decision in favor of the Freeport Sulphur Company.

On November 30, 1911, the Simms-Swenson option contract was executed.[20] By warranty deeds[21] Hamman as trustee transferred title to some 10,000 acres and simultaneously, S. M. Swenson & Sons turned over this property to the Vanderlip-Swenson-Tilghman Syndicate. On July 12, 1912, the Freeport Sulphur Company was incorporated in Texas, with $200,000 paid in capital (2000 shares at $100 par value each), and it took over the sulphur property. At the same time the Freeport Townsite Company was organized to develop a city on the west bank of the Brazos and it acquired most of the land off the dome area. The Freeport Sulphur Company had contracted to have a sulphur extraction plant on-stream by June 1, 1913. The task involved much more than building the operating unit.

The storm of 1909, the year before Mudd and Browne

investigated Bryanmound, had all but wiped out the town of Velasco and wrecked the old, single track railway from that town to Anchor where it connected with the International-Great Northern Railroad. On the west bank, the location of Swenson's dream city of Freeport, was a dilapidated dock, terminal of the Velasco ferry, about which clustered a few little corrals and shanties. A mile away, on the edge of the Gulf stood the fine old Bryan residence and a little west, the home of the Munson family. Except a cowhouse and a corral, there was nothing else on the landscape —a vast spread of low-lying prairie, only two or three feet above sea level, frequently submerged by an extra-high tide. Crossing this marsh, the old road had to be rebuilt three miles from the river to the mound. To protect it and the proposed townsite, a six-foot levee was thrown up all along the edge of the river. To provide ample water supplies for the Frasch operation, wells were driven and a three-mile canal, ten feet deep, was dug from the Brazos to a big storage basin beside the mound. The townsite was laid out; a hotel, the Tarpon Inn, built; a large warehouse erected on the opposite riverbank. Since it was proposed to burn oil from Mexico, receiving tanks were erected close to the river and storage tanks provided at the mound. All this work had to be synchronized with the building of the plant itself.

Perry Bryan, who lived with his wife, Octavia, in the big house near the Gulf, had a little 12 x 24-foot storm refuge, a tiny house anchored by two heavy wire cables, on the top of the mound. The big, easy-going rancher permitted the company to use this building with the distinct understanding however, that he retained all right to it as a haven in case of emergency. Here, Ben Andrews set up working headquarters.[22]

Andrews, who had worked for Union and had made the first report on Bryanmound for the Brazos Syndicate,[23] was hired by Freeport as general manager. He was an active-minded, genial man, a competent engineer, but opinionated and

prone to hold tenaciously to his own ideas. Freeport contracted with Westinghouse, Church, Kerr & Company to
build the power plant, and they called Homer S. Burns, one
of their field superintendents, from a job in Canada which
he left with the temperature at —30° to land in Texas where
the thermometer stood at 80°.

Transportation and labor were basic problems. Every
pipe coupling, every bag of cement, every tenpenny nail,
had to be brought to Velasco, either over the rickety railroad or by the old barge canal from Galveston. Shipments
were irregular and much delayed. Everything must be
brought across the river on a rope cable ferry and then hauled
to the minesite. To get one of the big air compressors on
location took three days and the help of 28 mules. After
every rain the country became a sea of sticky gumbo. While
the surveyors were laying out the town lots of Freeport, it
became a standing joke that "of three places not to build
a town, this is all three of them."

It was hard to find good construction workmen, until one
day a big, raw-boned Irishman turned up, "Dusty" Sullivan,
whom Burns recognized as just the right type. He asked
him, "Where do the gang hang out?"

"At Sixty-six," he answered, a saloon in Houston. Burns
went up there and soon got together a good working crew.

Amid all this activity, the drilling crew were driving three
wells to be steamed when the plant was ready. Bryanmound
was, as the oilman says, very "gassy." Lucas had been driven
off by hydrogen sulphide, and during the oil prospecting days
a number of times the gas pressure had blasted great craters
in the surface, sometimes blowing up the drilling rig. Most
of this pressure had by now been taken off. But there was
still enough gas to be inconvenient—even dangerous—due
to its poisonous character.

All this work was completed far ahead of schedule on
November 12, 1912. From the veranda of the new Tarpon
Inn, an auction of town lots in the embryo city of Freeport

was held. Back in the shadows, in a big cane rocking chair, sat E. P. Swenson. At five o'clock news was brought to him that the sulphur was flowing. So interested was he in the sale of lots and the thriving city he visualized that he refused to go out to the mine.

Out on the mound, George Hamman, tinkling with excitement at this consummation of his ten years' work, had a dump cart filled with great yellow chunks and delivered that night in front of the Tarpon Inn. In the morning when Swenson and his associates came down to breakfast, there it stood. There it remained for several months, a bright yellow monument of reality, a sample of the first sulphur ever mined in Texas.

8

From Pyrite to Brimstone

LIKE A GIGANTIC oval-shaped cookie—4000 feet long, 2400 feet wide, 20 feet thick—Big Hill lies but a mile from Matagorda Bay, a shallow strip of water separated from the Gulf of Mexico by a low, narrow sand spit, 50 miles long. It is 20 miles south by east from Bay City; 80 miles southwest of Houston. In the oil rush following the Spindletop boom, this was one of the first domes drilled. As an oil producer it was a conspicuous failure.

The earliest petroleum prospectors at Big Hill were William Cash of Bay City associated with A. B. Mayes and Cash & Luckel of Houston. Their first well reached 840 feet in January 1902, where it struck a tremendous flow of poisonous hydrogen sulphide gas. They drilled two more wells without success and abandoned the location.[1]

Shortly afterwards, a little north of these three test holes, a significant well was drilled by the Lane-Sutherland Syndicate in which T. W. Lane of Lane City and John Sutherland of Bay City, were partners.[2] They struck a modest flow of oil in the caprock and at 900 feet ran into a 93-foot layer of sulphur-bearing limestone. They persisted to 1200 feet where they abandoned the well in salt water. Lane sold his interest in the syndicate to Dr. T. S. Griffith who made a new location on the very top of the hill. In May 1904, after penetrating the caprock a short distance, this well began flowing an estimated 2500 barrels of oil with 3000 to 4000 barrels of water a day. This moderate success revived interest in Big

86

Hill and about fifteen wells were driven so that in 1904 production from the dome reached 151,936 barrels of heavy,
green oil. Late that autumn, however, salt water suddenly
appeared in almost every well on Big Hill, and in such
serious quantities that output dropped abruptly to 1200
barrels a day and within a couple of months had fallen off to
400 barrels.

Just at this time oil was struck in the Humble field and
Big Hill was deserted. Only John Sutherland was left. By
means of windmills he continued to pump several wells,
taking from 150 to 200 barrels a day. The hurricane in the
autumn of 1905 destroyed his derricks and windmills. Oil
production at Big Hill ceased.

During 1908, two St. Louis men, A. C. Einstein and John
W. Harrison, came to Texas prospecting for sulphur. Their
first exploratory work was done at Liberty where they failed
to get promising returns. Having heard from Joe Embry, a
driller who had worked at Big Hill, of the conspicuous sulphur showings there, they negotiated through C. F. Stevens,
a lawyer from Liberty, a sulphur lease with the Matagorda
Oil Company which had acquired the old Sutherland-Griffith
rights. The wildcat drilling for oil here had generally been
on the top of the elevation and most of the oil was produced
in the caprock from moderately shallow wells. However,
deeper drillings had brought up substantial cuttings of sulphur. Although, owing to the porous character of the caprock, these showings proved later to be misrepresentative
samples, they encouraged Einstein and Harrison. Their first
test on the northeast slope obtained results so tangible that
they were able to interest a fellow St. Louisan, Theodore F.
Meyer, the president of the Meyer Brothers Drug Company.

This St. Louis group organized the Gulf Sulphur Com-
pany. The incorporators were E. B. Pickett of Liberty, John
S. Sutherland and John M. Corbett of Bay City, R. O.
Middlebrook and Hugo Spitzer of Matagorda, A. C. Einstein,
J. W. Harrison, Theodore F. Meyer, and J. M. Allen, all of

St. Louis. Except Meyer and Pickett, these incorporators were elected directors and Einstein was named president.[3]

Exploratory drilling had just gotten under way during the summer of 1910, when Spencer C. Browne appeared on the scene. While waiting for the Bryanmound negotiations between Bernard Baruch and the Simms-Harman-Staiti Syndicate to reach the option stage, he was scouting for any likely brimstone deposits. He heard rumors of sulphur at the Matagorda property and came over to investigate firsthand.

If commercial quantities of sulphur were indicated, the St. Louis group originally intended to go into sulphur mining themselves. The expense of drilling proved greater than they had anticipated and they quickly learned that a steaming plant would call for a far heavier outlay than they were prepared to provide. Knowing that Browne was assistant to Mudd, who in turn was consultant for the important New York interests represented by Baruch, they appreciated the opportunity to interest through him people with ample means to develop the property. Accordingly, Spencer Browne was made welcome and shown everything. He was immediately and favorably impressed with what he saw. Back in Houston, Browne reported to Baruch and Mudd, indicating quite plainly that in his opinion the Matagorda property was surely as promising as Bryanmound, probably more so.

After Baruch's Brazos Syndicate had secured options on Bryanmound and Spencer Browne had explored and reported on the property, Browne accompanied Major Pemberton to Charleston to confer with the fertilizer people who were interested in the project. It began to appear likely that the Bryanmound negotiations would come to naught, so Browne went to St. Louis to meet with the owners of the Matagorda property. After talking with them he went on to New York, persuading Einstein and Allen to follow him there for a conference with Baruch. Nothing definite developed at the time. As far as the Brazos Syndicate was concerned, any sulphur deal had been called off.

Mudd, however, continued to be actively interested in sulphur.[4] At his instigation negotiations with the Gulf Sulphur Company were reopened in 1916. Mudd without much difficulty revived Baruch's interest in sulphur and together they approached J. P. Morgan. Morgan called in William Boyce Thompson. Colonel Thompson was won over by his professional colleague's enthusiasm for sulphur potentialities in general and for the Big Hill prospects in particular. Acting upon his recommendations, Morgan agreed to take part in the financing necessary to develop Big Hill.

Although the St. Louis people still held an interest, Bernard Baruch and Seeley Mudd had obtained control of the Gulf Sulphur Company. The company was reorganized and Mudd was elected president and he set about quietly acquiring the entire dome area.[5] Henry F. J. Knobloch, one of Boyce Thompson's associates, was sent down to Matagorda County in 1916 as secretary and director of Gulf Sulphur in charge of corporate matters during the period of land negotiations.[6] When, on July 16, 1918, the name was changed to the Texas Gulf Sulphur Company and the capitalization increased to $5,000,000, Knobloch continued as secretary and in 1919 he was elected treasurer.

The original plan was to develop the property modestly: one 4000 h.p. boiler to steam but one or two wells at a time in order to test the practical operation of the Frasch process in this dome and to try out the sulphur market. A new producer could expect to meet determined competition.

The field work was under Spencer Browne, but as his headquarters were in New York, he called in W. T. Lundy, a young consulting mining engineer from San Francisco who had graduated from the College of Mines, University of California, with a M. E. degree in 1907. Lundy took charge of the field operations.

Our entrance into the war abruptly changed all these plans. Colonel Mudd resigned to go into war work and his place

as president was filled by Walter H. Aldridge, chief engineer
on the staff of William Boyce Thompson. Baruch had been
appointed the head of the War Industries Board, and out in
the field both Browne and Lundy had resigned to go into
military service. Despite these upsets in the organization
and in the face of their incomplete control of the dome area,
came the pressing, patriotic need to increase the country's
sulphur supplies to meet war needs. The Government
began urging that Big Hill, which they considered the most
promising means of quickly enlarging the nation's sulphur
output, be brought promptly into production.

The war's drastic effects upon sulphuric acid were immediate and direct: it became at once a critical material.
Demand ballooned and quickly shifted to military uses. In
peacetime the largest consumer of sulphur in the United
States, the fertilizer industry, takes about one-third of our
sulphuric acid output. War certainly does not cancel out
the need for crops, but the need for ammunition is even more
pressing. Ninety days after we entered the war, August 1917,
American consumption of sulphur in acid, on the basis of 100
per cent H_2SO_4, was estimated as follows:[7]

INDUSTRIES	TONS PER MONTH	PER CENT OF TOTAL
Explosives (direct and indirect, including phenol and nitric acid)	140,000	35.0
Fertilizers	111,000	27.8
Oil refining	45,000	11.2
Chemicals, drugs, etc.	38,500	9.6
Steel (pickling and galvanizing)	36,500	9.1
Storage batteries, metallurgical work, including plating	15,200	3.8
Textiles, rubber, paper, etc.	5,200	1.3
Lithopone, paints, dyes, glues, glycerin	5,300	1.3
Miscellaneous	3,800	0.9

Explosives head the list, but as the War Industries Board
recognized, nine-tenths of all acid consumption was essential

for war purposes. Furthermore, the chemical uses of the acids are such that substitutes were hard to find. Conversely, it was not easy to divert any considerable part from the 10 per cent so-called nonessential uses.

When we entered the war our production of sulphuric acid (figured at 100 per cent H_2SO_4) was 4.8 million tons a year. November 1, 1918, just before the Armistice, our total capacity had been increased to 501,000 tons per month, or at the rate of 6 million tons annually. In 16 months sulphuric acid production had been raised one-third. This had been accomplished in the face of shortages and a dire need for high-test acid which compelled changes in raw materials and in techniques. In 1914, American sulphuric acid makers had all but completely switched from their traditional raw material, Sicilian brimstone, to Spanish pyrites. During the war this raw material cycle was again reversed. The percentage of sulphuric acid made from the various raw materials reveals this graphically:[8]

YEAR	FROM BRIMSTONE	FROM PYRITES		BY-PRODUCT RECOVERY FROM ZINC AND COPPER ORES
		DOMESTIC	FOREIGN	
1885	85	13	1	1
1891	80	10	9	1
1895	75	7	17	1
1901	16	26	55	3
1909	2	20	64	12
1914	3	17	60	20
1919	48	15	21	16
1925	68	6	13	13
1929	69	7	10	14

Modern ammunition strongly favored the contact process fed by brimstone. Black powder, a simple mixture of saltpeter, charcoal and sulphur, had been replaced by smokeless powder based on nitrocellulose. Two new weapons, high powered disruptive explosives, such as trinitrotoluol (TNT), and combat gases had been introduced. All these complex compounds can only be made with pure, high-test sulphuric acid.[9]

Although relying chiefly on imported Spanish pyrites, American acid manufacturers did not seriously lack this raw material until 1917.[10] Then pyrites imports, which in 1916 were 1,224,662 tons, dropped to 967,340 tons and next year were further cut to 496,782 tons.[11] A shortage of sulphur-bearing materials was plainly imminent.[12] It became critical when imports of Canadian pyrites were reduced from 400,000 to 200,000 long tons because of the shortage of lake steamers and the delivery of domestic pyrites dropped from 800,000 to 600,000 tons because of labor shortages.[13] For lack of pyrites, acid output would be a million tons short of requirements.[14] A switch to brimstone was the only solution and the War Industries Board bestirred itself mightily to promote this technical revolution. In accomplishing this feat, it also revolutionized the American sulphur industry.

When in 1912, Frasch cancelled his agreement with the Sicilian Consortium it promptly withdrew from the American market which was then consuming about 250,000 tons a year, most of which went into sulphite pulp. Consumption in insecticides and fungicides, and in rubber for vulcanization was steadily increasing. The brimstone then bought by chemical manufacturers was insignificant.

Herman Frasch resented the arrival of the Freeport Sulphur Company which he naturally considered an illegal, unwarranted invasion of his own domain. But his strong feelings did not cloud his appreciation of the situation: he foresaw a three-cornered battle royal for the world's markets. Accordingly, he stepped up Union output to 786,605 tons in 1912, which was over 100,000 tons more than the entire 1911 world consumption.[15] He strengthened his four European sales offices and added two new steamers to Union's fleet of freighters.[16] The Panama Canal had just opened, presenting an opportunity to invade the West Coast and Oriental markets then held by Japanese volcanic sulphur. When Freeport came into production, November 12, 1912, Union was poised for a sulphur war. Armed with a seven-figure bank account and a stockpile of 690,000 tons, led by a determined, daring president, the battle promised to be historic. It was never fought: two unexpected, unrelated events intervened. On May 1, 1914, Herman Frasch died in Paris.[17] On August 4, Germany invaded Belgium.

Overnight the promised competitive battle was transformed into a struggle for greater production. Every ton of brimstone Union and Freeport could bring to the surface was wanted by the Allies and by our expanded munitions industries. Frasch's stockpile became literally a lifesaver.

To prevent runaway prices, the natural result of these exorbitant demands, Union agreed with the Council of National Defense, July 1917, to sell to munitions and fertilizer makers at $22 a long ton, f.o.b. mine. While not signing this agreement, Freeport concurred in principle and co-operated fully. This voluntary ceiling price, the first adopted during the war, was religiously maintained.

In order to obtain this price, fertilizer plants using pyrites in the chamber process were required to report monthly their stocks of this raw material on hand. They could burn sulphur to enrich their SO_2 gas from pyrite, but were required to use up their stocks of the ore before completely turning their operation over to brimstone. A technical booklet was written and distributed, instructing how sulphur might be burned in a pyrites furnace at small expense for the changeover and how a simple low-cost burner for sulphur could be built. In the contact acid plants the use of sulphur was also encouraged. Since it eliminated the elaborate gas purification to remove arsenic and other impurities in pyrites gas, the use of sulphur simplified the construction of new plants. Furthermore, sulphur insured maximum production from existing equipment.

During October 1917, engineers detailed by the Bureau of Mines visited the Union and Freeport properties to determine the stock of brimstone on hand and explore the possibilities of increasing production. Both plants were thoroughly inspected. Both companies made their technical data and statistical reports freely available.[18] Combined stocks were 1,440,000 tons and it was estimated that in the ensuing year 1,400,000 tons could be surfaced—500,000 tons from Freeport, 900,000 tons from Union. At this time Freeport had drilled 124 holes and Union nearly 600. Reserves at Bryanmound were estimated at 2,675,000 and at Sulphur Mine, 4,706,000, a total for both domes of 7,281,000 long tons. The report continued:

Freeport has three plants with a total capacity of 23,800 hp maintained in operation constantly at from 150 to 175% of the rating, heating in all about 8,000,000 gallons of water for 24 hours, which is adequate for the steaming of six wells under ordinary circumstances, producing 1,500 tons of sulphur daily.

Union has eight boiler plants with a total rated capacity of 21,480 boiler hp, six plants with a rating of 16,230 boiler hp at present in use about 150% of rating and heating some 8,000,000 gallons of water for 24 hours. Lower temperature for water is maintained at Union and seven wells in operation are producing 2500 tons daily. Their plants are old and built on sunken ground and so it is considered unsafe to depend upon continuous operations. Construction of a new boiler plant requires about a year's time under favorable circumstances.

It was also pointed out that the companies were each burning approximately 4000 barrels of fuel oil a day. Freeport drew its supply from Mexico by boat. Union was buying partly in Mexico and partly in Louisiana and Texas.

A month after war was declared on Germany, General Pershing authorized military protection for the Freeport plant, situated at the mouth of the Brazos River and hence vulnerable to attack by a sea raider, and the company approved the expenditure of $2500 for barracks.[19] In June, a guard under a Deputy Marshall was established on the property.[20] In August, Company A, Third Texas milita arrived, and having previously voted an addition to the barracks, the directors authorized the purchase of a car for the use of the officers.[21]

Production at Bryanmound grew markedly. Experience in drilling and steaming this very porous formation raised the average output per well. Under C. A. Jones, a reorganized personnel increased the efficiency and economy of the whole operation. In January 1914, Jones named P. George Maercky his assistant and shortly afterward Homer S. Burns, who had been supervising the boiler plants as engineer representing the contractors, Westinghouse, Church, Kerr, & Co., became superintendent of the steam plants. Jones had recommended this appointment to E. P. Swenson, and one day when the president was on one of his periodic visits to Texas, they stopped in Burns' office and he said:

"Isn't it about time we put Burns on our payroll? And let's make it retroactive to January first."

"But, Mr. Swenson," the engineer protested, "that is not right. I am working for WCK and I hope they'll soon be sending me to another job."

"What, you don't like Texas?" To Swenson such a thought was unthinkable.

"No, I certainly do not."

"Well, Jones, we'll have to make this man like Texas, won't we?"

The superintendent nodded and the president named a salary calculated to have this effect.[22] And so Homer Burns entered upon his lifelong career with the Freeport Company.

Another wheelhorse of the organization, Lewis Mims, came from the Southern Pacific Railway. To expedite rail shipments in and out of Bryanmound in 1915 a spur track from

Freeport to the loading dock was built. Swenson was a director of the Southern Pacific and Jones went to the road's president, asking for a good man to get materials and to help build this three and a half mile line. Mims, with 20 years' experience in engineering, operation, and maintenance departments, was assigned to the task. This was not his first

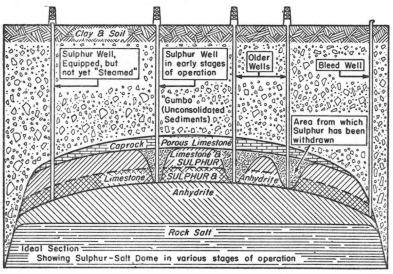

FIG. 5. Cross section of typical Gulf Coast sulphur deposit showing various stages of the Frasch mine operation.

experience at Freeport since he had supervised the treating of all piling and timbers for the dock and the five-mile trestle for the fuel pipeline. After the spur line was laid, Mims became permanently connected with Freeport in charge of all loading and shipping.[23]

The Union mine in Louisiana was in no danger of attack from German submarines, but the operation had its own difficulties. Back in 1911, the flow of sulphur had suddenly dwindled and then stopped. No amount of steaming brought results. It was feared that the melted sulphur was escaping through some great underground fissure, and for six months the staff worked on this problem. Finally they called upon

Herman Frasch, who was in Europe, a seriously ill man, to find the answer.[24] He came to Louisiana and diagnosed the difficulty as an excess of cold ground water in the sulphur horizon. By installing bleed pumps, he drew off as much as 9,000,000 gallons of cold water a day, thus permitting the hot water to do its work. This withdrawal of cold water soon became a standard Frasch process practice. (Fig. 5.)

By 1914 subsidence at the Union mine had become serious. In places the surface area had sunk as much as 20 feet, forcing a continuous shoring-up to sustain the foundations of the boiler houses.[25]

But the outstanding event at Sulphur Mine during the war was the cyclone of August 1918. A 90-mile twister turned the wooden derricks into a pile of jackstraws and seriously damaged every plant building, ripping off roofs and in some cases demolishing the structure. Fortunately, the furnaces, boilers, heating units, pumps, though temporarily put out of commission, were not irreparably hurt and a great deal of the equipment was salvaged. Nevertheless, the storm completely shut down operations. Since two months of extra production preceded the shutdown, the stockpile was able to fill the gap until by Herculean effort—everyone worked feverishly day and night—a few wells were again pumping within the amazingly short period of three weeks.

This catastrophe shocked the authorities in Washington. The margin of safety in sulphur supplies was much too thin. To manufacture 4,500,000 tons of 50° acid required 880,-000 long tons of sulphur and the paper, rubber and chemical processing industries needed 300,000 more tons. The Allies must have 150,000 tons. The total of 1.35 million tons was dangerously close to the expected production of 1.4 million from the two Gulf Coast mines.

Brimstone was placed under strict allocation by the War Industries Board.[26] A survey of Western surface deposits concluded that they could make no considerable contribution to the threatened sulphur deficiency.[27] There remained

the possibility of extending sulphur production from the
Gulf Coast saltdomes. The records of oil-drilling operations,
which had revealed sulphur showings, were supplemented
by owners and promoters who flocked to Washington seeking
Government financial aid to exploit various properties. Generally what they had to show was not very impressive. The
notable exception was Big Hill where Texas Gulf was still
exploring but already had approved blueprints for its projected plant.

Charles H. MacDowell, chief of the Chemicals Division
of the War Industries Board; Van H. Manning, of the Bureau
of Mines; and Major W. H. Gelshenen for the Procurement
Division of the Ordnance Department of the Army, all agreed
Big Hill was the most promising means for quickly increasing
the sulphur output. All began pressing for this promising increase in sulphur supplies. For the company W. H. Aldridge
replied: "We will bring the property to a production stage
at the earliest possible moment, and will provide all necessary
funds for this purpose.[28]

9

The Third Competitor

I F   B IG   H ILL were to be quickly brought into production, priorities must be gotten to build the plant. But priorities on needed equipment and materials were only given to firms with contracts for essential supplies for our Armed Forces or Allies, and Texas Gulf was in no position to make commitments to deliver any definite quantity of sulphur at any given time. Having a financial interest in the company, Bernard Baruch and Edward R. Stettinius of the Morgan firm scrupulously kept hands off, and priorities were only granted because the Bureau of Mines insisted and Charles H. MacDowell of the War Industries Board made a personal plea.[1]

Construction at Big Hill started August 13, 1918, and a few weeks later Charles Biesel, who had worked with Thompson and Aldridge on several mining jobs, became general manager. Production started March 15, 1919 and for ten years, until July 1928, when ill health forced him to retire, Biesel had charge of Texas Gulf's mining operations. He was succeeded by H. E. Treichler who had joined Texas Gulf in September 1918 after leaving the International Nickel Company.

The original plant at Gulf, as the Big Hill property came to be known, followed closely the plan Frasch successfully used at Sulphur Mine, namely, individual pumps and air compressors on each well. It was hoped there would be sufficient water for melting enough sulphur to raise a thousand tons daily. Three years later they were producing 4000 tons from the same 1000-ton equipment. The Big Hill deposit required much less water than had been calculated from the experience at Sulphur Mine where there was no tight, thick blanket of gumbo over the caprock. At Bryanmound, on the other hand, thermal efficiency was handicapped by the exceedingly fissurous character of the caprock and by large quantities of cold ground water. But physical conditions at Big Hill were almost ideal for the Frasch process. The area of the caprock was some 300 acres and the average thickness of the sulphur zone about 60 feet. This dome yielded more than 12,000,000 tons of brimstone.

On March 19, 1919, four months after World War I ended, when Big Hill was first steamed, oil and water spouted from a score of forsaken wells all over the dome area, and there was wild talk of Matagorda reviving as an oil field. But the flow was only the dying gasp of the dome as a producer of petroleum. All these wells soon went to water.[2] Some of them spouted like geysers, with a serious loss of hot water, so that all were sealed with cement.[3]

In the initial operation the unusually favorable structure of Big Hill was surprisingly demonstrated. After steaming 24 hours, the first flow of sulphur was most disappointing. Not until the second day was it learned that the water was being sent down too hot. Sulphur melts at 240°F. and at 315° is quite as liquid as water. At 330°, however, it becomes as thick and viscid as cold molasses, so the water temperature at the surface must be held below this point.

The war was over and where was this lush, low-cost production of brimstone by Texas Gulf to go?—a good question; one that worried the executives of all three sulphur companies.

The abnormal munitions demand had vanished. The stockpiles of Union and Freeport held more than a million tons. Excess war stocks of brimstone and acid and various sulphur chemicals were being dumped on the market. The Government itself had on hand over 150 million pounds of oleum and sulphuric acid.[4] Even the normal demand for sulphur was down, for industrial activity had slumped and American farmers, anticipating the loss of their wartime exports, were planting fewer acres and buying less fertilizer. The future of the American sulphur market seemed dark and threatening.

In its marketing system the American sulphur industry paralleled closely the sales methods of the chemical industry.[5] This was logical since like most common chemicals sulphur has many uses in many fields. The intensity of demand varies from user to user all the way from compulsory, as in the vulcanization of rubber, to optional, as in insecticides where sulphur has acceptable substitutes. As is also true of many chemicals, sulphur has one major use—production of sulphuric acid. Since World War I this acid has consumed never less than 60 per cent of our brimstone. The immense amount of pyrite available has always been a controlling factor in the price of all sulphur. In addition to pyrite, brimstone must meet the competition of recovered sulphur from various metallurgical processes and from petroleum or gas refining. Supplies of by-product sulphur have grown steadily, and with improved techniques recovery of spent or so-called "sludge" acid from petroleum refineries and from steel-pickling plants has also increased. These competitors of brimstone fix limits above which the price of sulphur cannot go. And it is to be noted that being by-products, the costs of recovered sulphur and sulphuric acid are largely a matter of bookkeeping.

Prior to World War I, except for a handful of manufacturers who specialized in strong acid of great purity, there were few big, regular brimstone buyers in the chemical industry. Domestic consumption was chiefly in paper and rubber, both of which were expanding rapidly, and in agricultural insecticides.[6] Changing demands and new competition was forcing continual revisions in the sulphur marketing system.

Frasch, who dominated the commercial as well as the technical activities of the Union Sulphur Company, sold direct to large industrial consumers, chemical jobbers, and the sulphur refiners who produced the sublimed grade known as "flowers of sulphur." He quoted all buyers one open price, f.o.b. plant, in carloads, his minimum sales unit.[7]

When Freeport came in production, E. P. Swenson appointed the established chemical merchants, Parsons & Petit of New York, sales agents for domestic business. The marketing situation he faced made this a wise move. Unlike Frasch, who had no domestic competitor, Freeport must break into the established trade of Union. Neither Swenson nor his associates were familiar with this business, while as former agents of the Sicilian cartel, Parsons & Petit knew the uses of sulphur and had contacts with consumers. Later, a group of Freeport stockholders sharply critized the commissions paid to these sales agents, but by that time conditions had again changed. Texas Gulf had entered the field and sulphur marketing methods must be revised again.

The third competitor arrived at a critical time, but fortunately there were favorable factors in the situation. Pent-up demand for all sorts of consumer goods, frustrated by war shortages, quickly revived industrial activity. The acid makers had been encouraged to employ brimstone, so instead of attempting to slash out a share of the existing market, Texas Gulf's management, led by Walter H. Aldridge, determined to make this switch from pyrites permanent. With this objective, he launched an intense educational sales campaign throughout the fertilizer industry. To gain quick entry into this field, he appointed the old house of H. J. Baker & Bro., dealers in fertilizer raw materials, sales representatives on a commission basis. William Gelshenen of the Baker firm signed up Virginia-Carolina Chemical Company, and Aldridge himself sold the first chemical contract, 75,000 tons to the Grasselli Chemical Company and secured the first carload order from the Marathon Paper Company. While working closely with Baker, Aldridge took pains to build his own sales organization. Thus the cycle of merchandising method—from individual proprietor to sales agent to a company's direct sales—was completed.

Herman Frasch's selling policy helped the industry during the excessive competition following World War I. Surface stocks were then nearly five times annual prewar consumption and current production of the three companies was twice annual prewar demand. Furthermore, domestic pyrite was again an active competitor and foreign pyrite, cut off during hostilities, reappeared in 1919.

The prices of these sulphur-bearing materials had to adjust on the basis of their use in acid manufacture by competitors employing the chamber or contact processes. The logic of this price adjustment, which took place between 1919-26, becomes clear[8] if expressed in the cost per unit of sulphur (dollars per ton) which these rival materials contain:

YEAR		U. S. BRIMSTONE (f.o.b. Mine)	IMPORTED PYRITES (best) (ex-vessel N. Y.)	U. S. PYRITES (f.o.b. Mine)
1919	Jan.—June	18	17	15
	July—Dec.	15	17	
1920	12 mos.	15 to 16	16.6	12.9
1921	12 mos.	15 to 16	14.25	10.6
1922	12 mos.	14	13	8.5
1923	12 mos.	13 to 14	12.25	8.8
1924	12 mos.	13 to 14	12	9.7
1925	Jan.—Apr.	13 to 14	12	
	May—Aug.	15	13	9.3
	Sept.—Dec.	15 to 16	13	
1926	12 mos.	18	13.5	9

During this seven-year readjustment the contact process established a new price basis for sulphur. At the same time, all three American companies eagerly cultivated export sales to relieve domestic pressures. The old Union-Consortium agreement on the European market had been cancelled back in January 1913, but as the Sicilians pointed out at the time, the arrival of Freeport would have nullified the agreement unless the new producer subscribed to its terms and was given a place in the allocation of markets.[9] At that time any such agreement was utterly impractical. Union was suing Freeport for infringement of the Frasch patents and any marketing understanding between the two companies would have been interpreted as tacit recognition.

During the war, with American exports shut off and European demand greatly increased, the Sicilian industry enjoyed a period of great prosperity.[10] However, contrary to American wartime experience, different technical and transportation conditions in Europe cut down the use of brimstone by acid makers and encouraged the employment of other sulphur-bearing raw materials. Postwar, the vigorous efforts of American producers to dispose of sulphur abroad aggravated this situation, and after the sharp decline in ocean freight rates, the Consortium was plunged in 1921 into a financial crisis. This was staved off only by direct government assistance.[11]

With this official backing, the Consortium determined to fight the American invasion. They cut prices and negotiated with the National Sulphuric Acid Association of London, the biggest buyer in Europe, a sale of 25,000 tons for delivery during 1922 and renewed this for 124,000 tons for 1923-25.

Negotiations were also opened with the American companies. At the first meeting at Geneva in August 1922, the Americans were represented by Clarence A. Snider for Union, E. P. Swenson for Freeport, and Wilber Judson for Texas Gulf. This conference could reach no agreement: the conflict of interests was formidable. The Sicilians naturally claimed all the Mediterranean area, including Marseilles where Union had a refinery producing flowers of sulphur for the important vineyard trade. During the war the Montecatini chemical interests had successfully sold brimstone from their own mines and sulphur springs on the Italian mainland, winning a notable share of the Continental business. This powerful organization was entirely outside the Consortium and remained aloof from these negotiations. The Americans felt strongly that no agreement could be successful without Montecatini. An added complication was the inability of the three American companies to act in concert.[12]

This obstacle was removed by the formation of the Sulphur Export Corporation, commonly known as Sulexco, organized under the Webb-Pomerene Act,[13] which permits American manufacturers to associate themselves for unified action in foreign markets. Reopened negotiations in New York got off to a bad start because Guido Jung, at one time the Italian commercial attaché at Washington, stood firm for the Mediterranean markets, including the vineyards of Spain and southern France. Subsequent meetings were held in London and Paris where a representative of Montecatini gave assurances that in the future their production would be solely for their own consumption. Later in Rome a virtual agreement was reached, but the representative of the Italian government continued to haggle over details. Snider, president of Sulexco and as such the sole American representative, forced the issue.

"It is useless, gentlemen," he said, "to continue these discussions. I am returning to America by the next boat."

As he was packing his bags, Luigi Delabretoigne, secretary of the Sicilian representatives, rushed into his hotel room exclaiming, "You must not leave. We must come to amicable terms." [14]

The following day, March 14, 1923, the agreement was signed. It was not necessary even to consider the Italian or the North American markets. By royal decree the importation of sulphur into Italy had been banned. The American domestic price was lower than export quotations, so Italian sulphur was as effectively barred from the United States and Canada. The agreement thus fulfilled the Webb-Pomerene requirements forbidding allotment of markets or control of prices within the United States. A minimum of 135,000 tons was guaranteed the Sicilian producers; above this, world markets were divided: 75 to Sulexco, 25 to the Consortium.

This agreement, which remained in force until 1934, provided that year by year minimum prices were to be agreed upon. A statistical office to compile data for pricing and allocation of markets, was set up in London under A. Hughes, formerly of the English firm of chemical merchants, Chance & Hunt, and more recently European agent of Texas Gulf Sulphur. After his death in 1936, his son, B. C. Hughes took over. The harmonious working of the Sulexco-Consortium agreement owed much to these two Englishmen whose disinterested honesty won the confidence of both parties. To handle Sulexco's sales in Europe, Snider appointed Pierre Chaubert, who formerly represented Freeport—in France, and Charles E. Hope, manager of Union's Marseilles plant.

The arrival of the third competitor had not upset the domestic market. The price war everyone dreaded never materialized because during the booming 1920's American consumption of sulphur grew greatly. Conditions for this expansion were trebly propitious. First, it was a period of extraordinary industrial activity and the direct use of brimstone in paper, insecticides, and rubber increased enormously. Secondly, the switch of acid makers from pyrite to brimstone came just when the two greatest sulphuric acid users, fertilizers and petroleum, were enjoying a great boom. Finally, the decade was one during which phenomenal chemical progress in this country demanded many more tons of sulphur.

In this expanded consumption of sulphur the manufacture of sulphuric acid was the most important element. At the close of the war, about half of this acid was made from brimstone. During the 1920's consumption of sulphur in acid manufacture alone reached a total greater than the entire output in 1919, and by 1929 more than two-thirds of the acid came from this source. During this latter year, according to *Chemical & Metallurgical Engineering,* domestic consumption of sulphuric acid (50° Bé) was 7,925,000 tons. Of this total, 5,606,000 tons, or 70.8 per cent of the acid produced was made from 1,135,000 tons of brimstone.

In the fertilizer industry, during this period, production of superphosphate grew from 3.3 to 4.4 million short tons.[15] In plant practice phosphate rock is converted into normal superphosphate by treating it with approximately an equal weight of 55° Bé acid.[16] In other words, half the tonnage of superphosphate produced represents sulphuric acid.

In the second largest field of acid consumption, petroleum refining, the 1920's saw the American output of gasoline grow from 94 to 435 million barrels.[17] At this time nearly all the gasoline was being produced by straight-run distillation, in the chemical refining of which three pounds of 66° Bé acid were used per barrel of crude oil.[18]

Outside of acid production, the largest use of sulphur has been in the manufacture of sulphite pulp. During the 1920's our per capita consumption of paper doubled, reaching a peak in 1927 of 210 pounds for every man, woman, and child in the United States.[19] Most of this growth, preceding the recent expansion of kraft paper, was due to sulphite paper in which 220 to 300 pounds of sulphur are used per ton of pulp.[20]

Chemical production grew more rapidly than any other American industry, and except for alkalies, sulphur compounds[21] led the list. Important technical developments demanded more sulphur chemicals: diversification of organic synthesis required increasing amounts of high-test sulphuric acid and sulphur chloride; expansion of household refrigeration created new demands for sulphur dioxide; the rayon industry called for more and more of its most important solvent, carbon bisulphide.

This broadening and deepening of the brimstone market

was indeed fortunate for the American sulphur industry. In 1919 a production of 1,190,575 tons with a domestic consumption of 453,622 tons was an overproduction that held a serious threat. Although output almost doubled during these ten years, that threat was eliminated by sales which almost quadrupled. The market situation which in March 1919, when Texas Gulf first came into production, seemed so gloomy changed so completely that within a few years the three sulphur producers were all exploring new domes.

10

Additional Domes

HAD HERMAN FRASCH not died, on May 1, 1914, the history of the industry his hot-water process created would have been different. While he was battling to make his invention practical and profitable, his courage and self-confidence were good assets. But they betrayed him later into ignoring the depletion of his sulphur reserves and tempted him to belittle competition. Frasch was not bluffing when he brusquely dismissed Staiti's offer to sell him Bryanmound. He firmly believed the Calcasieu mine had abundant reserves for years of profitable operation. Besides his patents had not yet expired. He died before the Union Sulphur Company had to face either contingency; sulphur exhaustion or direct competition.

Veterans of the industry, men who knew Frasch, agree that had he been at the helm, his process would not have been completely upset in court nor would Union have been caught without sulphur. Frasch, so they reason, realized the dubious validity of his supplementary patents. His basic claims having expired, he would have accepted some such royalty agreement as E. P. Swenson proposed when Union first brought suit against Freeport for patent infringement. He was familiar with similar arrangements in the petroleum industry and knew from personal experience the financial advantage of leasing the right to use his patents. It is also inconceivable to his contemporaries that Frasch would have failed to recognize the coming depletion of Sulphur Mine or to have taken prompt steps to find another workable dome. He certainly had ample capital, nor was the opportunity lacking. The first thought of any wildcatter who found brimstone was to offer the dome to the oldest, wealthiest company.

During 1920-21, the coming exhaustion of Sulphur Mine spurred the Union management to seek actively for a likely deposit. They prospected Palangana, down near the Mexican border, and at least three other domes. During the summer of 1922, they optioned the sulphur rights at Damon Mound.[1]

J. M. Guffey, one of the financial backers of Lucas at Spindletop, had drilled here in 1901. During the next four years he struck six dry holes, then withdrew for more promising fields. Ten years later Henry T. Staiti, who had developed the Bryanmound sulphur, secured mineral rights to the greater part of the Damon dome. He drilled his first test on the western face of the mound. At 650 feet, this well gushed oil and gas, running wild for a time, making 5,000,000 cubic feet of gas and 100 barrels of oil a day that sprayed the countryside for 2500 feet. Owing to insufficient storage, this flow was shut in and the well filled with sand. None of the 15 wells drilled during the following year struck oil, but several clearly indicated sulphur. Staiti, following his experience at Bryanmound, deliberately prospected to outline the sulphur deposit during 1917 and drilled 37 wells, 10 of which produced oil, 13 were dry, and 14 were frankly sulphur-test drillings. Subsequently he drilled 14 more sulphur tests which so impressed the Union Sulphur Company that they optioned the rights to Damon. During 1923 Union drilled nine wells adjacent to which they built a small battery of steam boilers, but the plant never operated. Staiti and Union had in all made 52 tests for sulphur in this dome and all the important sulphur-bearing horizons were mapped. While sulphur occurs spottily throughout the area, the only large deposit is confined to less than 120 acres on the north side of the dome.[2]

Having abandoned Damon, Union moved its exploration

crew ten miles to Big Creek. As elsewhere, this field had first been explored for oil and cores had indicated a promising sulphur deposit. Union leased some 400 acres and began test drilling. They moved over their small plant from Damon and during 1925-26 steamed six wells, production from which was only 1070 tons. Although this was the sole dome the company actually steamed, they explored twelve others.

On December 23, 1924, the Sulphur Mine operation in Louisiana closed down. During its life it produced 9.4 million tons of brimstone and while for three years the Union Sulphur Company continued to sell from stockpile, it ceased to be a producing factor in the industry.

The pioneer company's plight underscored the need of adequate reserves and during the 1920's every known salt-dome with showings of sulphur was investigated. This feverish hunt pointed up the limited and unpredictable character of prospecting for sulphur. Geophysical surveys and drilling have indicated more than 200 salt domes along the Gulf Coast between the Mississippi and the Rio Grande Rivers,[3] and while 80 per cent of them have shown the way to petroleum-producing fields,[4] admittedly most known saltdomes are poor sulphur prospects. Only 24 domes (including four in Mexico) have been successful commercial producers of brimstone and by 1958 12 of these (including one in Mexico) had been exhausted and abandoned.

During the Booming Twenties the Gulf Coast hummed with sulphur activities. Optimistic prospectors besieged all the companies, toting heavy valises packed with beautiful cores splotched and streaked with yellow. Sulphur executives had become callous to bargain offers for fabulous brimstone deposits. No longer were they excited by rumors of new companies organized to exploit caprocks as yellow as butter. But a different story did disturb them.

A strong, efficient petroleum producer, the Texas Company, was deliberately prospecting for sulphur at Hoskins Mound in Brazoria County. Their drills, it was said, had

penetrated a sulphur horizon 200 feet thick. Most disconcerting, their exploring was being done by that outstanding
appraiser of sulphur deposits, Spencer Browne.

The early history of Hoskins Mound is a story of repeated
efforts to develop a profitable petroleum production. Lucas,
himself, examined this dome, but could not make a satisfactory lease with the owners, the three Hoskins brothers.[5]
Inspired by the obvious interest of their celebrated visitor,
the Hoskins picked out 500 likely acres of their 42,000-acre
ranch, and cutting it into one-acre tracts, sold 55½ of these
plots to various people.[6] They picked well—these acres
were right in the chief sulphur-producing area to be.

Between 1903 and 1915 two groups got a small, short-lived
production of oil from six shallow wells. But almost every
hole they drilled turned up significant showings of sulphur.
These were so consistent that had working capital been available, they would have built a Frasch plant. Since they were
working on a shoestring, they were compelled to lease the
property, first to J. M. Guffey who drilled three dry wells,
and then to the Producers Oil Company, a subsidiary of the
Texas Company.[7] This lease covered all surface and mineral
rights to 3000 acres, 2500 of which covered the Hoskins dome
proper, and only mineral rights to 37,564 acres, the balance
of the ranch property.

These leases were taken on the recommendation of the
company's chief geologist, E. G. Woodruff. Previous drilling
in Hoskins had all been shallow wells on the top, and he
believed that if oil existed in large quantities, it would be
found on the flanks of the dome. All wells of the Producers
Oil Company, and later of the Texas Company, were drilled
in accordance with Woodruff's theory.

Producers' No. 1 was a perfect blank: no oil, no gas, no
sulphur. Producers' No. 2, a shallow well on top of the dome
to find fuel oil, seemed to be a big strike, but it soon petered
out. Producers' No. 3, on the south flank, went through a
sulphur-bearing formation 200 feet thick.[8]

None of the Producers Oil people felt this amazing showing of sulphur important enough to justify taking even a single sample or making a single analysis. In fact, although two other wells showed remarkable indications of sulphur, there was no interest in them until Texas' No. 10 was drilled. Only then did C. N. Scott, vice-president in charge of production, write the president of the Texas Company, June 19, 1918:

> In our Hoskins Mound Well 10, located on the southwest side of the Mound . . . the first well we have drilled in that direction, we have encountered at a depth of something over 900 feet, 20 feet of practically pure sulphur, and are still in it with fair prospects of having considerable more of it before we get out of this stratum.
>
> Our Mr. Schroeder, who has charge of this district, was in the employ of the Union Sulphur Co. in Louisiana as driller for many years, and who also is well posted on the sulphur development at Freeport, tells us that in all his drilling he has never encountered so rich pay as this is.
>
> We are immediately shipping in two more light drilling rigs so that this prospecting can be crowded . . . This looks like the biggest thing we have uncovered in a long time and I will keep you posted.

With an eye now focused on sulphur, the Texas Company drilled eleven wells during the next two years. They were experts in oil, but had no experience in core drilling for sulphur. Their haphazard prospecting indicated an extensive deposit on the south and west sides of the mound, but they had no accurate information as to its richness. Recognizing their limitations, yet intrigued by these sulphur prospects, the Texas Company called in Spencer Browne who recommended a sulphur survey, employing his reverse-flow method of taking cores. This report was approved and Browne again called upon W. T. Lundy, who had returned to his private consulting practice in San Francisco since the war, to take charge of the tests which began during the summer of 1920 and continued until April 1921.

Four drilling rigs bored thirteen prospect holes. Samples were scrupulously collected from every foot of the sulphur horizon, chemically analyzed, and the sulphur content conservatively calculated.[9] Lundy submitted a detailed report and the Texas Company engaged Col. William Couper to draw plans for a Frasch sulphur-mining plant.

Despite the enticing prospect of a profitable enterprise, the Texas top management hesitated. To exploit the Hoskins Mound brimstone required a considerable investment. It was an excursion into an entirely new and unfamiliar business against well-established competitors. Accordingly, they approached the Texas Gulf Sulphur Company, but were unable to agree on the value of the sulphur showing. Negotiations were therefore started with the Freeport Sulphur Company.

Freeport's fast-depleting Bryanmound was balky to operate and had a higher water ratio than Texas Gulf's Big Hill, so E. P. Swenson had good reasons not to forget that this Matagorda dome had been offered to him and refused, even as Bryanmound had been turned down by Frasch. Swenson wanted very much to find a second dome for Freeport. Accordingly, on March 4, 1922, the Texas Company's Hoskins Mound lease was taken insofar as it related to sulphur, and plans were drawn to install a sulphur-mining plant there.[10]

Just as construction was getting under way, serious floods of the Brazos River upset the operations at Freeport and delayed these plans. Eleven vessels lay in the roadstead at Freeport awaiting a cargo of sulphur which at that time was loaded here to 18 feet and then topped off at Texas City. The flood ruined the dock-loading facilities and washed out about eight miles of the branch railway to Freeport. The water was several days in receding.

In the midst of this crisis, Lewis Mims, who was in charge of shipping, disappeared. While the flood was still raging, he had gotten into a skiff, rowed back to dry land, tramped on foot until he found an automobile to take him to Houston. There he collected a forty-car wrecking and construction train with 300 laborers and when he was found two days later, he already had a mile and a half of the track relaid.[11]

There were different difficulties at Hoskins. The royalty contract with the Texas Company called for operation within a year and April 1, 1923, was the deadline. The spur line of the railroad to bring in supplies was to be completed by August 1, 1922, but was not in running order until October. To get the work through on a rigid schedule Homer S. Burns was moved over from Freeport in charge of construction. He drove and coaxed his 400 men to the utmost of their capacity, while carefully seeing that they were well fed and always had dry clothes.

About a month before the job was completed, the book-keeper started one day to tell him that one of the stewards was stealing hams and selling them to the commissary which was feeding a gang of Mexican laborers. Burns did not dare upset the camp; even a half day's work would pay for many, many hams. So he cut the bookkeeper short saying, "I don't want to know anything, murder included, if only they will wipe up the blood." [12]

Four days before the deadline they started steaming Hoskins Mound. On March 31, Saturday, the first well pumped sulphur.

To avoid the difficulties of subsidence, the new plant was built 2000 feet off the mound. It had cost $2,000,000, including warehouses, pumping stations, water treating plants, and so forth. Its rated boiler capacity was initially 8400 h.p., capable of developing a 50 per cent overload. Reservoirs had a water storage capacity of 280 million gallons—an estimated three-months' supply—fed by a gravity canal dug from the Bastrop Bayou.[13]

From the first there were extraordinary operating difficulties. For the amount of superheated water pumped down, the return of sulphur was poor and uncertain, making for low production and high costs. P. George Maercky suggested to Swenson that Spencer Browne, who was in France on vacation, be invited to take charge at Hoskins. Browne declined to join in competition with his old associates in the Texas Gulf Sulphur Company, so Swenson turned naturally to Browne's assistant, Lundy, who accepted and reported at Freeport on January 1, 1923, as production manager at both the Bryan and Hoskins Mounds. When Maercky resigned as general manager at the end of 1930, Lundy succeeded him.

For three grief-packed years Lundy struggled under conditions which he described[14] as "persistently and characteristically adverse to satisfactory production,"—a real sulphur-mining chamber of horrors. Willy-nilly, the Freeport staff had to perfect new equipment and methods.

Because of its geological formation, the Hoskins dome presented a combination of drilling problems. Its surface area is a low mound of 2000 acres.[15] In the center, 1100 feet down, the salt plug proper has a circular top of only 500 acres. Scattered through the sedimentary deposits of sand and gumbo between the surface and the salt plug are big boulders, nasty obstacles to drilling. The 100-foot caprock overlying the sulphur is dense and hard, thus difficult to drill. Finally, the richest sulphur strata are not on top of the dome but along its flank, necessitating drilling 2000 feet in some wells. To cope with these problems, Freeport had a special crew of trained engineers and skilled drillers, under J. B. Gaffney, which patiently learned the hard way new drilling techniques.[16]

When hot water was pumped down to the sulphur horizon, it migrated rapidly through the barren caprock to the center of the dome: exorbitant quantities were needed to melt precious little sulphur. Pumping chopped hay into the operating wells helped somewhat and proved that greater thermal efficiency underground would result if the main channels of the formations could be filled with a material of sufficient body and strength to check the escape of hot water. A crudely designed mud mixer was installed and fed by teams of mules with scrapers. The mud was ground to a pulp, settled in a small pit, and the thickened sludge pumped into the well. This primitive equipment proved so promising that experiments were continued until a good mudding operation was perfected.[17]

After sulphur had been pumped for some time another production handicap appeared. Subsidence, which greatly increases the efficiency of subsequent operations because it fills the cavities created by the extracted mineral, did not occur. At Hoskins, after five years' operation, it amounted to only four inches. As early as August 1924, nine tons of nitro-glycerine were detonated in three wells to induce subsidence.[18] Results were disappointing, but this trouble cured itself and eventually greater thermal efficiencies were obtained at Hoskins than had even been achieved in the spotty, irregular formation at Bryanmound. Output for 1927 reached 489,534 tons, an increase of approximately 70 per cent, while production costs increased only 12½ per cent.[19] The company reported to its stockholders "production at Hoskins Mound is limited only by boiler capacity."

During 1921, the second full year of production at Gulf— the first mine of Texas Gulf Sulphur Company—output reached one million tons. This dome had a known reserve of 10 million tons and a possible reserve of 12 million. Clearly more sulphur deposits must be found if the company were to stay in business longer than a decade. Albert G. Wolf, who joined Texas Gulf in 1919, went into the field to study all possibilities, not only saltdomes, but even surface deposits. At that time, this graduate of the Colorado School of Mines was the entire geological and scouting force. During his 35 years of service with Texas Gulf, Wolf earned a reputation as one of the greatest of all sulphur and saltdome geologists. His early exploratory work began before geophysics had been introduced as a dome finder. Indications

of new domes were limited to topography, paraffin dirt, salt
water and "sulphur water" (containing hydrogen sulphide)
in wells, and gas seeps. Therefore, any shallow Gulf coastal
saltdome not thoroughly drilled was a potential sulphur-
bearing prospect.

In 1922, B. D. King, County Surveyor of Wharton County
called the attention of James F. Weed, an independent oil
operator, to an old 100-foot-deep water well which made
considerable hydrogen sulphide and also to a gas seep in the
San Bernard River about a mile to the northeast. Years before, this Missouri Land Company holding in the east corner
of Wharton County had been subdivided and sold in 60-
and 80-acre tracts. The surface, partly farmland and partly
jungle, was flat, giving no topographic indication of the
immense saltdome beneath. The gas showings were in-
triguing, and with King's help, Weed took mineral leases
from the various owners of this subdivision, which leases he
assigned to the Gulf Production Company.[20] Gulf Production started an exploratory well near the old sulphur-water
well on May 28, 1922. Drilling was stopped on August 31,
1923, one and one-half feet in the limestone caprock with a
trace of sulphur and oil shows. The existence of a saltdome
was proved. The area under lease was large enough to cover
any dome of average size, but other oil companies now took
leases around the edges of the original block; Texas Company to the south and west; Sun Oil to the east on the Fort
Bend County side of the San Bernard River; and Marland
Oil to the northwest.

Wolf scouted the region right after the completion of
Gulf's first well and recommended it to his company as a
likely sulphur prospect. As all the apparently desirable acreage was under lease, he began to buy, with the approval of
Wilber Judson, then vice president of Texas Gulf, mineral
fee and royalties from land owners who had granted leases,
leaving part of the royalties to the original owners.

Gulf Production then subleased the oil on some of the

tracts back to Weed who drilled a number of shallow wells
on this and adjoining tracts, even making a small producer
out of Gulf Company's dome discovery well. The development of this little, shallow oil field effectively stopped Wolf
from acquiring fee to all minerals because land owners would
not part with their oil. Texas Gulf had to change its policy
and from that time on, just sulphur fee and royalty were purchased. Some of Weed's wells, which were drilled a few feet
into caprock, showed sulphur cuttings. In April and May
1925, Texas Company drilled its S. T. Taylor No. 1 well

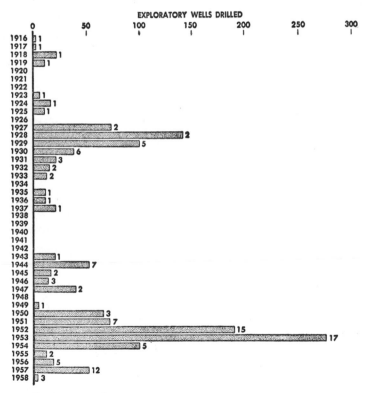

Figures at end of bars represent Structures Drilled

FIG. 6.   The endless search for sulphur: exploratory wells drilled (ex-
cluding development and production wells at producing mine) by
Texas Gulf Sulphur Company.

some 8000 feet southwest of the Weed oil field, extending considerably the caprock area. More important, this well showed a good sulphur formation, the best up to that time. Limestone was topped at 1196 feet and the well was bottomed at 1511 feet in salt. Even then, apparently, none of the oil companies sensed the immense sulphur possibilities.

Early in 1925, Texas Gulf established an office in Houston, with Wolf in charge, and two scouts, one to cover the coastal area from Houston, the other the coast west of Houston. This work, coupled with exploratory drilling, ultimately paid off handsomely; witness Boling, Long Point, Clemens, Moss Bluff, Spindletop, Starks, and Lake Bullycamp. (Figure 6.) After the first well was drilled on the Long Point Dome, Fort Bend County, Texas Gulf, on Wolf's recommendation, bought mineral fee there and also at Clemens and Allen in Brazoria County. Of these, Boling was the "best bet."

On May 16, 1926, Neilan No. 1 Bay well, three and one-half miles west of the discovery well, encountered caprock and sulphur at a depth of 914 feet, extending the dome far beyond the limits determined by the geophysics at that time. In fact, there was speculation that there might be twin domes. Subsequent drilling proved Boling Dome to be five miles by three and one-half miles in extent on the 1500-foot contour, the largest shallow salt structure on the Gulf Coast.

Further drilling by Gulf Production on its leases found no significant amount of oil but did extend the dome to the south and southeast. Finally Gulf Production cored Chase well No. 3 on Lot 4 of the Missouri Land Subdivision from March 8 to 20, 1927, as a caprock test. Top of cap was found at 636 feet and the well was extremely rich in sulphur to its abandoned depth of 671 feet. Wolf predicted Boling Dome would have reserves of 50 million tons; he was considered a dreamer by his own bosses. Nevertheless, Texas Gulf redoubled its efforts to acquire more sulphur fee and a few more purchases were closed by Wilber Judson. Judson, an-

other recruit from William Boyce Thompson's staff, was
trained at Harvard and the Michigan College of Mines. He
joined Texas Gulf in 1921, became Vice President in 1926,
came to Boling in 1927, eventually taking charge of all field
operations. He cherished deep, well justified pride in "the
largest Frasch plant on the biggest sulphur dome."

Many Gulf Production leases were now about to expire.
If they ran out, the sulphur would fall into the lap of Texas
Gulf, so the natural thing for Gulf to do was to trade with
the sulphur company. The deal was made, Texas Gulf paying Gulf Production $3,000,000 cash and agreeing to pay
one-half the net profits after Texas Gulf had recovered its
capital and development costs. The agreement included an
option on all other sulphur deposits discovered on properties
controlled by Gulf Production in the Gulf Coast.

Because the leases to the sulphur and oil rights on Boling
were due to expire shortly, Gulf Production and Texas Gulf
moved in 28 rigs, all of which were in operation on the expiration date, thus maintaining the leases in force. Texas
Gulf now started a thorough exploration. More than 200
development wells were cored from caprock to salt. This
survey revealed a brimstone formation of more than 1500
acres, a great crescent around the eastern and southern slopes
of Boling Dome, ranging in grade from traces to as high as
50 per cent and varying in thickness from thin edges to more
than 200 feet.

This exploratory work took over a year and a half, so that
by the time plant construction started May 31, 1928, several
individual landowners had become impatient for production
to start. Mining sulphur under leases is quite a different
matter from operating a property where the company owns
the land. For the most efficient operation of the Frasch process the wells are grouped closely together, starting at the
highest point of the sulphur-bearing area, working down the
side of the dome. In this way subsidence closes in the area
from which the ore has been extracted. This procedure can

only be used when the land is owned or the sulphur leases are pooled. Otherwise, operations must take place on each individual lease. This increases the investment since distribution lines for hot water, receiving stations for sulphur, and other facilities must be provided for this multiple operation.

Every effort was made therefore to have the owners at Boling pool their leases and about half did so. The others demanded that their leases be operated individually. To arrive at just royalties on the pooled leases and a fair number of wells allotted to the others, it was agreed to abide by the estimates of two mining engineers named by the U. S. Geological Survey and the U. S. Bureau of Mines.[21]

Except for small farms, Boling Dome was a semitropical jungle of trees and scrub timber with poor dirt roads. All supplies and rigs had to be hauled four miles from the Southern Pacific Railroad. In rainy weather, it took a six-horse team with an eight-wheel wagon to drag in two joints of eight-inch pipe needed for casing every single well. The last month before the leases expired rains were heavy and men and mules slithered frantically through Texas gumbo to complete the job on schedule. It was hoped to produce the first sulphur on March 19, the tenth anniversary of the company's first pumping at Big Hill, but none of the steamed wells sealed until a few hours after midnight.

Obligatory, scattered, simultaneous operation meant that hot-water requirements were going to be extremely large at Boling. The plans drawn by Texas Gulf engineers, collaborating with the J. G. White Engineering Corporation, called for 8,000,000 gallons every 24 hours. Most of this water was taken from the San Bernard River two miles from the powerhouse and enough well water high in sodium bicarbonate was added to the surface water to furnish the "soda" for the hot process of lime-soda softening. The large area of the deposit also necessitated transporting superheated water, steam, and compressed air great distances, costs which were increased by the location of the power plant sufficiently clear of the dome not to be affected by subsidence. Over 90,000 feet of 4- to 6-inch pipe were used in the main feed lines and 26,000 feet in branch lines leading to the mining zone. The main sulphur return lines from the pumping stations to the storage plant, with auxiliary steam lines to prevent freezing, totaled 80,000 feet of pipe.

Unlike the other Texas domes, Boling lies 30 miles inland in a relatively thickly populated farming district, so that evil-smelling, salty bleed water from the mines could not be run directly to waste or impounded and released into fresh water streams during the flood period. A special disposal plant was built to aerate the bleed water, which after settling was run to waste into the San Bernard River below tidewater where the river water was already salty. Mechanical difficulties and high chemical costs necessitated building a new plant, designed by Koppers Company, in the summer of 1930.

While Boling Dome was being equipped, the Taylor brothers' old hog pasture had been transformed into the attractive town of Newgulf. There now stands a town of more than 300 modern homes owned by the company and leased to its employees. The community is served by two drygoods stores, two grocery stores, two pharmacies, a barber shop, a tailor and cleaning shop, three garages, and one moving-picture house. All of these business buildings have been erected by the proprietors and held by them on only 30-day leases; none are company-operated. They are all competitive with the town of Boling and to a lesser extent with Wharton and Houston. There are Methodist, Baptist, and Catholic churches.

The company makes provision for health, educational, and recreational facilities. There is a modern hospital. Water and milk supplies are checked regularly to assure their safety. Newgulf public schools are second to none in Texas in academic standing. The Newgulf public library is much larger than those in most towns of its size. A nine-hole golf course is maintained and is open to all employees for nominal greens fees or monthly dues, while the golf clubhouse has rooms for games or dancing that can be used exclusively by any employee who wishes to entertain on a scale larger than is possible in his own home.

The beneficial social effects of this large-scale industry in the midst of the typical Texas farming community do not stop at town limits of Newgulf. Wharton County is famous for its public buildings, its hospitals, and its well paved roads, which have come, thanks to increased tax values, since sulphur was found on Boling Dome.

There remained one improvement to assure the most efficient operation at Boling. The contract with Gulf Production called for a 50-50 division of profits after deducting the costs of development and operating expenses incurred in getting the property on a paying basis. These terms might well furnish grounds for disputes arising from different interpretations of property charges and the exact date when the operation became profitable. Accordingly, in the autumn of 1934, the Delaware Gulf Oil Company, to which this contract had been assigned, exchanged its profit-sharing rights for 1,300,000 shares of Texas Gulf Sulphur Company's common stock.[22] This amicable exchange, authorized by the shareholders, increased the total of Texas Gulf shares to 3,840,000.

To January 1958, almost 50 million tons of sulphur have been brought to the surface at Boling Dome, roughly 38 per cent of all the brimstone raised by the Frasch hot-water process.

11

Two New Companies

WITH BOLING, the Texas Gulf Sulphur Company acquired from the Gulf Production Company all other sulphur prospects which it might discover or control. Only 12 miles northeast of Boling was Long Point where a seismograph survey indicated the presence of a saltdome. This having been proved by a well drilled in December 1924, Texas Gulf decided to develop the two properties simultaneously.

After drilling 26 holes in 1929-30, Long Point seemed to be a minor deposit: sulphur was proved only along the edges of the north and east flanks of the dome. Accordingly, Texas Gulf installed boiler capacity to pump but a single well. For use at Long Point, Texas Gulf bought some equipment from a dealer in Houston who had purchased it from the Union Sulphur Company after they withdrew from Big Creek. Among the apparatus were some of Clarence Snider's old pumps from the original Union operation.[1] Production at Long Point came in March 19, 1930—exactly one year after Boling—and was continued regularly until October 19, 1938. A total of 402,000 tons had been extracted when these leases where abandoned.[2] The company retained its rights over the major part of the sulphur-bearing area.

Up to this point, two small domes had been exploited: Big Creek by Union and Long Point by Texas Gulf. It was not a spectacular introduction to one of the most interesting phases of the industry during the between-wars period: the exploitation of little deposits by small companies.

In the southeast angle of Texas, midway between Corpus Christi on the Gulf and Laredo on the Mexican border, is a saltdome with a sulphur horizon whose history opens familiarly but ends unexpectedly. This Palangana dome is also unusual in that underground water, dissolving away the salt plug, caused a central depression, rather similar to the formation at Sulphur Mine. Its surface indication is like a great doughnut and the surrounding country in this part of Duval County is much more hilly than the flat coastal plain, so the outward signs of this dome are obscure. It did not, however, escape Capt. Anthony Lucas who drilled here during 1901.[3] Results were negative and he moved on.

Hit-and-miss exploring was done on and about Palangana until 1917. Empire Gas & Fuel Company then began deep drilling during which the salt plug was identified and approximately outlined. In 1919 National Oil Company drilled down into salt at the center of the dome and then bored a series of holes due east until their No. 4 reached the edge of the salt plug. Both Empire and National found repeated signs of sulphur.

These yellow cuttings attracted Edward F. Simms, one of the syndicate that developed Bryanmound, and in 1920 he drilled into the southern section of the dome until salt was reached.[4] Four years later, under a lease from Simms, J. W. Cain and A. H. Smith found no oil but made the best showing of sulphur to date. They interested two of the three sulphur companies, and Texas Gulf cored 25 test wells and Union Sulphur, four. Results were contradictory: undoubtedly, a considerable sulphur body existed; obviously, it was uneven and discontinuous. Both companies declined the opportunity to develop this South Texas mound. Nevertheless Cain and Smith were still optimistic about Palangana's brimstone potential. They drilled more test wells; found more sulphur; organized the Duval Texas Sulphur Company to build a small hot-water process plant. It came on-stream early in 1928.

The Houston investment house of Moody, Seagraves & Company, prominent in developing oil and gas properties, had a substantial financial interest in the Duval company. In 1930, when Moody-Seagraves sold their gas properties to the United Gas Corporation, subsidiary of Electric Bond & Share, their interest in the sulphur company was included. Keen to develop this property, the new owners found for their manager a big, deep-voiced Californian, George F. Zoffman, a mining engineer from Stanford, with 20 years' hardrock mining experience in Mexico. Zoffman had no firsthand knowledge of the Frasch process, but suspecting that pumping brimstone out of Palangana was no job for a bungling amateur, he hunted out the best practical sulphur miner available and found him in August T. Drachenberg.

A veteran of the Frasch regime at Sulphur Mine, "Gus" Drachenberg had an uncanny skill. Like a violinist tuning his instrument, Drachenberg's long knotty fingers would play with the controls while he squatted on his haunches, his head cocked on one side as if listening to what was happening far underground. A bit more hot water: cut down the air pressure a little: a call for greater heat to the boiler house. The discharge pipe would gradually stop spitting and sputtering. What had been a tiny trickle of molten sulphur would become under his manipulation a respectable gushing stream.

Asked how he did it, Drachenberg would shrug his shoulders and say, "I don't know, I just sort of get the feel of the lines." [5]

This is probably the literal truth. It is indisputable, however, that he could coax a lot of sulphur out of a balky well. Such talents had been sorely needed to cope with the initial production difficulties at Bryanmound and he had been engaged there at a salary which tradition says was $20,000 a year.[6] When Texas Gulf opened its mine at Big Hill, Gus Drachenberg had been the first production man. This dome was not one that needed a trouble shooter, so in a couple of

years, he was back again at Bryanmound which was beginning
to show signs of exhaustion. Again he lived up to his reputation, stepping up production from 600 to 1200 tons a
day.[7] On all these jobs he combined rare skill with a happy
disregard of orthodox methods. His wide experience and
nimble ability were needed on Palangana Dome.

Out in the hills of South Texas, Drachenberg was lord of
all he surveyed, and with plenty of balky wells to tend, he
was thoroughly happy. As he himself confessed,[8] "This is a
small operation, worked economically and modestly. But I
like it here. It's high and dry; cool and no mosquitoes; and
if we are little, we are good. On the big domes they're disap-
pointed if they don't get from 15 to 20 tons an hour from a
well. Here I'm pleased to get five or ten tons. We are all on
a small scale, but it's comfortable and we are independent
and happy."

The sentiments of that sunburned operator with sulphur
under his nails sum up the philosophy of the smaller sul-
pher mining company's management. By taking every advantage of low overhead and mining costs, they can profitably
work a deposit too small to be attractive to the larger companies. Knowing their operation on any location will be
short-lived, they build no great powerhouses of re-enforced
concrete, but put up neat little buildings of pine planking or
corrugated sheets which can be dismantled and moved to
another dome. Much of their machinery, boilers, and pumps
is second-hand and almost all of their piping.

After surmounting numerous mining handicaps, the
Duval Texas Sulphur Company operated the Palangana
Dome to exhaustion, producing 237,689 tons. They closed
down in the spring of 1935. Two years before, however, they
had wisely taken steps to acquire another sulphur deposit.

In a section of the great Boling Dome known as Bear
Camp Plantation, a block of leases on sulphur rights covering about 1100 acres had been collected by Lindsay H. Dunn,
an oil lease trader, and Lee Hager, a geologist expert in

dome formations. Texas Gulf Sulphur had an undivided fee interest in certain tracts in the Bear Camp area, insuring not only ownership of the minerals, but also the right to the use of the surface, including the necessary right of ingress and egress, the erection of the buildings, and so forth. When Duval took over the Dunn-Hager block of leases, George Zoffman went to Wilber Judson and Texas Gulf agreed to lease these rights and some adjacent interests to Duval on a royalty basis, with the option of taking payment in brimstone. Duval started steaming this location in 1935. A total of 571,237 tons of sulphur was raised before exhaustion in 1940.

Two years before Duval had begun steaming still another dome known as Orchard. This had been located by geophysical methods by Gulf Production Company after its third well in 1924 struck oil with a production of 2000 barrels daily.[9] Texas Gulf had automatic rights to explore here for sulphur and did so during 1929-30. Further tests, three years later, found no commercial sulphur. However, Gulf Oil in overhang drilling, that is, drilling down beneath the overhanging caprock along the flanks of a dome, ran unexpectedly into a good showing of sulphur, and the landowners insisted on more tests for sulphur. Accordingly, Texas Gulf drilled five more holes. One of these was fair; the other four almost barren. At this point Duval took an option on these sulphur leases from Texas Gulf and its first test well showed more sulphur than anyone dreamed existed in the Orchard Dome. Encouraged by its tests, Duval acquired these leases on a royalty basis and successful steaming began in 1938. In charge at Orchard was J. O. Tyree, an operator with 20 years' practical experience.

Among all the various types of sulphur-topped salt plugs, Orchard is something of a freak. The top of this dome has a thin, almost barren caprock, much faulted, that is the structure is cracked and folded, impractical for hot-water mining. All the workable deposits are along the flanks. They occur as

pockets in step faults in the overhanging limestone at from
1200 to 2500 feet down or beneath a second cap in long
narrow structures between faults at from 2500 to 4000 feet.
Thus Orchard exhibits some real curiosities, such as sulphur
found in salt and one pocket above another so that here two
wells, one on top of the other, have been steamed and
pumped simultaneously.[10] If it is to be profitably worked, a
dome of such unusual formation demands some exceptional
changes in the conventional methods of the Frasch process.

When Duval's Boling plant closed, Xerxes T. Stoddard
moved over to Orchard and has become a specialist in the
highly specialized job of probing deep down along the side
of this dome and finding limestone impregnated with the
yellow material. He emphatically disclaims being an artist
or a genius.

"I'm sort of sulphur bird dog," is how he phrases it, "but
like a wise old setter who knows that the quail are out in the
fields feeding in the morning and huddling along the fence
rows in the later afternoon, I've learned where the hunting
is apt to be good."

That explanation may be as true as Gus Drachenberg's
"feel of the lines," but Stoddard plays no hunches. He works
upon a scientific basis. After several seasons of night work
he earned a Master's degree from the University of Houston
in Reservoir Geology. He has the "night school habit" and
regularly takes extension courses at Houston. He also has
one of the finest set of property maps in the industry.

"Like any gambling, it's exciting. We keep poking
'round," he explains, "and sometimes we find a pocket with
only 5000 tons, but sometimes we hit ten times that much."

One can see how in this dome Texas Gulf happened to
miss signs of a commercial deposit, and also how Duval, the
smallest of the four American companies, has worked this
single dome profitably for 20 years. The company's management keeps an eye open for likely domes in Louisiana and
Texas. They feel that Mexico is not a proper field for opera-

tions such as theirs nor offshore, since mining under water involves extraordinary capital investment.[11] The change of the company's name to Duval Sulphur & Potash Company is descriptive. In March 1952, it began mining potash salts in New Mexico and since then has also staked a substantial claim in the potash area of Saskatchewan, Canada. In March 1955 Duval began exploring for copper in the foothills of the Sierrita Mountains, some 30 miles south of Tucson, Arizona. A year later it raised $7,500,000 by the sale of warrants to its own shareholders to build a grinding mill and flotation cells to concentrate ore rich in both copper and molybdenum.[12]

Our American sulphur narrative now moved back to Louisiana, between Abbeville and New Iberia, not far from the Frasch mine. Skirting Joe Jefferson's island in the famous Five Sisters group is Lake Peigneur, a part of a navigable stream flowing through Vermilion Bay to the Gulf of Mexico. As such, the mineral rights here, according to Louisiana law, belong to the state.

Back in 1924 Arthur Barba, an engaging and enterprising Spaniard, who had come to New Orleans as a youth and won a prominent place in the city's business life, organized a syndicate with Adolphe D'Aquiñ, John Vaccaxo, and other friends, to explore for oil around the Jefferson Island salt dome. They secured from the state a mineral lease on 2500 acres, including the surface of Lake Peigneur—which later became important—perpetual so long as they kept on exploring and producing. It stipulated the usual one-eighth royalty on all oil, gas, and minerals sold.[13] The Syndicate engaged Richard B. Thacker, a consulting geologist, to supervise exploring and put the operation under Edward LaGuerre, graduate of Sorbonne University in Paris, who had previously been in the Baku oil fields and for 15 years had worked on the Gulf Coast. They did considerable drilling but struck no oil.

Lack of capital forced a couple of reorganizations and by 1932 the Jefferson Lake group had spent close to a million dollars and found no oil. Cash on hand was enough for just one more try. After much debate it was agreed to drill in the center of the lake. From this forlorn-hope Edward La-Guerre turned up a significant showing of sulphur. Subsequent drilling established that about 650 feet beneath the lake is a submerged salt plug with a cap of limestone covering 200 feet of sulphur-bearing formation, obviously a commercial deposit.[14]

Still interested primarily in oil, Jefferson Lake leased all sulphur rights in Lake Peigneur to the American Cyanamid Company, which six months later withdrew. Again the Jefferson Lake directors faced a momentous decision. Their resolution to go into sulphur changed their company not only from petroleum to brimstone, but from a prospecting to a producing enterprise. They engaged as chief engineer Lawrence O'Donnell, previously with Texas Gulf, and called into consultation James M. Todd, a professional mechanical engineer of New Orleans. A. A. Mayer, a New Orleans exporter, surveyed the world sulphur markets and was invited to become sales manager, which he did in October 1932.[15]

To mine sulphur underneath six feet of water, though familiar practice in the petroleum field, was quite new for the Frasch technique. Oil experience was capitalized and drilling rigs mounted on floating barges were anchored on location until a well was bored, then moved for the next drilling. This aquatic mining has its disadvantages, but a rig can be moved to a new location in a couple of hours instead of as many days.[16] The power plant was built on high ground 6000 feet from the mining field, but accessible to a concrete highway and where it was possible to bring in a three-mile railroad spur to the main line of the Southern Pacific. This was built at a cost of $40,000 prior to construction of the plant, which was designed to heat 1,500,000 gallons of water a day in three Babcock & Wilcox boilers of 600 hp rating each. The furnaces burned fuel oil and Cochrane hot-process, lime-soda ash water-softening equipment was installed. Water came from two artesian wells of six-inch diameter, pumped to a reservoir of 20 acres with storage capacity of 50,000,000 gallons.[17]

When this new plant went on-stream, October 18, 1932, the devoted supporters of this Jefferson Lake enterprise, who had swallowed so many disappointments, held a great jollification in the new town of Barba, Louisiana. After two days steaming the first sulphur was pumped.

The operating crew at the mine were a notable trio. The field superintendent was Harvey A. Wilson, still with Jefferson Lake and now (1959) vice-president in charge of their Frasch operations. The other two were native Louisianans, descendents of the French Huguenots who settled in the Evangeline Country after being driven from Nova Scotia: Gaston Etie and Harold Jaquet. Etie, now dead, was field superintendent, famous as one of those skilled operators who can wring the last drop of sulphur out of a difficult structure. His assistant, Jaquet, has made a name for himself, as we shall see, for his efficient development of the Jáltipan dome in Mexico.

Production at Lake Peigneur started with a rush, but it soon petered out:

YEAR		PRODUCTION (Tons)	TOTAL SALES (Tons)
1932	(Oct. 20—Dec. 31)	13,401	
1933		303,787	127,584
1934		76,135	178,861
1935		24,473	94,458
1936		8,439*	22,449
1937			6,458

* To the end of June, 1936.

Depletion stopped production in June 1936, with a total output of 426,235 tons.[18] This disappointing performance divided the company's directors: some were for going ahead with sulphur at another location, others wanted to return to

oil exploration. In the end sulphur prevailed, and with
A. A. Mayer as president, prospective deposits were studied
and turned down at San Felipe in Mexico and Damon
Mound in Texas, and another test made at Clemens Dome
near the San Bernard River in Brazoria County.

This dome was found by torsion balance survey in 1925
and proved by drilling the following year. The Shell Oil
Company controlled most of the area, but one substantial
tract was under lease to the Texas Company. Sulphur rights
were optioned from these companies by Texas Gulf which
started prospecting in August 1927. This did not indicate
what was considered a commercial deposit, so the leases were
abandoned in February 1928. However, prior to the exploratory work, Texas Gulf had bought sulphur fee interest in
several tracts on the dome.[19]

While drilling ten test wells for Jefferson Lake at Damon,
Harvey Wilson hired a driller who had worked on the 22 test
holes of Texas Gulf at Clemens. This man was so enthusiastic about the sulphur possibilities at Clemens that Wilson
drove over to make a little informal investigation. He met
Pabst, the principal landowner, who showed him some exceptionally good-looking cores. A. A. Mayer, who was then
Jefferson Lake's president, had little difficulty in leasing
Pabst's 50 acres. When testing turned up sulphur in tempting quantities, Jefferson Lake gathered together practically
the entire dome area.[20] In this section Texas Gulf had an
undivided sulphur fee interest on some property and one
tract it owned outright.[21] To facilitate mining as a unit, the
companies agreed that Jefferson Lake have full control of
operations and deliver to Texas Gulf that company's pro
rata share of the brimstone produced; revised in 1949 to
royalty payments.

The first Jefferson Lake test well was begun September
21, 1936, on the Pabst tract. Within two months 22 wells
had been sunk, roughly delineating the sulphur deposit and
furnishing log data that justified mining. On December 21,

they began dismantling the plant at Lake Peigneur and transferring it to Clemens. By the end of April construction work, handled by Harvey A. Wilson, was finished and April 25 the fires were lighted under the boilers. April 27 steaming began, and at 2:30 P.M. May 3, Pabst No. 24, was brought into production. Within two hours two others came in.

For five years Clemens produced profitably. Toward the end of 1941 operations moved to the lower end of the dome where they could get no production. As a result in 1942 Jefferson Lake ran into the red, a loss of $327,000 for a mined total of 76,586 tons.[22] There was sulphur below, but it could not be brought up, so Harold Jaquet, field superintendent, visited the plants of Duval at Orchard and Freeport at Hoskins where he was generously permitted to study their mudding operations. Next year production jumped to 152,-433 tons and although at times there have been fears of its exhaustion, the dome has continued to produce profitably ever since, with a total to December 1, 1956, of 2,626,130 tons.[23]

While Clemens has been Jefferson Lake's backlog, the company had explored other possibilities and operated two other domes. They drilled, for example, 18 holes at Hawkinsville in Matagorda County, Texas, and this prospect was abandoned. Early in 1929 sulphur rights on 175 acres on the dome known as Bay Ste. Elaine in the southwest coastal section of Louisiana were obtained from a syndicate of local people. Jefferson Lake decided that the character of this dome and its location required an investment beyond the resources of a small company. At Spindletop the company got leases on some 50 of the 500 acres. These were small lots, some of them as little as 40 sq. feet, just large enough to hold a derrick. Drilling showed excellent prospects, but the area controlled was so small and scattered that these leases were assigned to Texas Gulf in exchange for leases at Long Point where Jefferson Lake built a plant in 1942, half of the production to go to Texas Gulf.

Long Point has proved a good second string to the Clemens Dome bow. It is a dome of some 500 acres, rather easy to work, with sulphur 700 to 1000 feet down under a 150-foot layer of caprock. The principal difficulty has been rapid subsidence which sometimes shears off pipes.

From 1930 to 1938, Texas Gulf had mined 402,000 tons from a 50-acre tract here and Jefferson Lake started alongside this depleted area working toward the south. There a sulphur area was opened up where the wells are very long-lived. After Jefferson Lake took over Long Point, other people explored a part of this dome. First, the National Lead Company, which gave it up, and then the Lone Star Sulphur Company, followed by the Admiral Sulphur Company, both of which were soon closed as unsuccessful operations. Jefferson Lake's plant, with a water capacity of 3,380,000 gallons a day, came on-stream June 7, 1946, and through 1957, produced 2,396,000 long tons, half going to Texas Gulf.[24]

Having gone wholeheartedly into sulphur, the company's name was changed from Jefferson Lake Oil to Jefferson Lake Sulphur Company, and its oil properties were farmed out. The 1700 acres, the bed of Lake Peigneur, were leased to the Texas Company for a 1/16 overwriting royalty on all petroleum found, saved, and marketed. Rather ironically after fourteen years of exploration by Jefferson Lake and its predecessors, Texas struck oil on its first well, and in the first year (1939) produced 70,047 barrels of petroleum.[25] The 2500 acres in the proved oil field at Valentine Dome were turned over to an independent operator and for several years paid Jefferson Lake good royalties.[26]

Having committed itself to a sulphur future, the company's annual report of 1938 gave its shareholders some wholesome instruction in the economics of sulphur marketing when it said:

It is to be remembered that sulphur is a basic material. The volume of consumption in any country, or in the world, depends upon the general industrial activity. . . . When there is a demand for automobiles, iron and steel, fertilizers and insecticides, pulp and paper, oils, textiles—or the manufacture of cannon, battleships, airplanes, and explosives—there is demand for sulphur. . . . The demands of peace are best and the most dependable in the long run. The situation means that our sales effort must be in competition with other producers for the patronage of manufacturers of other products and goods who need sulphur for their processes. We cannot stimulate sulphur consumption by any mass appeal of advertising: we can only struggle for our share of a total consumption over which we can exercise no control, and in these days of troubled economics the purchasers of raw sulphur are seeking their material at the lowest possible prices.

12

Web-Foot Mining

THE GHOST of the dead Frasch mine in Calcasieu Parish haunts every sulphur-mining company. Always, therefore, they carry on explorations. Not a likely dome is located but their scouts begin inquiries and executives open negotiations for test drilling.

Accordingly, when it was gossiped in early 1928 that the Gulf Refining Company's geophysical staff had found an enormous salt dome buried under the marshy fringes of the Delta of the Mississippi, P. George Maercky, then general manager of Freeport, sent Earl Dissinger to investigate.[1]

Two years earlier Maercky had succeeded C. A. Jones, who retired November 12, 1927. Before he left, this sulphur pioneer wrote a number of his old associates. To Lew Mims he said:

> As I write I am looking at the wonderful framed picture of Freeport which hangs over my desk and I am contrasting the appearance of what it was when I first saw the ground which it now occupies—there was one little Negro shack about where the schoolhouse is now with its hard-packed yard full of little kinky heads.[2]

An even more marvelous transformation was destined to be wrought by the Freeport Sulphur Company in the swamps of the Mississippi Delta.

Having succeeded Jones, Maercky himself resigned in

138

December 1930. After the stockholders took control of the
Freeport management away from E. P. Swenson, Maercky
felt, no doubt, that he was a man of the old regime. He left
and opened an office in Houston as sulphur consultant. In
June 1931, he joined the staff of Texas Gulf as assistant to
the New York executives.

From the inception of the Swenson-Vanderlip-Tilghman
syndicate, E. P. Swenson had been its very active head. He
was a resolute, self-reliant man. Since youth he had handled
large affairs on his own initiative with conspicuous success.
Neither by nature nor by training was he an executive to
brook interference with his plans or policies, and he regarded
this sulphur enterprise as his personal responsibility.

Associated with the Freeport Sulphur Company, also since
its beginning, was the private banking house of John L.
Williams & Sons of Richmond. From the first this firm was
inclined to be critical of the Swenson management, and John
Skelton Williams, son of the bank's founder and Comptrol-
ler of the Currency during the Wilson Administration, maintained that his company's big interest had never been properly recognized or adequately represented.

When the stockholders began asking questions, particularly about the cost of sales and the reserves at Bryanmound,
Swenson ignored their inquiries. Later, when they pressed
for a reply, he said flatly that the details of sales management
were no concern of theirs and that information about reserves
was more valuable to his competitors than to his stockholders. This dictatorial attitude naturally irked many shareholders, and John Skelton Williams' brother and nephew,
Langbourne Sr. and Jr., headed the growing opposition to
what many felt was Swenson's arbitrary and unreasonable
stand. A proxy battle to control the company was climaxed
at a stockholders' meeting in Wilmington, Delaware, April
10, 1930, when the Williams group overturned the Swenson
control.[3]

Langbourne M. Williams, Jr., took charge of Freeport af-

fairs just when the big sulphur dome in the Mississippi Delta
was under investigation. Preliminary reports were discouraging. Dissinger went so far as to say, "In my opinion this will
prove to be an impossible sulphur-mining proposition."
There was good reason for this pessimism.[4]

This Grande Ecaille dome is some 35 miles below New
Orleans, situated ten miles southwest of the Mississippi and
within four miles of the Gulf. It lies beneath a tidal marsh
of peculiar formation. Sand from waves and tide and fine
sediment from the river accumulate on the bottom of the
lagoons till the salt grasses eventually obtain a foothold.
Successive growth and decay of this vegetation form a brown-
ish, fibrous mat which literally floats on an ooze of sandy
mud. The whole overlies a stratum of clay. These floating
islands are intersected with sluggish streams. Not a bush or a
tree grows in the area. These grass marshes are uninhabited
save for muskrat, mink, herons, thousands of red-winged
blackbirds, billions of mosquitoes. All materials had to be
shipped in by a circuitous 75-mile course from Harvey, opposite New Orleans, through the Harvey Canal, twisting
about through a series of bayous into Barataria Bay and
thence to Lake Grande Ecaille. Barging and towing in these
shallow winding bayous were not only costly but dangerous.

In the exploratory drilling by Humble for the Gulf and
Shell companies, barges carried the rigs to location and supported them. Swarms of mosquitoes so pestered the crews
that airplane propellers driven by Model T. Ford motors
to serve as blowers were set up on the barges. In the third
well drilled sulphur in a limestone formation was reached at
1527 feet. Subsequent cores showed brimstone in considerable quantities. On February 10, 1932, Freeport acquired
all sulphur rights to Lake Grande Ecaille and the vicinity.[5]

During 1932-33, a picked crew of Freeport engineers and
drillers from Hoskins sampled 18 wells at Grande Ecaille.
They worked from two welded-steel barges designed to support and house the entire drilling unit. This consisted of

The five-master schooner and wooden loading equipment contrasts dramatically with the ore-type freighter with five holds and the million-dollar loader with its ¾-mile conveyor, all controlled by a portable, pushbutton panel at Port Sulphur, Miss.

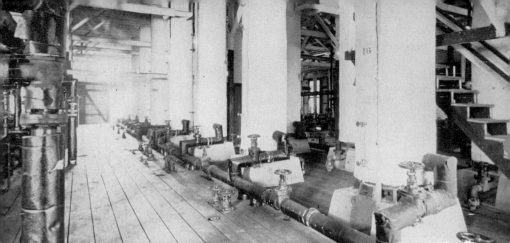

Union Sulphur Co.

Steam direct from boilers to heaters raises the water temperature to about 325°F. Great efficiencies have been achieved since the first operations (*above*) and the five heaters at Newgulf delivering 9,000,000 gals./day and the newest type at Pan American's Jáltipan installation.

Texas Gulf Sulphur.Co.

Photo by Author

Union Sulphur Co.

Freeport Sulphur Co.

Pipelines for hot water and compressed air from plant to mine are the life lines of the industry. The wooden-box insulation stuffed with Spanish moss is primitive indeed compared with pipe layout at Garden Island Bay where remote control regulates the water- and air-flow and measures the sulphur output at each well.

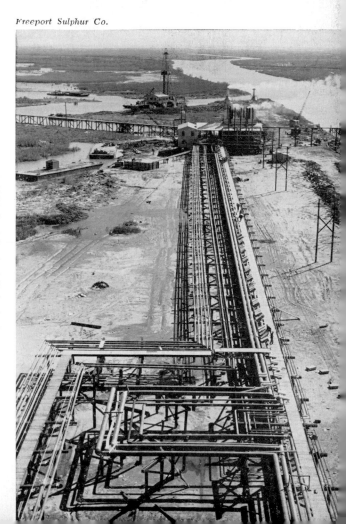

Replacement of wood by metal is but the visible sign of very great advances in drills and drilling techniques which have reduced time and increased accuracy many times over.

Mine head, showing set up of the four concentric pipes.

A vat is essentially a gigantic bin in which the molten brimstone solidifies into a great block; first made of wooden planks; later of adjustable metal sheets; recently of sulphur itself cast in the form of retaining walls.

Union Sulphur Co.

More even distribution and hence quicker freezing have been accomplished by a long series of improvements in the discharge of melted sulphur over the top surface of the vat area.

Freeport Sulphur Co.

Texas Gulf Sulphur Co.

From the pick-and-shovel methods of breaking down a vat for shipment to the bulldozer and completely mechanized loading into box cars or gondolas, into trucks or ships epitomized the advances of this distinctively American industry in the past 60 years.

Vats vary in height from 20 to 50 ft. and small charges of dynamite are exploded to break up the solid mass. Mechanical cranes have loaded as much as 17,000 tons/day of solid sulphur.

British-American Oil Co.

Freeport Sulphur Co.

Texas Gulf Sulphur Co.

Molten sulphur becomes more and more popular with big consumers and is now being shipped in insulated and heated barges by water, in tank cars over the rails, and by tank-trucks over the highways.

Freeport Sulphur Co.

Photos by Texas Gulf Sulphur Co.

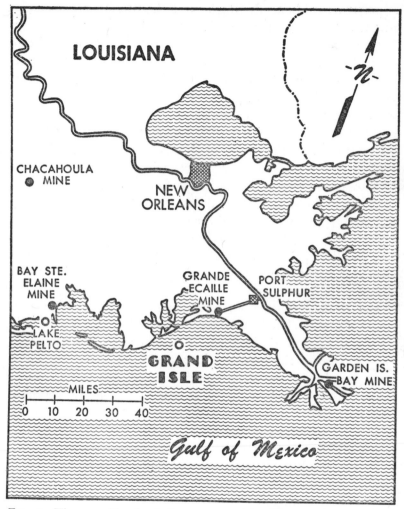

Fig. 7. The marshland, shallow-water, and offshore sulphur mines in operation or under development by Freeport Sulphur Company.

96-foot derricks with 100 hp engines for the draw works, 50 hp motors for the slush and water pumps, electric lights, mosquito blowers, and all tools accessory to rotary drilling rigs.[6] The derrick and draw works' engine stood on an 8-foot superstructure beneath which were the pumps, other equipment, and five gasoline engines to power each unit. The barges measured 80 x 36 feet and were six and one-half feet deep, divided into watertight compartments whose bulkheads strengthened the barge to withstand the shocks and vibrations of rotary drilling. The two rear compartments were used as slush pits for the drilling mud. The forward compartments were filled with water as ballast to maintain an even keel. In the center of the bow, a 4-foot opening extended to the middle of the barge which provided a means of moving on the well location and off again once the well casing had been set. A 45-feet-wide, 6-feet-deep canal was dredged to the spot selected for drilling and around this the canal was enlarged to a working bay about 70 feet wide and 175 feet long. The drilling barge was then towed to position and anchored, a method which saved time and cost in moving and setting up.

Dr. Donald C. Barton, consulting geologist of Houston, made a torsion balance survey that revealed a caprock area of about 1100 acres, only 200 of which were proved before the erection of the plant. This caprock lies generally about 1250 feet below the surface and averages 250 feet in thickness. The overlying sediment is chiefly of sand and gumbo, easy material to drill. Barton's survey was exceedingly valuable in locating wells and selecting the site for the powerhouse and auxiliary buildings.

In the sulphur industry the problem of plant location is never complicated by considerations of markets, freight rates, labor supply, or any other economic, political, or social factors. Over the dome, there the plant must be.

Imagination could hardly picture a less inviting site for a Frasch operation than Grande Ecaille: ten miles from fresh water; in the midst of a swamp where a dropped pair of pliers disappeared within moments; far from highways or railroad and with no means of building solid transportation; wide open to every hurricane and any tidal wave;

plagued by swarms of mosquitoes. What a site for a power plant to heat over 2,000,000 gallons of water every 24 hours! As Homer Burns, who built this plant, once said half jestingly but with a big element of truth,[7] "The first man on the job stepped gingerly out of a rowboat in hip boots and standing on a plank, drove a pile on which to perch his coat and lunchbox."

A picture of the country helps one appreciate the novel and peculiar difficulties of Grande Ecaille. As it twists through the Delta, the right descending bank of the Mississippi is protected by a high levee behind which lies a narrow strip of dry land built up by the river sediment, a rich unctuous soil, famous of old for its oranges and now for its Easter lilies. It is inhabited by an easy-going population: Indian, French, Slav, Negro, with colonies of Chinese shrimp fishermen.

Tucked away behind the levee is a strip of land, maybe a mile wide or a mere ribbon. That land is sold, not by the acre, but by the front foot on the river, extending south and west through the marshes out to the Gulf of Mexico anywhere from five to 20 miles distant. Grande Ecaille Lake— it literally means "big scale" or in the French patois of the country "big fish," which is the tarpon—lies ten miles south of the river and about four miles from the Gulf.

Water for the plant must come from the Mississippi and the dry land near the river was obviously the place for the townsite and offices. Also, shipments of sulphur must be made from the river bank, and so 2800 feet along the Mississippi extending back about 7600 feet, was purchased with a strip 1000 feet wide extending to Lake Grande Ecaille. The first job was to dredge a ten-mile canal from river to dome, approximately 100 feet wide, nine feet deep, involving the moving of 2,000,000 cubic yards of dirt. At the river a dock 1000 feet long was built to accommodate vessels with the draft of a battleship. The river water here is sufficiently low in salt for mining purposes, and a reservoir to hold 50 million gallons was constructed. The earth from this was used as fill for the townsite.

When it came to building the plant to house the big boilers and gigantic air compressors, no stratum was found sufficiently close to the surface to be of any value for supporting the piling upon which the buildings were to be erected. It was therefore necessary to depend upon the friction between soil and piling. After much testing, for the ordinary engineering formulas were of little use under these unusual conditions, it was found that a 75-foot piling would support eight tons.

"After that," as Homer Burns put it, "the rest was just like a good golf swing—all a matter of timing. We had to plan every step so that the right materials would be on hand at the right time because we didn't have any room for a box of tacks before the carpet was ready to be laid."

The construction plan was to lay heavily reinforced concrete mats supported by piling as the foundation of all buildings. The mats distributed the load uniformly over the piles. They were reinforced to compensate for any variation in the individual supporting power of the piles. Future requirements must be anticipated since it was impossible to alter these foundations once they were installed. Almost all moving had to be on traveling piling, for soil conditions did not permit any skidding. When the job started, the construction crews lived in houseboats, and the first buildings were a cookhouse and men's quarters equipped with electric lights and all conveniences.

In all 18,000 pilings 35 to 80 feet in length were used.[8] Under the power plant the pilings were laid approximately on 2-foot 8-inch centers. The floor of the plant is elevated 12 feet above mean tide and about 11 feet above the surrounding marsh, ample protection against storms and high tides. The space between this floor and the concrete mat is used for water storage. The superstructure of the power plant and all permanent buildings is a steel framework designed for a 125-mile wind, covered with corrugated asbestos roof and sides fastened with aluminum bolts and clips. All steel framework, tanks and walkways, flue gas pipes, stairways, pipe supports, and so forth were fabricated in the company's own shop and barged to location down the canal.

The power plant equipment consisted of six 860 hp Sterling boilers provided for combustion of oil, gas or pulverized coal. Three 750-kilowatt noncondensing turbine generators provided current for the drilling wells, water pumps, sulphur loading, and other operations, and three 800-pound high-pressure compressors supplied air for pumping sulphur. The steam used in driving such auxiliary services as generators, compressors, and pumps is returned to the mine water system through low-pressure heaters and the water-treating plants. Approximately 30 per cent of the heat that goes down to the sulphur formation is first passed through these auxiliaries. In the layout particular pains were taken to assure the greatest thermal efficiency, and this important factor has been continually studied and improved.

On January 2, 1933, it was reported to Freeport headquarters that "the dredge has arrived at Rattlesnake Bayou to start the canal." A month later the first pilings for the plant were driven. Ten months later, December 7, the first wells were steamed and initial production was secured the following day. During the first month daily production averaged 708 tons.

To build this plant all materials were barged from the new town of Port Sulphur on the Mississippi ten miles through the canal to the mine in the marshland: 18,000 piles, 2,500,-000 board feet of lumber, and 2700 tons of steel and metal piping. Over 5,500,000 cubic yards of earth had been moved.[9] This was at the time an incomparable accomplishment in the Frasch sulphur industry. It gave Freeport unique experience in what Wilson T. Lundy, who had charge of this construction job, well called "web-foot sulphur mining," an experience invaluable in the subsequent development of the domes at Bay Ste. Elaine and Garden Island Bay.

Picture this unique sulphur mine—on the banks of the Mississippi, the big, half-mile long, loading docks with their vast storage bins and highly mechanized, rapid handling equipment close to the end of the canal. Nearby, the town of Port Sulphur,[10] laid out on the garden city plan with schools, churches, hospital, community house, flood-lighted tennis courts and baseball diamonds. Off to the southwest as far as the eye can see green marshes cut through by the canal lying straight as a ruler between the river's dock and loading dock at the plant, on which silvery lifeline the operation men commute to work in high-speed launches while barges bring back the yellow product of the mine. Parallel to the canal, a 9-mile pipeline carrying water from the reservoir is flanked by an electric transmission line for power for the pumps.

At the producing end of the canal, in the marshland, stands a modern power plant a mile away from the mining area to provide against subsidence. Nearby, on sites 200 by 700 feet, two great sulphur bins are supported by piling on a fill built up and leveled off 11 feet above low water. From the vats the sulphur is loaded by electric caterpillar shovel and permanent conveyors take it about 400 feet to barges in the canal. Originally it was planned to drill from floating barges, but after actual operations began, filling in with hydraulic dredges over the area to be mined was adopted and the working surface built up four or five feet above tide level.

When a new dome is first steamed everyone looks for trouble. Initial production is almost always small and comes hard. At Grande Ecaille difficulties similar to those at Hoskins were caused by the underground formation. Again they had to resort to mudding, but swamp mud has the consistency of a thin pea soup. So they forced down 8000 cubic yards a day of dredged material in order to get the Frasch system working.[11] A year later the management reported to its stockholders, "The program of pumping mud into the formation at Grande Ecaille to bring about better thermal efficiency . . . has been continued. Substantial progress has been made in these operations, but the program is not yet completed. In the meantime, production has remained relatively low, costs consequently high." [12]

During the next year, however, this phase of the problem was solved. But a new difficulty arose. Grande Ecaille sulphur is low in ash content and commercially free from arsenic, selenium, and tellurium, but traces of crude oil discolor it to grayish-brown. It was the industry's first experience with "off-color sulphur" in quantity.

This problem was immediately recognized as serious, and a research program was undertaken to develop the most suitable method of removing the oil. Freeport developed a unique distillation,[13] but as this problem is now familiar in other Louisiana domes and in Mexico, several methods for converting off-color to bright sulphur have since been developed.[14]

When, thanks to Grande Ecaille, the state of Louisiana again became a producer of sulphur, the late Huey Long drew to a head the long festering sore of sulphur taxes. Levying a just *ad valorem* tax on any mineral property is admittedly a knotty problem: the perplexities of valuing sulphur underground are multiple.

Even disinterested experts have great difficulty in accurately determining reserves. It is not forgotten that the original engineering report placed the reserves at Bryanmound at 17 million tons but the dome actually produced 5 million. Even the words 'mine' and 'mining,' conjuring up a tunnel in which miners with pick and shovel dig ore from the bowels of the earth, are quite misleading when applied to the Frasch process. Nobody ever gets down to the sulphur horizon of a saltdome to study its strata and estimate its ore content. Experience proves how irregular these deposits are.

Mining by the melt method is a gigantic physical refining

process. The caprock becomes a great autoclave within which brimstone is converted from the solid to the liquid state. No man can foretell where the injected hot water will flow, nor the direction of the flow of the melted mineral. Being twice as heavy as water, it must follow the lowest open fissures. These may lead to the bottom of the well whence it can be pumped to the surface. They may lead off to some crevice from which it can never be recovered. Experience is the sole guide, experience that must work blindfolded. The operator knows but one safe rule—no two deposits are alike. Accordingly, the amount of recoverable sulphur in any given sulphur horizon cannot be determined exactly nor can costs or recovery be estimated with precise accuracy.

Furthermore, equipment of a brimstone mine calls for a big investment. Under the most favorable conditions but a fraction of the heat supplied performs the useful operation of melting sulphur underground. It is therefore necessary to build power plants of ten to twenty times the capacity needed for the direct application of the heat to the mound. In addition to the costs of drilling and equipping the wells are the costs of a big water supply system, king-size boiler plants, heating and pumping machinery, as well as transportation and housing facilities.

With the best will in the world, sulphur taxation is difficult. Because of its highly localized character, the industry has little statewide influence. In Texas, for example, all the Frasch sulphur is being produced from seven domes in six counties out of a total of 254. Accordingly, the entire area in which brimstone industry is located is represented in the Legislature by four Senators out of 31 and by eight members out of 150 in the House. In political years sulphur is dangerously apt to be set up as a "straw man" to be buffeted about, a target for uninformed criticism and demogogic appeals. The record of the severance taxes levied against sulphur and other mineral resources of the state, show how the industry has been singled out for unfavorably preferential treatment. The following table sets forth the growth of the natural resources taxes in Texas:

MONTH	YEAR	"NATURAL RESOURCES"	TAX
April	1905	Oil	Beginning of tax of 1% of value
May	1907	Oil	Tax reduced to ½% of value
March	1919	Oil	Tax increased to 1½% of value
June	1923	Sulphur	Beginning of tax of 2% of value
		Oil	Tax increased to 2% of value
*April	1930	Sulphur	Tax increased to 4% of value (55¢)
		Oil	Tax remained at 2% of value
April	1931	Sulphur	Tax remained at 4% of value (55¢)
		Gas	Beginning of tax of 2% of value
		Oil	Tax remained at 2% of value
*August	1931	Sulphur	Tax increased to 5¾% of value (75¢)
		Gas	Tax remained at 2% of value
		Oil	Tax remained at 2% of value
*October	1936	Sulphur	Tax increased to 8% of value ($1.03)
		Gas	Tax increased to 3% of value
		Oil	Tax increased to 2¾% of value
		Cinnabar ore	Beginning of tax of 10¢ per ton
		Other ores	Beginning of tax of 5¢ per ton
		Marble	Beginning of tax of 10¢ per ton
		Carbon black	Beginning of tax of 3% of value
August	1943	Cinnabar ore	Tax repealed
		Other ores	Tax repealed
		Marble	Tax repealed
March	1950	Sulphur	Tax increased to $1.40 per ton
		Gas	Tax increased to 5.72% of value (This tax was later raised to 9% of value, then reduced to 8%, and, in 1956, further reduced to 7% of value.)
		Carbon black	Tax increased to between 4.51% and 5.72% of value.

* Based on value of $13 per ton at well. Oil and gas also based on value at well. Sale price of sulphur f.o.b. cars of $16 per ton.

In Texas the sulphur producers pay three full taxes. First, the $1.40 per ton paid to the State is theoretically a severance tax and set up in the State Comptroller's records as a gross receipt tax. Second, in figuring the *ad valorem* taxes, sulphur above ground is taxed year after year so long as it remains unsold. Finally, to the *ad valorem* levies must, of course, be added the many increasing federal and local taxes which have been estimated to run up the overall tax bill of more than $6 a ton.

Taxes paid by the Union Sulphur Company in Calcasieu Parish, Louisiana, from 1919 to abandonment of the mine in 1925 illustrate how easy it is to place prohibitive values on a sulphur-producing property. Although the company protested in the Federal Courts,[15] valuations were sustained so that during the last five years of operation the company was compelled to pay taxes on over 1,000,000 tons of sulphur underground which did not exist, or if they did, one must logically conclude that the Union Sulphur Company was forced to abandon the property because of the burden of taxation.[16]

Remembering this experience and fearing the Huey Long Administration and its openly avowed tax policy, Freeport hesitated to begin operations at Grande Ecaille until Louisiana placed sulphur on the same basis as oil and gas in its tax program. Back in 1921, the Louisiana Constitution had been amended to provide that "no further tax should be levied or imposed on gas or oil rights or leases, nor shall any such additional values be added to the assessment of land by reason of the presence of gas or oil therein, or the production therefrom."

The New Orleans Association of Commerce and other groups interested in the industrial development of the state, anxious to see the reestablishment of the sulphur industry in Louisiana, pressed the Legislature for action. Accordingly the constitution was amended to put sulphur on the same basis as gas and oil, with a compensating upward revision of the severance tax from 15 cents to 27 cents per ton. The company, taking this action as a pledge of the State's good faith, began construction at Grande Ecaille.

At the very next meeting of the Louisiana Legislature, however, the sulphur severance tax was raised, August 1, 1934, to 60 cents per ton. At the next session, July 28, 1936, it was this time raised to $2 a ton. Naturally, the result of this $2 tax against a $1.03 tax in Texas was that during 1936 Texas showed a 38 per cent increase in sulphur production while Louisiana production decreased by 23 per cent.[17]

While the highly localized sulphur industry has no wide political influence, its product goes through every channel of trade to many different industries. Accordingly, the bad faith and discrimination of the Louisiana sulphur tax became widely known in industrial circles. Just at this time Governor Richard Leche, who had succeeded Huey Long, was staging a sensational campaign to build up the industrial resources of the state. In little over a year this campaign brought $47,000,000 worth of new industrial construction to Louisiana.[18] That energetic governor's vociferous slogans, "Ten years property tax exemption," "Fair play to industry," "No political harassments," were given the direct lie by a sulphur tax which was raised from 15 cents to $2, repudiating the Legislature's own acts. The Freeport taxes in Louisiana jumped from $399,860.04 in 1936 to $816,468.81 in 1937.

The State Board of Commerce and Industry intervened and upon its assurance that the tax matter would be dealt with fairly in the coming session of the Legislature, Freeport stepped up production at Grande Ecaille and went ahead with plans for expansion. Pressure of public opinion became so forceful that the State Legislature referred the entire matter to a state referendum, and a constitutional amendment embracing the revision of the sulphur tax was adopted in November 1938. Thus by direct vote of the people the taxation of Louisiana sulphur was placed entirely within the framework of the state constitution. The *ad valorem* tax on unmined sulphur was restored with a ceiling established at twice the value of the physical property used in the production. The severance tax was reduced to parity with that in effect in Texas, namely $1.03 a ton. But this was only the first round in a long tax fight.

Eighteen years later the Louisiana tax battle was reopened by a brother of Huey Long, Earl K. Long, who ironically had campaigned for Governor pledging no increase in state taxes and then immediately introduced a bill raising, among other industrial levies, the severance tax on sulphur to $3 a ton. This triple increase would have cost Freeport, the biggest Louisiana producer, about $4 million a year. Again the company fought this discriminatory tax proposal—it takes courage for a corporation to oppose a Long in Louisiana—and won a second time with the aid of aroused public opinion.

Obviously, a $3-a-ton severance would place Freeport at a competitive disadvantage with producers in Texas, where the severance tax is $1.40, and also at this time Mexican sulphur was just coming on the market. Pointing out that since the present tax was established in 1938, the company had opened four new Louisiana mines, increased employment fourfold, and multiplied its severance tax payments six times over, a publicity campaign was launched. Through its own employees, its stockholders, suppliers and customers, through chambers of commerce and service clubs, thousands of copies of a little booklet, "Don't Put the Brakes on Progress" were distributed. The cover showed a pelican, state bird of Louisiana, chained to a ball labelled "H.B. 671," and the text was illustrated with similar eye-catching cartoons. (Figure 7.) To tell the story to the general public an advertisement headed "Open Letter from a Taxpayer to the Members of the Legislature" was printed in the newspapers.

Letters, telegrams, telephone calls began bombarding the lawmakers in Baton Rouge. Indignant letters and warning editorials appeared in the Louisiana press. Outside the state,

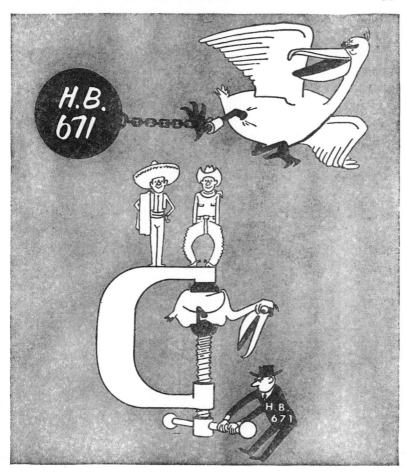

Fig. 8. Cartoons used by the Freeport Sulphur Company to dramatize the unfairness of the proposed increase in Louisiana tax and its damage to the State's industries.

the Texas newspapers commented rather gleefully and national chemical, mining, and financial journals pointed out the unfair and antagonistic attitude betrayed by this legislation. Despite this wave of public disapproval, Governor Long insisted on bringing the bill to a vote and appeared in person to cajole, threaten, chide, and deride the legislators. Although the bill was twice amended on the floor, reducing the $3 tax, first to $2.75, and then to $2, the measure was defeated. Furthermore, the Governor's effort to repeal the provision of the State Constitution requiring a two-thirds majority vote for the passage of any tax bill was later beaten by the voters. The protracted Louisiana sulphur tax battle is a parable in drastic and arbitrary taxation to be pondered alike by legislators and industrialists.[19]

13

War and Postwar

WORLD WAR II affected brimstone much as did World War I—only more so. However, its aftermath was quite different.

The four American companies operating the Frasch process in five domes met the second war's exorbitant demands for sulphur by pumping up a million more tons a year.[1] Most of this increase came naturally from the two biggest operations, Texas Gulf's Boling and Grande Ecaille where Freeport spent $7,000,000 in wartime expansions.[2]

YEAR	FREEPORT	%	TEXAS GULF	%	OTHERS	%	TOTAL U. S.
1940	860,000	31.5	1,428,000	52.5	444,000	16	2,732,000
1941	905,000	29	1,839,000	59	395,000	12	3,139,000
1942	1,014,000	29.2	2,173,000	63	274,000	7.8	3,461,000
1943	1,028,000	40.5	1,187,000	46.6	324,000	12.9	2,539,000
1944	1,003,000	31	1,842,000	57.3	373,000	11.7	3,218,000
1945	1,178,000	31.4	2,203,000	59	372,000	9.6	3,753,000
Total	5,988,000	31.7	10,672,000	56.6	2,182,000	11.7	18,842,000

Throughout hostilities, brimstone was never in short supply. But the industry accomplished this vital effort only by increasing production and digging into the great yellow blocks adjoining its plants which between 1940 and 1945 were cut down from 4.0 to 3.5 million tons.[3]

Following Japan's surrender, September 2, 1945, came a series of events so unforeseen, so contradictory to past experience, they seem almost an economic miracle. Four "highly improbables" became flinty realities.[4]

1—The postwar business recession, which had regularly

followed every major conflict since the Napoleonic Wars, did not materialize.

2—On the contrary, around the Free World, industrial activity—especially in chemical fields—bounded forward, and the demand, further raised by military needs in Korea, far exceeded even World War II's record-breaking sulphur requirements.

3—American producers of brimstone shoved up their output an additional million tons per year.

4—Yet they could not overtake the galloping demand so that by 1950 their stockpile was blasted down to 2.7 million tons, less than six months' supply.

Here is a statistical picture of this miraculous market:

BRIMSTONE (FRASCH) IN THE U. S., 1940-50

(In 1000 long tons)

YEAR	PRODUCTION	APPARENT SALES	EXPORTS	DOMESTIC
1940	2,726	2,558[a]	746	1,812[a]
1941	3,130	3,076	729	2,347
1942	3,456	3,032	568	2,464
1943	2,539	3,191	657	2,534
1944	3,218	3,580	654	2,926
1945	3,753	3,850	919	2,931
1946	3,860	4,094	1,189	2,905
1947	4,441	4,840	1,299	3,541
1948	4,869	5,015	1,263	3,752
1949	4,745	4,871	1,431	3,440
1950	5,192	5,637	1,441	4,196

[a] Mine shipments.

In 1950 there was a real sulphur shortage. Fortunately, it did not last long, but it did have far-reaching effects. It stimulated a world-wide search for sulphur and resulted in a markedly increased supply of this element in various chemical forms and from several new sources. This new competition inevitably unsettled prices. The situation is now more complicated as to the relative positions of brimstone and its substitutes and of the individual suppliers of these sources of sulphur.

The key to these revolutionary changes, as always in the steady evolution of sulphur, is the market actions and chemical reactions of sulphuric acid. U. S. production of this acid had risen, during the between-wars years, to 4.8 million tons a year, a million tons more than at the end of World War I. This increase mirrored the amazing expansion of the American chemical industry.[5]

This industry has always sold to other industries the chemical "tools" for tanning leather and vulcanizing rubber, bleaching and dyeing cloth and paper, turning fats into soap and sand into glass, and for hundreds of similar chemical-processing operations. Chemicals have been so used for ages to modify all sorts of natural materials better to serve man's uses. Now the chemical industry has taken on a new job. It is supplying other industries with man-made raw materials. In two decades synthetic fibers, rubbers, plastics and resins, gum and waxes, dyes and scents, detergents and lubricants, many others, have come to rival, and sometimes replace, their natural counterparts. Manufacture of these synthetic raw materials has become the chief business of the chemical manufacturers; the secret of their great growth; the reason why during the 1940's our domestic consumption of brimstone (most of it in acid) increased so much more than our use of the other basic industrial commodities:[6]

	1939	1949	INCREASE
Brimstone (000 long tons) (1)	1620	3442	113%
Steel (MM net tons) (2)	32.5	54.6	68%
Petroleum (MM barrels) (3)	1229	2118	72%
Coal (MM tons) (4)	428	478	12%
Lumber (MM board feet) (5)	2133	2710	27%

U. S. Bureau of Mines; Iron & Steel Inst., Total shipments of steel products, less exports; *Minerals Yearbook*, Total Domestic Demand; *Minerals Yearbook*, U. S. Consumption of bituminous coal and apparent consumption of anthracite; *Business Statistics*, 1957 U. S. Dept. of Comm., Shipments of lumber plus imports, less exports.

When the Nazi armies invaded Poland, September 1939, our production of 4.8 tons of sulphuric acid came from 183 plants. Over half of it was made by the contact process.[7] By 1945, the victory year, 174 acid plants were making nearly twice as much, 817 million tons, more than two-thirds of it by the contact method. Fought with modern munitions on a global stage, the Second World War's much greater acid needs were filled by more efficient production in larger units by the contact process fed by brimstone.

Improved chemical procedure in making modern munitions cut down sulphur requirements. For example, in 1918 the billion pounds of TNT consumed at the Front required 13,000 tons of sulphur to make: in 1941, the 600 million pounds of TNT ordered for the Defense Program required only 8000 tons of sulphur.[8] Regardless of these improved efficiencies, the demand for sulphur kept step with that for acid, so that during World War II, shipments of brimstone jumped from 2.5 to 3.8 million tons. Part of this increase went to our Allies, an average of 712,000 tons each year, approximately a third greater than our prewar exports.[9]

All these pressing needs were met. Nobody was concerned about sulphur. Many were much concerned, however, about the expected postwar slump and the labor-financial upsets accompanying the change-over to a peacetime economy. Bitter experience, backed by every economic statistic, forecast a serious let-down in industrial activity. Against everyone's jittery anticipations, business boomed. By 1950 sulphur was definitely short but while unforeseen, this shortage arose from understandable causes.[10]

Fundamental among these was the switch from the chamber to the contact process, promoting the use of brimstone at the expense of pyrites. A contact plant costs roughly half as much as a pyrites-burning unit and employs only two-fifths as much labor. The contact method produces high strength acid; is more flexible; gives better yields; and is being constantly improved in design, in materials of its construction, and in the catalysts it employs.[11] Except under special conditions these advantages are irresistible.

The contact process had appeared, in several modifications, shortly before World War I.[12] With Spanish pyrites (the highest grade available) cut off and Canadian and domestic pyrites cut back in the face of urgent need for high-test acid, war conditions furnished strong incentives to adopt the new process. World War II repeated this situation, heightened by greater demands for acid, so that both in North America and Europe adoption of the improved method was speeded. Ever-growing postwar demand for acid turned this technological trend into standard practice. In Europe, where chemical plants had been favorite bombing targets, the need for acid was almost desperate, and the switch to the contact process was much accelerated. With few exceptions new plants, here and abroad, were contact units.

The increased postwar demand for acid also had understandable causes. Most of the increased output of acid went to manufacturers of fertilizers and chemicals. Hunger, even starvation, threatened many lands in the war-wrecked world, and the great need for more food continued. In the United States various acreage restrictions adopted for farm relief during the 1930's taught farmers that greater crops can be raised on fewer acres by using more fertilizer.[13] They applied this lesson and fertilizer sales doubled from 8.2 million tons in 1940 to 18.0 in 1950.[14] This meant some 3.33 million tons more of 100 per cent H_2SO_4 in the production of superphosphate and ammonium sulphate. In the next two years, fertilizer sales increased to 22.1 million tons and the climb has continued. In Europe, farmers had long used more fertilizer per acre than was American practice, but there, too, they increased its applications.[15] Furthermore, during these years, in Australia and New Zealand, Japan, India and Pakistan, Israeli, Egypt, in many other countries, new fertilizer plants were the first tangible signs of economic development programs.

At the same time the American chemical industry was growing amazingly. Between 1939 and 1951 the value of its products advanced from $4,399 million to $18,472 million;[16] its consumption of sulphuric acid rose to 3.8 million tons,[17] an increase of 3.2 million tons.

, A significant feature of the postwar world-wide boom was the immediate recovery and rapid advance of synthetic fibers. World production of rayon, 1940-1950, increased from 2.5 to 3.5 billion pounds: in the United States, from 471 to 1238 million pounds.[18] Since it takes 1.25 pounds of sulphuric acid to make a pound of rayon, the world's increase in rayon output called for about 4,500,000 more pounds of acid.[19] During this decade, big gains in pigments, in synthetic rubber, and in the products of the new petrochemical industry, all helped boost the uses of the acid from 682,000 tons in 1925 to 3,226,000 tons in 1950 and by 1956 to 4,350,000 tons.[20]

Nor did the direct use of brimstone lag. Its consumption in pulp for paper went to more than half again as much as prewar. As a fungicide sulphur slipped because new organic compounds became serious competitors, but this was more than compensated by its use in making carbon bisulphide, for aluminum, and in vulcanizing natural and synthetic rubbers. While the curve of non-acid consumption was not as steep, it was definitely up.

All these accumulated demands kept gnawing into the sulphur stockpiles. The price of brimstone, held at $16 a ton throughout the war, advanced to $18.[21] Shipments to Europe continued to mount. Brimstone was an important commodity in the Marshall Plan and Washington was committed by the Atlantic Pact to build up the military strength of Free Europe. Then suddenly, in June 1950, the Chinese Communists overran Korea, and in the closing months of that year, an impending shortage of sulphur was apparent.

Fully aware of the obligatory military needs in Korea and the mandatory exports to Free Europe, the managements of Texas Gulf and Freeport eyed their vanishing vats with apprehension. No one knew better than they the grave effects of a sulphur shortage. Accordingly, first Texas Gulf and then Freeport took the only step open to them to conserve their above-ground reserves. They told their domestic customers that during 1951 they must reduce deliveries to between 80 and 85 per cent of the 1950 shipments.[22]

The first official conservation move followed quickly. The National Production Authority put brimstone for export under allocation in January 1951, calling forth protests throughout the chemical world. In Great Britain, especially, the consternation was great. A third of our exports, 420,000 tons, had gone there, and for the first quarter of 1951, their allotment was only 81,000 tons, a cut of 23 per cent. Actual first-quarter shipments in 1950 were 84,000, a cut of only 4 per cent.[23] Since 1938, when only 22 per cent of the United Kingdom's acid was made from brimstone, the switch to the contact process had raised this to 55 per cent, so the situation was critical. Sulphur was put in the hands of the International Materials Conference, which already controlled molybdenum and tungsten, and they set the quotas for the third quarter.[24]

Several war-built powder plants were reopened to fill Korean demands and in June the NPA put all sulphuric acid produced in the eleven Western states under limited allocation. Under a revised NPA order, all but the smaller users throughout the United States were restricted to a monthly brimstone consumption no greater than their average monthly rate of 1950 and to a three months' inventory. After July 1, sulphur producers could make deliveries only on specific authorization by the NPA. On November 9, the inventory limit was cut to 25 days. The amendment reducing to 90 per cent of the 1950 use, became effective January 1, 1952, with exceptions for special cases and the defense plants.

Dramatized by these controls and widely publicized, the sulphur shortage sparked a hunt for new supplies from any source from everywhere. Surface deposits of native sulphur were exploited from California and Wyoming to Ecuador and Argentina, from Japan to Turkey.[25] The Government in Spain, a combination of four companies in Australia, five different projects in Canada, and others ranging from South Africa to Sweden, proposed to increase the supply of pyrites. Scores of installations were made in the United States and Canada to recover sulphur from sour natural gas, from refinery gases, from smelter gases. Production of sulphuric acid from gypsum was undertaken in Germany by the I. G. Farbenindustrie, and in England by the Imperial Chemical Industries and United Sulphuric Acid Corporation. From this frantic stampede, the most tangible results came in sulphur recovered from the various gases and in more brimstone by the Frasch process from Louisiana and Texas and now also from Mexico.

The first new Frasch operation in production after the Korean War was Jefferson Lake at Starks in Calcasieu Parish, Louisiana, on June 25, 1951.[26] Texas Gulf had located sulphur in the lower edges of this dome. The exploring leases were due to expire shortly and to be renewed would require building a plant and actually working the dome. Since Texas Gulf was developing Moss Bluff, Spindletop, and Worland they turned Starks over to Jefferson Lake on a royalty basis. In the midst of the shortage Eugene H. Walet, Jr., who became president in 1947, saw an opportunity for their type of operation. Accordingly, Jefferson Lake built a 1.5 million gallon plant and during 1951 (six months of operation) Starks made 39,488 tons, raising its year-by-year output to 110,528 tons in 1955.

Realizing the vital need of an adequate supply of sulphur,

if the United States were drawn into war, Texas Gulf Sulphur had begun planning to bring its Moss Bluff dome into production back in 1939. Sulphur rights at this dome in Liberty County, Texas had been acquired from the Gulf Oil Company back in 1927, along with the sulphur rights to Boling, Long Point and several other domes. The first exploratory work was in 1931-32 when Texas Gulf drilled five wells and the Gulf Oil Company thirty-two. Sulphur was found over a widespread area in what appeared to be a large commercial deposit. Because of the depression and an existing surplus of sulphur, a five-year lease extension was negotiated. Similar conditions existed in 1937 so that Texas Gulf, in view of the lack of adequate sulphur markets, negotiated another five-year extension to 1942.[3] However, with war in Europe imminent, plans were pushed forward in late 1939, and by the Fall of 1940 purchase orders had been issued for almost the entire plant. In 1941 planning proceeded as rapidly as possible; low-pressure turbines were promised by October 1941; pumps and other equipment used in the old Gulf operation had been reconditioned.

However, when the United States entered the war, unforeseen obstacles appeared. After Pearl Harbor, Government controls and priorities were established. Delivery of necessary equipment was slowed down and finally halted. As a result, Texas Gulf was forced to obtain further extensions of leases by paying additional advance rentals. By 1942 it was becoming more difficult to obtain the necessary priorities and shortly after this the Government requisitioned some of the equipment on hand for use in other industries. In August 1944, the War Production Board finally refused to recommend the application to build the Moss Bluff plant because in their opinion sulphur requirements were not as critical as the manpower and material which could be used better elsewhere. Accordingly, Texas Gulf was again forced to obtain another extension of their leases.

Not until after the war, in October 1946, was permission given to proceed with the Moss Bluff plant. Construction began in 1947 and the plant went in production June 24, 1948, more than 20 years after the sulphur rights to the dome had been acquired and almost seven years after the plant would have been operating had the war not intervened. However, this plant was in full production in time to help during the 1950 sulphur shortage. Through December 1957, Moss Bluff had produced 2,613,747 long tons of brimstone and is still producing at its rated capacity.

The Moss Bluff story aptly demonstrates the time interval that can sometimes elapse between discovery and production in the sulphur business.

One reason why Texas Gulf was willing to turn Starks over to Jefferson Lake was its desire to bring Spindletop into production. Albert G. Wolf had studied this dome in 1924 and wrote a favorable report. R. C. Coward, a driller who had worked there, was employed to examine old records and contact old-timers who knew of drilling operations on the caprock area. As a result of these investigations, in 1926 Texas Gulf purchased the sulphur fee of Higgins Oil & Fuel Company, and in 1936 acquired from Gladys City Oil, Gas & Manufacturing Company their sulphur rights covering almost half of the entire dome area. In 1939, Texas Gulf acquired the sulphur from the McFaddin, Weiss and Kyle families and Unity Oil Company covering a very substantial tract on the dome, giving them approximately three-fourths of the dome area.

Early in 1941 Jefferson Lake Sulphur purchased some leases on the east side and on top of the Spindletop caprock and drilled. Results were encouraging, but their holdings were too small and scattered to warrant exploration, and the ownership in adjoining tracts was so complicated Jefferson Lake decided to go no further. Then a trade with Texas Gulf was made in 1942 whereby Jefferson Lake acquired rights to the holdings of Texas Gulf at Long Point, and Texas Gulf took over Jefferson's Spindletop holdings.

During the latter part of 1941, Texas Gulf started leasing and buying to block up the balance of cap area of this dome. Perhaps no suburban district in the world had a more complicated ownership. During the great excitement following the Lucas gusher, the area was minutely subdivided, some tracts being as small as 8 x 10½ feet and hundreds of tracts being only large enough for one well. Hundreds of corporations had as their only asset title to one of these tiny tracts. Wells were drilled, produced, and were abandoned by the individuals and corporations without any further ado. Two generations had passed; officers and directors were dead; stockholders scattered and dead; all records of most of the corporations disposed of, lost or destroyed.

It took several years to assemble the multitudinous leases, in all, hundreds necessary to cover the area of interest. Texas Gulf landmen traveled all over the United States and corresponded throughout the world.

Texas Gulf drilled 42 exploratory wells in early 1950. They proved and outlined a substantial sulphur deposit. It was decided to construct a plant, which was started in 1951. The first production from the field was on May 12, 1952 after solving numerous problems attendant upon operating a plant adjacent to the city of Beaumont. Through 1957 Spindletop had produced 2,110,000 long tons of sulphur. This new 4,000,000-gallon per day plant was important in helping relieve the sulphur shortage.

In May 1955 Freeport's Hoskins Mound plant was closed after 32 years during which nearly 11 million tons of brimstone had been surfaced. Having gotten their feet wet at Grande Ecaille, Freeport officials in 1949-50 entered into the famous "four point deal" with the Texas Company, thus receiving sulphur rights to four marshy, along-shore locations. These were Garden Island Bay at the tip of the Mississippi Delta; Bay Ste. Elaine on the Gulf 100 miles westward; Lake Pelto almost alongside; and Dog Lake prospected with discouraging results.

Garden Island Bay, the largest single brimstone project in 20 years, had been explored by the Texas Company for oil and a sulphur area of 1200 acres found 1600 to 1700 feet below the surface. Freeport drilled 12 exploratory wells, and, as had the oil men, ran into high-pressure gas at three levels. During the drillings Texas had lost three rigs in blowouts, and Freeport had one rig thrown over and another burned.

The terrain is similar to Grande Ecaille, and the Garden Island Bay plant is also built on a 16-inch mat of concrete supported by piles, 2260 of them.[27] Because spring floods cover this marshland, the plant is raised 16 feet. It houses boiler capacity to deliver 3.5 million gallons of water a day at 325°F., although the usual working schedule is 3 million gallons steaming 10 to 12 wells.

The water problem, not unlike that of the Ancient Mariner—"everywhere, and not a drop to drink"—was solved by a 600-acre reservoir, holding a billion and a half gallons. Water is taken in by three pumps, each moving 15,000 gallons per minute, during June and July of each year. At this season water from the nearby pass is comparatively sweet. From the reservoir the water goes through the Permutit hot-water process and then to the high-pressure heaters.

The plant was built and equipped by a picked crew from shut-down Hoskins Mound—the veterans were handsomely pensioned off—and it is largely manned today by these experienced men. A distinctive feature of this unique setup is how extraordinarily bad working conditions—miles from a square foot of dry land—have been turned into an Eve-less Eden where jobs are at a premium.

Every five days speed boats bring in from the town of Venice, a dozen miles away, a full replacement for the working crew, and return the other shift to terra firma. Everyone works a 12-hour day, in five days 60 hours, 20 of them overtime, or 22½ per cent more "take home" than the regular base pay. On the job everyone from William S. Donner, the superintendent, and his assistants, Douglas King and Richard Wormat, to the youngest recruit out in the field, lives in a long row of ultra-modern quarters, two- and three-room apartments, each with its own bath and living room, complete with air conditioning and TV. There is a big recreation hall with a paperback library, ping pong and card tables, and an adjoining softball diamond beyond which some fanatical golfers have constructed a three-hole course. The sportsmen find wonderful fishing and duck shooting all around. The food at the Commissary is superior and served help-yourself.

"There's not a petticoat on the reservation and do we love it!" was how a big burly Texan with 20 years' service as a pipe fitter explained why Garden Island Bay is considered a premium job. "Five days down here and then you'd be surprised how you really appreciate Home, Sweet Home, and the missus and the kids. Besides," he chuckled, "in five days off you can do a lot of things. I run an egg ranch, 30 or 40 dozen a day. Most of us have some job and we live all over. Some even commute way to Mississippi. I wouldn't go back to dryland and an eight-hour day—well, not unless I get fired."

Garden Island Bay has but two roads with a total mileage of about six. They cross at right angles above the landing docks, and this crossroads of marshland is famous as the scene of a classic automobile accident. Here the pickup truck and the jeep, unaccustomed to traffic jams, met in a smash-up: no casualties, but for months the Eve-less Eden's No. 1 joke.

No. 2 deals with Louisiana's efforts to compel this pair of cars to carry license plates. The drawn-out argument ended with the company's ultimatum: delighted to pay car license fees for both vehicles provided the State will take over and maintain the two highways of "Freeportland."

Garden Island Bay came on-stream November 19, 1953. Since it is not practical to vat half a million tons of brimstone on top of a swamp, the sulphur is poured molten into "hot barges," gigantic Thermos bottles afloat, and ferried to Port Sulphur. In the first four years, to the end of 1957, Garden Island Bay produced 2,318,000 tons.

Exactly one year before Garden Island Bay, on November 19, 1952, another along-shore dome, Bay Ste. Elaine, was brought into production by Freeport. On the Gulf, 20 miles from fresh water inland, it was set up as a pilot plant to experiment with marine mining. To save the heavy extra costs of construction on concrete mat and piles, a floating plant was built at the company's Grande Ecaille shop and towed 65 miles through the bayous and anchored at the mining area. It measures 200 feet long, 40 feet wide, 12 feet deep. Costing about $2 million, the plant is equipped with five gas-fired boilers, producing 2,000,000 gallons of super-heated water daily, and developing the electricity and air pressure needed for this operation.[28] The first man in charge here was William S. Donner, M.E. from Minnesota, 18 years with Freeport, who, after Hoskins closed down, was succeeded by Samuel Muery and later Robert Fitzhugh.

The $64 question posed at Bay Ste. Elaine was: can salt water be used in the Frasch process? Scanty data on heating various concentrations of sea water to high temperatures were inaccurate, and the heat-exchange manufacturers agreed that it would quickly scale the evaporators. Forgetting everybody's preconceived notions, the Freeport men, under assistant vice president B. A. Axelrad, made their own experiments. They found two particular types of scale. First alkaline scale, chiefly magnesium hydroxide and calcium carbonate, and the second type, gypsum scale. Control of these was but the first forward step. After four years of heartburning, brain-twisting, callus-making work, both scale and corrosion have been overcome and Axelrad and his associates now declare, "Yes, we can operate the Frasch process on salt water."

Almost alongside Bay Ste. Elaine is the Lake Pelto dome, lying under eight feet of water, where water salinity is somewhat higher. However, the size and character of the deposit make it attractive and engineering studies are being conducted towards its development.[29]

Forty miles inland lies one of the oldest domes and Freeport's latest operation, Chacahoula. The first to drill here was Gulf Refining in 1926. Then Gulf, in 1927, inspected for Texas Gulf Sulphur, drilling 23 wells, and two years later Union Sulphur prospected this dome. In 1931 States Production, a subsidiary of Du Pont, drilled here but abandoned this project. Sun Oil leased the property in 1937 and the following year began the production of oil. At best, the cores at this time were poor, and the data obtained was contradictory. Freeport is now mining nearby where previously there had been no drilling.[30] The dome area here is large, some three miles long and three-eighths of a mile wide. On the southern edge is a rather thin sulphur seam.

Allegedly a dry land operation, the Chacahoula plant is in the midst of a cypress swamp above three different layers of rotted trees, and in case of heavy rains, the plant must be bailed out with pumps. Fresh water is brought in through a two-mile canal from Bayou Black. A heavy stand of cypress was cleared and turned into piling under the plant which has a capacity of 3 million gallons a day and supplies electrical power and compressed air. E. J. McNamara, who was in charge here, admits production is spotty, only 291,000 tons from February 1955 to December 1957. But again Freeport had been experimenting here, partly to solve the vatting problem, and partly to test out a new form of sulphur. The molten mineral is being run over steel belts and flaked.

Seven new domes exploited—Starks by Jefferson Lake; Nash, Bay Ste. Elaine, Chacahoula and Garden Island Bay by Freeport; Moss Bluff and Spindletop by Texas Gulf Sulphur. Nash was short-lived, producing 149,000 tons before its abandonment in November, 1956. Bay Ste. Elaine and Chacahoula as yet but marginal and probably short-lived producers. Starks is a small producer; Spindletop, Moss Bluff and Garden Island Bay, however, are substantial producers —this was the Frasch industry's answer to the gloomy forecasts of depletion.

14

Birth of the Mexican Industry

SIR WEETMAN PEARSON believed in experts. Accordingly, when his Mexican Eagle Petroleum Company found what was supposed to be a saltdome he called Capt. Anthony Lucas to the Isthmus of Tehuantepec. Who better than the discoverer of Spindletop to find similar formations and place a drill just where it would strike oil?

For three weeks Lucas sweated through the jungles and was quoted in the *Mexican Herald*,[1] "The oil is there in large quantities." He made no sensational discoveries, but he spotted about 20 drilling locations, some of which paid off.

Pearson's first manager, J. B. Body,[2] also believed a salt-dome was a sign of oil. It is quite a different matter finding a mound amid a thick stand of mahogany and cedar, entangled with barbed vines and creepers as long and strong as wire hawsers, than in the wide open spaces of Texas. But the urge to find petroleum will hack through any jungle, and after 1908, when the first refinery in Mexico was built at Minatitlán, the need to feed its stills with 12,000 barrels of crude every day was an added spur.

Penetrating the jungle in dugout canoes up the Coatzacoalcos and its tributaries, the Eagle's explorers combed the Gulf side of the Isthmus, and in 1912 two American geologists, Paul Weaver and Willard Hayes, later manager of the Eagle, going up the Tonalá River, carried explorations into the adjoining states of Tabasco and Chiapas.[3] By the time of the 1917 Revolution, 70-odd salt domes had been found and 50-odd drilled. Two score of these showed sulphur.

Among the hardy men who struggled through swamps, battling insects and snakes, facing fever and dysentery, several were trained geologists.[4] Their scientific interest was caught by those mounds. Descriptions of these strange structures, speculations about their origin, theories as to how the caprock became impregnated with sulphur, were appearing in geological journals. Out of the Isthmus came many contributions to this growing literature.[6] Juan Villarello[7] and Walter Ver Weibe[8] were there during the early drilling and they described the domes, quoting from logs and noting particularly the sulphur formations. Three Americans, Burton Hartley, Arthur H. Redfield, and Sterling Huntley, wrote valuable papers.[9] The first explorations of the Mexican saltdomes repeat almost word for word the familiar story. If they found no petroleum, they dragged the rigs to a new location. But frequently there were signs of sulphur.

In 1910, a real gusher, Potrero del Llano No. 4, transferred Mexico's petroleum capital from Minatitlán to Tampico. In 1921, Pearson added his Mexican Eagle Petroleum Company to the Shell-Royal Dutch merger. There followed an era of international competition and exploitation. Then, in 1938, Mexico expropriated its oil industry. Amid these stirring events in petroleum history, brimstone was quite ignored.

In 1936, two years before the expropriation, Frederico Deschamps upbraided the oil companies for neglecting Isthmus sulphur.[9] He was ten years ahead of the time when these deposits would become economic prospects for development. But if Deschamps' protest was futile, he did a useful job. Soundly, he emphasized the early geologists' descriptions[10] of four domes, Petrerillos and Jáltipan, close to the railroad, Teterete and San Cristóbal on the riverbank, because they had ready transportation to the port of Coatzacoalcos. His paper became a guide to the birthplace of the Mexican sulphur industry.

A tropical jungle encourages mythology. Already the birth of the Mexican sulphur industry appears as miraculous as the finding of Moses in the bulrushes, as incredible as the rescue of Romulus and Remus by the she-wolf. The core of the story is, of course, the trials and triumphs of the three Brady brothers. Within two decades the Brady saga has been so embroidered that even neutral by-standers do not see the same events eye-to-eye. Yet the bare facts are romantic enough to claim the pen of a Scott or a Dumas.

The first man to do something about the brimstone buried in the Isthmus was Gen. Alfredo Breceda,[11] alert as a catcher in a World Series game, as self-contained as a judge in court, as smartly turned out in mufti as a U. S. Marine on parade. He learned about sulphur because he and four fellow students in the Durango Technical High School went to Mexico City to see a bullfight.

In the cattle-raising states of northern Mexico the idol of all healthy, ambitious lads was the great matador, Montes, and young Breceda himself had fought in several country bullrings. In Mexico City, flashing newspaper headlines told of the oil boom in the jungle—fabulous wealth, swamps and palm trees, bananas and pineapples, monkeys and parrots— the boys from the desert country were captivated. Alfredo and two others decided to go, but Breceda's money ran out and he was stranded in Veracruz. He found a job with the Tehuantepec Railroad as inspector of way stations. For eighteen months he shuttled across the Isthmus between Coatzacoalcos and Salina Cruz. He heard a lot about sulphur and saw several cores. He never forgot those cylindrical gray stones veined with bright yellow.

Thirty years later, in 1935, that venturesome lad, now a revolutionary hero and prominent citizen, was associated with Engineer Manuel Urquidi in an antimony mine. While prospecting in Sonora and Lower California they found surface deposits of sulphur. But they were hunting for antimony.

In 1937 at Stockholm, Breceda, now Mexican diplomatic agent to the Scandinavian countries, was talking over cakes and coffee with a geologist who had spent several years in Mexico.

"I am surprised, General," he said, "that nothing has been done about the saltdome sulphur in the Isthmus of Tehuantepec."

Thus reminded of those interesting cores, Breceda en route to Mexico, learned in Washington that the U. S. Bureau of Mines was making a sulphur survey of the Western Hemisphere. Through the Mexican Minister, a chum of his Durango school days, he was given free run of the Bureau's records and files—much material about surface sulphur in Mexico; about the Tehuantepec saltdomes, little except a bibliography.

Two years as ambassador in Panama, then back in Mexico and Breceda with Urquidi went to the Isthmus to study the sulphur possibilities. They toured the old oil operations— a really rugged journey afoot and on muleback—and at Minatitlán they had access to the logs and files of the now expropriated Eagle Company. Particularly interesting was the correspondence between the saltdome enthusiast, Body, and his employer, Pearson. They did no drilling, but made a thorough surface survey. They returned to Mexico City enthusiastic about Isthmus brimstone, little realizing where this would lead them.

The first sulphur concession in the Isthmus was granted to Breceda by the Secretaria de Economia, June 15, 1942.[12] In Mexico in colonial days, all minerals belonged to the King of Spain regardless of the ownership of the surface land. After the Independence, they became the property of the people of Mexico, vested now in the Fomento de Minero (Commission to Promote Minerals). This conception of mineral rights differs markedly from the English law, followed generally in the United States, under which surface ownership includes the minerals beneath.

The concessions of the Fomento naturally have restrictions and conditions. To mine brimstone by the Frasch process was a novelty in Mexico and these provisions have been modified from time to time. A fundamental change was the creation of a Sulphur Reserve (Zona Azufrosa) suggested by General Breceda to clarify the Government's interest in the mineral and adopted June 12, 1943.[13] The Reserve is a roughly oblong block of land on the Gulf of Mexico at the eastern end of the State of Veracruz. It includes about a million hectares, approximately 2.5 million acres, and encompasses all the better sulphur structures identified during the Eagle-Shell explorations. In 1957 it was increased some 60 per cent in area by adding a large tract in the state of Tabasco.

A Fomento sulphur concession is legal permission to explore for sulphur in a definite area and to work any deposit found.[14] It may be granted only to a Mexican citizen, and any company organized either to explore or to produce and sell must be incorporated in Mexico. Accordingly, the American companies operate through Mexican subsidiary corporations.

The policy of the Fomento is to be rather generous in the initial exploring rights, but a much smaller acreage will be eventually controlled by the concessionaire. For example, the concession granted in June 1953 to the Central Minera, S. A., later subsidiary of Texas International Sulphur Company, was for 968,384 hectares (2,392,877 acres) but the mining contract entered into September 7, 1953 granted the right to exploit 50,000 hectares, from which 6000 hectares must be chosen for final working.[15]

Acreage and time periods vary, but within a given period, usually five years, the concession holder must carry on a minimum of exploring work and upon definite dates must select a specified limited number of acres for exploitation. Once such a territory is selected, a contract under the standard Mexican mining law replaces the concession. It stipulates a date when a plant of agreed capacity must be completed; the royalty to be paid, and other operating conditions. These contracts are usually for a term of 20 years with an option to renew.

In June 1952, with their sulphur concession in hand, Breceda and Urquidi must do their obligatory exploring and also raise working capital for the entire venture. They went first to President Miguel Aleman with the proposal that, if the Government would provide half the money necessary to establish this new industry, they would provide the balance. It is the national policy, so they were informed, that such developments should be done by private industry.

They went next to the National Financieroa, an official organization charged specifically with fostering the industrialization of the country. They asked help in financing a stock company. The reply was, "The Financieroa cannot finance mineral prospecting. Prove up a commercial deposit and we shall be glad to consider assisting in financing a Frasch plant."

They went to all the larger private banks, Mexican and international. Everywhere they were told, "It is not the function of a bank to provide venture capital. Come back when you have some tangible assets and we will be glad to discuss a loan."

They talked with a number of close friends, wealthy Mexicans. Since the days of Cortéz, Mexican investors have been familiar with all sorts of mining propositions. They have been the chief source of this country's wealth. But the favorite investment has always been land, vast acreages for farming or ranching, choice real estate in the cities. Mexicans are just beginning to be interested in industrial enterprises. As for building a multi-million dollar plant to mine sulphur with hot water—they were not at all interested. Besides any lukewarm enthusiast would be cooled off by the Isthmus of Tehuantepec's "unlucky" reputation—the railway ruined by the Panama Canal; rubber plantations abandoned by

German and American companies during the Revolution; bananas and pineapples killed by diseases. After several promising starts, the ill-fated region had reverted into primitive undeveloped country, taken over by the native Indians.

Amid these discouraging negotiations, General Breceda with a friend who had formerly worked for the English in the Isthmus, sat down one noon at the lunch counter at Sanborns next to a big, good-looking American, a hearty, friendly man with twinkling eyes and a great shock of curly hair. Introductions followed: "Senor William Brady: General Breceda. You two should know each other. Bill Brady and his brothers have a drilling rig and they're looking for work for it to do."

The General explained the brimstone proposition: would the Bradys be interested in doing exploring work in the Isthmus?

"Maybe so. It sounds interesting. Let me talk it over with my brothers. Call me up sometime."

That evening the Brady brothers discussed this brimstone venture. It appealed to them much more than contract drilling water wells which Wells Fargo wanted them to undertake. It was plainly a tough job, but if they hit it right, it promised a "jackpot."

Next morning Ashton Brady went to the library of the Mexican Geological Institute. He found so many references to saltdomes and sulphur in the Isthmus that he engaged a young Mexican geologist to make copies of all this material. Meanwhile, Lawrence and Bill conferred with the concession holders on a working agreement.[16]

The brothers are a remarkable team. Born in Louisiana, all are well trained: Lawrence at St. Mary's College, San Antonio; Bill at Holy Cross, New Orleans; Ashton at the University of Texas. Lawrence studied law; Ashton specialized in geology; Bill went into the real estate business. They combined forces in various oil wildcatting projects in Texas, in Venezuela, and in the new field discovered just over the border in Mexico. They were drilling there when the oil industry was nationalized.

Intimately allied with this triumvirate has been Eugene Rossi. Vigorous, strong, handsome, known throughout Mexico as "Count Rossi," he has been the dashing, romantic character in the Brady saga. The Rossi family had brought in a profitable oil field near Benevides, Texas, and Gene was living in Corpus Christi when the Bradys were wildcatting nearby. He cast his lot with the brothers. They all liked Mexico and with a stable government now well established, they agreed that here was a land of opportunity.

The Bradys and the Breceda-Urquidi partnership set up Azufre S. A. upon a 50-50 basis. But when it became clear that money for the project could not be found in Mexico and that the financing was going to be up to the Bradys, the concession was put upon a royalty basis. The immediate job was to survey the first concession to be explored. They picked San Cristóbal. This dome was under concession to Portez Gil, so the Bradys made another royalty deal with the ex-president. Over 100 wells had been drilled here by Eagle and Shell. Several logs had been examined and the plan was to off-set the wells that recorded the best sulphur strata.

Ash Brady and the Count, accompanied by a Mexican civil engineer, went by train to Minatitlán and hired a boat with a captain and a cook. They loaded aboard their gear, and hours later than planned, they shoved off in pouring rain. The river was high, and especially after they left the Coatzacoalcos and started up the Coachapan, they met many floating logs. When the early dusk closed in, the captain headed for shore announcing they were tying up for the night. The engineer protested noisily and finally pulled a gun. Grabbing him by the wrist, the captain whipped out a knife.

"Young fellow," he thundered, "I'm captain, and when I say we dock, we dock."

Next morning, around two bends in the river, they reached a group of palm-thatched huts, the village of San

Cristóbal. Blowing a cow's horn the headman, Don Julio Blanco, summoned a town meeting, and they hired six Indian machete men. They began the survey by slashing a path along an old road, deserted 40 years. A couple of hours later one of the Indians suddenly let out a terrified shriek. He had been bitten by a deadly bushmaster snake. He must be hurried back to the village and the *curandero*, the native witchdoctor. By some magic, unknown to our physicians, he was alive and ready for work next day.

After a hard day in dripping rain, without lunch because of the accident, the surveying party came back to the boat at 5:30, clamoring for food. The cook calmly announced that dinner would be served at seven o'clock. There was almost a riot and again the excitable engineer drew his gun.

"Senores," said the cook, mimicking the captain, "I am the cook and when I say dinner is at 7 P.M., you eat at 7 P.M." To make amends, he served a glorious meal; fresh-caught robala—most delicious of fish—in a rich tomato sauce.

Four sopping days of forced work and they had surveyed the concession, "tying in the property" with wooden stakes. In January the engineer returned with a bargeload of sand and cement to replace the stakes with concrete markers.

A frustrating year and a half went by. Lawrence and William Brady scurried about trying to raise money. They formed the Cia. Mexicana Minerales, financed cautiously for exploring by some Californians and Texans. Ashton Brady and Gene Rossi moved the drilling rig by rail down to Minatitlán and struggled to collect pipe and other supplies. In the midst of World War II with all oil equipment at a premium, getting supplies and replacements was no benefice.

It was April 1, 1944, before their rig reached San Cristóbal and weeks before it was on location. The driller, Lauren Smith, an experienced operator and a great fisherman, mounted the rig and spudded in. Within an hour, as told in the first chapter, a burned-out bearing, caused by a clogged oil strainer, abruptly shut down operations.

Ashton went down the river in a dugout canoe paddled by two Indians to get a replacement or improvise one in Minatitlán's only machine shop. A long series of breakdowns kept Ash Brady in Minatitlán a lot of the time and one day at the Hotel Jara—nicknamed the Hotel Horror—the manager buttonholed him begging a job for an old friend of the Eagle days. He recommended James "Cowboy" Reynolds as being fully acclimated to the jungle and its people and as knowing more about a drill than the man who invented it. Tempting qualifications, so he was brought in.

A little, loose-framed man in low-hung baggy pants, Reynolds looked like Barry Fitzgerald, the movie actor. He had the disconcerting habit of tucking each set of his dentures into his two hip pockets with the frank confession, "Lordy, lordy, I just can't talk with my teeth in." But he was obviously a two-fisted operator, so Brady made a diplomatic proposal.

"You know, Cowboy, a driller always hires his own people, but our drill always needs fixing. Suppose I introduce you to Smith as a good mechanic with a local background and we'll see what happens."

In Cowboy's capable hands the drilling went much better and Smith formed the habit of slipping off more and more frequently to go fishing. When "Swede" Jensen came down from the Jefferson Lake Sulphur Company to check the drilling and study the cores, he made the bald suggestion.

"Lauren," he said, "why don't you let Cowboy run the drill? Then you can go down to Coatzacoalcos and get in some really good deep-sea fishing."

By the time they had found sulphur in the third drilling and the Mexican Gulf Sulphur Company had taken over the dome, it was imperative to do exploring on the Breceda-Urquidi concessions. A second-hand Kelly drill was shipped down by rail to Jáltipan and Ash Brady and Cowboy

Reynolds went over by bus to unload it. On horseback, with an old Shell worker as guide, they explored the relics of the petroleum activities. They found plenty of oil seepages and old casings. Reynolds left to work for the Texas Gulf Sulphur Company which was exploring Nopalapa above San Cristóbal on the river. The new driller, True White, with a rusty piece of cable as a clue, hit sulphur in the first hole.

To keep the concession alive it was now necessary to drill at nearby Potrerillos. There was a little river, the Chachalatpa, to cross and they had no tractor to move their rig. But they built a makeshift log bridge, and by main force dragged their equipment over. Again they hit sulphur and the group of Texas oil men who financed this exploration took up their option. Their newly formed Pan American Sulphur Company sent down a new, ultra-modern drill.[18]

Ash Brady suspended operations. The old rig on the spot was misbehaving. He had no liking to do contract drilling for the new owners with his dilapidated equipment. Back to San Cristóbal went Brady.

"How lucky we were at Jáltipan," he admits in retrospect. "It was 'must hit' or 'go bust,' and I shudder to think that 50 feet in the wrong direction at either hole might have been a miss." [19]

Across the Coachapan from San Cristóbal lay two domes, Mezquital and Vista Hermosa, beyond the village of Salinas. The Mexican Gulf Sulphur people, who had taken over San Cristóbal, were offered these domes but, lacking men and money to develop both properties, they turned them down. The Bradys' battered, original drill was on hand, and again pressed by the exploring deadline, Brady determined to take it across the river. But how to get it over the 100 foot stream? They had no barge, not even a tractor. A bridge was out of the question. They planned to build a raft and float the clumsy, top-heavy machine across.

At this juncture, around the river's bend appeared a tug

escorting a big, new barge on whose deck stood a shiny red tractor with Cowboy Reynolds in the driver's seat. It was part of the equipment coming in for Texas Gulf Sulphur which, since 1949, had been exploring their nearby Nopalapa Concession. Frantically, everybody beckoned them ashore. The dilemma was explained, and in good neighborly spirit Texas Gulf was ready to lend a helping hand. The barge was swung stern to; eager hands shoved the aged rig aboard and hooked it to the tractor's draw bar.

Some 40 Indians had gathered on the opposite shore watching these proceedings. As the barge approached, two score machetes suddenly flashed in the sun. A couple of antique shotguns and a suspiciously new Army rifle appeared as if by magic. Clenched fists were shaken and a tumult of shouts broke out, "No can land! No can land!"

A hasty conference, and then, the bow still 15 feet from land, Bill Brady, the great negotiator, leaped ashore. With hands high above his head waving a white handkerchief, he scrambled up the bank. The Indians crowded around him threateningly, but he walked slowly towards the headman, a wizened, wrinkled, old Indian, bursting with anger and dignity. Bill took off his hat and bowed deeply.

"Senor," he asked, "what in hell's the matter with your people?"

The Indian proudly returned his salutation and replied, "The trouble is not with us, but with those robbers over the river."

Ancient tribal rivalry had exploded. The men of Salinas would not allow the San Cristóbal men to come into their territory and earn fabulous wealth working for the decidedly crazy, but admittedly friendly and generous, Norte Americanos.

"All our drillers are Mexicans, except the boss, but they are all trained men. They must learn. Have you 30 good men?"

Suddenly, the sputtering roar of a racing motor burst

from the barge. The big tractor, dragging the rig behind, climbed over the bank and did not stop until it had reached the location picked for drilling, a couple of kilometers away. Some of the Indians tried to stop the monster. They might as well have tried to stop a tank.

Despite this dramatic break in negotiations, Bill Brady pacified the Salinas rebellion. The headman was to name 30 picked men, and for two weeks they were to watch while the San Cristóbal men set up and started the rig. Then ten would take the places of ten over-river men, and so again, another ten in two weeks. In two months, all of the hated San Cristóbalans would be out.

Ashton Brady selected a 15-foot off-set to the casing that marked Amezquite No. 2 where, in 1904, Eagle had drilled to 1042 feet and hit sulphur. For the third time, the first drilling found brimstone.

The Bradys now called in the consulting geologist, Walter H. Maddox. Back in 1928 he had come to the Isthmus for the Richmond Oil Company, subsidiary of Standard of California, and after 14 years in Mexico, had gone prospecting petroleum in Australia and New Guinea. Escorted by Gene Rossi, Maddox surveyed the concession while drilling continued at five points he spotted. During his studies he discovered the Vista Hermosa dome, confirmed later by aerial photographs. This structure had never been drilled: the first dome in the region found by surface geology. Upon his geological reports, the Gulf Sulphur Corporation was organized, the third and last of the Brady-sponsored Mexican brimstone enterprises.

15

Three Wins: One Loss

WHEN the first showing of brimstone turned up at San Cristóbal, Lauren Smith, the driller, telegraphed a friend in Texas that they had found 80 feet of 12½ per cent sulphur. His figures were imaginary, but they caused a mild sensation. The Bradys' hobby—some called it their "folly"—attracted a number of hopeful intermediaries, brokers and promoters, and there was much talk, a great deal of it exaggerated, misleading, damaging, but little action. Outside of the Frasch industry there was no serious interest in jungle brimstone.

In Mexico eager speculators seeking concessions laid siege to the Fomento. Realizing that over-competition would be fatal, the Foment officials were wisely cautious in making grants. Only three new concessions were made between 1950 and 1956.[1]

The four American companies could not but know what was happening. General Breceda, himself, when he could interest no one in Mexico, wrote in 1942 to both the Texas Gulf and Freeport companies.[2] Besides, since the Union mine had failed, it has been their habit to investigate every sulphur rumor.[3]

Jefferson Lake had men at San Cristóbal in 1944, and Adolphe D'Aquin, chairman, and Joseph Mullen, president, visited John S. Waterman, a New Orleans manufacturer living in Mexico, who was trying to interest them in the Isthmus, and they were offered any or all the Breceda concessions. The Financiera even agreed to share exploration costs and build a plant. With limited capital and exploring costs unknown, but obviously high, the Jefferson Lake management turned down the proposal.[4]

The Duval Sulphur Company refused several offers. George Zoffman, with 20 years' hardrock mining experience in Mexico, decided that the Isthmus was no place for a small sulphur company.[5]

Even before the Bradys started drilling, Freeport had J. G. Baragwanath and William Bartlett in the Isthmus, and in 1941 Dr. Ralph Taylor, the geologist, met their H. C. Petersen at the Hotel Jara. They went together on several geological junkets. H. Layton Johns was in Mexico City much of this time, and he was at the Brady drilling of San Cristóbal No. 3.[6] Freeport finally decided not to take a concession largely because the Secretary of the Treasury could give no assurances as to future taxes on sulphur stocks, reserves, and exports.[7] Moreover in the 1940s sulphur was in abundant supply.

The Texas Gulf Sulphur Company was not less alert. In fact, Texas Gulf was the first company to negotiate a contract with the Mexican Government for the production of sulphur, and its basic terms concerning royalty terms, taxes, and so forth, signed August 1949, established the pattern for the new industry.

All the American producers had long been familiar with the early shows of sulphur encountered by the Mexican Eagle Oil Company in the Isthmus of Tehuantepec during the early 1900s. Following the expropriation of the Mexican petroleum industry in 1938, only Nationals were able to obtain a mining concession. During this period and throughout the war years, Texas Gulf was concentrating its exploring in Mississippi and Louisiana. The management reasoned that if World War II were prolonged, development of a sulphur industry in Mexico would be most difficult, if not impossible, whereas a deposit in the U. S. would be easier and better located to supply brimstone for the war efforts. March 15, 1954, the first sulphur ever surfaced by the Frasch process outside Louisiana and Texas gushed into the sump of the new plant of the Mexican Gulf Sulphur Company at San Cristóbal. It was a notable accomplishment, achieved like all "firsts" under peculiar difficulties, and largely because of these special handicaps, it did not succeed. As a seasoned sulphur man who was two years at San Cristóbal said, "Inexperience and impatience to get quickly into production, not guile nor negligence, caused the trouble." [8] He might have added that financial pressures had a hurtful influence upon many decisions and that too little sulphur was the final determining cause.

The Mexican Gulf Sulphur Company was organized January 22, 1950, by Eugene L. Norton to acquire two concessions on 1482 acres from the Bradys' American Sulphur Company for $150,000 and 405,000 shares of stock with certain royalty agreements.[9] The Bradys had drilled 14 holes, 10 of which were reported as showing sulphur.[10] Gilbert B. Ebarb, Sr., who had first come to San Cristóbal when Jefferson Lake was considering this property, returned in 1949 as general manager. With Walter Maddox as adviser, 10 more wells were sunk on 125 acres.

By this time the sulphur shortage was front-page news. Paul Nachtman, an attorney practicing in Washington, succeeded Eugene L. Norton as president after having secured from the Export-Import Bank a loan of $3,973,500 to build a plant in order to bring in a new source of brimstone. William P. Barnard, M.E. from Boston University, with 12 years' varied plant and mining experience on both sides of the border, was put in charge of plant construction. Barnard, a clean-cut, hard-working executive, later became vice-president in charge of all Mexican operations. A Mexican of good connections, Eugenio de Auzorena, was recruited from the diplomatic service to handle personnel. He later became domestic sales manager, and the first sale of Mexican brimstone was shipped by rail to the insecticide plant of the Pennsalt de Mexico, S. A.

Building the plant was badly complicated by war shortages and transportation difficulties. In the midst of construction, the engineering firm in charge was changed and Ebarb resigned to become president of the recently organized Standard Sulphur Company in Texas. The plant was nearing completion: an experienced sulphur miner was needed. Lawrence Brady and Nachtman found him in Chris S. Elliott, an engineer trained at the Univerity of Texas with 25 years' experience with Texas Gulf. He came down in August 1953. Urged to get into production as soon as possible, in December he made a trial run of two wells before all the facilities were installed. This test indicated that the structure was tight and that bleed wells would be needed. Three of these were drilled, and the installation being complete, the plant was brought on-stream March 15, 1954.

From the beginning production came hard. Pressures built up and more bleed wells became necessary. Though some wells produced as much as 250 tons a day, returns even from them were irregular. Production for September and October averaged 7454 tons per month with a water ratio of 4367 gallons per ton. The output was about half of what had been expected.[11]

To raise production to a profitable point, it was proposed to double the plant's water capacity of a million gallons daily. An offering of 200,000 shares of common stock at $11.25 was made,[12] the first that attracted any widespread favorable interest in Mexican brimstone among American investors. Though this stock was sold nationally, sulphur was naturally attractive in Texas, and thanks largely to two investment dealers, Claude Crockett of Crockett & Company; and Douglas Johnston, of Moreland, Branderberger, Johnston, & Currie, Houston became the financial center of the infant industry.

At the time Mexican Gulf Sulphur raised this additional

capital, December 1954, only 61 wells had been drilled. This points to the fatal mistake made at San Cristóbal: inadequate exploring to define the deposit and determine the reserves. Drilling had confirmed what had been recognized by geologists, that Isthmus brimstone structures are anticlines. These folds or ridges of stratified rock are obviously a less regular formation than the salt plug, and they may present exceedingly favorable or almost impossible structures for the operation of the Frasch process. Several of the early drillings at San Cristóbal hit it rich and had been optimistically misleading. But they had shown that the deposit was spotty. Chris Elliott resigned in June 1955, and James M. Todd, a consulting engineer from New Orleans was called in. Production was up for a couple of months, but soon dropped back, and after Todd left a systematic hunt for more brimstone was undertaken. From January 1956 to March 1957, two or three rigs were continually active. Although 92 wells were drilled, no new reserves were found. Ten new wells in the producing area were steamed, but their accumulated output was only 7000 tons. The Mexsul management, the Export-Import Bank, and the Fomento agreed this was not a commercial dome, and efforts were made to salvage the project by joining with either Pan American Sulphur Company or Gulf Sulphur Corporation which were now in operation at Jáltipan and Salinas. Both had nearby concessions that could be worked by the San Cristóbal plant. But this $6,000,000 property was a block in negotiations with the companies already operating new Frasch plants of their own.

In the belief that the dome was commercial, a stockholders' committee charged the management with incompetency and solicited proxies for the annual meeting to be held in Wilmington, Delaware, April 16, 1957. J. T. Claiborne, Jr., former vice-president of Freeport, who had succeeded Nachtman as president, placed before the shareholders the management's position and a proposition that Mexsul's drilling equipment and staff explore for the Texas International

Sulphur Company their concession south of and beyond the Texas Gulf Nopalapa property. If a commercial deposit were found, a merger was proposed and proxies were asked to support the management and this program. There was an exchange of sharp statements,[13] and at the meeting the management was upheld by a vote of 482,614 to 351,622.[14]

Meanwhile, the distinguished consulting geologists, De Golyer & MacNaughton, appraised the San Cristóbal deposits for the Export-Import Bank to determine the amount of recoverable sulphur and the efficiency of the extraction operations. After four months' study of the dome's geology, a review of production and drilling records, and the drilling of 17 new test holes, their report[15] concluded "no evidence of any deposits of commercially recoverable sulphur exist" . . . "conduct of the operations and the efficiency of the sulphur recovery have been quite satisfactory."

Under contract with the Texas International Sulphur Company, for a fee of $43,750, Mexican Gulf Sulphur moved three rigs over to the Nopalapa concession of International and drilled 20 exploratory holes with negative results. These wells were selected by International's geologist, and simultaneously their Mexican subsidiary, Central Minera, S. A., was also drilling with three rigs. They found some sulphur, but not in commercial quantities.

This project having failed, Mexsul tried to secure a further exploration concession, or as a contractor, to drill prospective brimstone areas for the Fomento. Nothing came of these negotiations,[16] and on April 11, 1958, the Mexican Gulf Sulphur plant, its accessories, marine equipment, machinery, pipe, etc., were put up for sale at auction.[17] Terms of the mortgage held by the Export-Import Bank did not permit sale at less than the appraised value of $1,656,800. No bidder could be found to meet this minimum.

In vivid contrast, the Pan American Sulphur Company, the second to bring brimstone to the surface in Mexico, quickly became the third largest producer of Frasch sulphur in the

world, showing substantial profits for the first year's operation.[18]

Pan American was incorporated April 17, 1947, by Texans
with ample venture capital and the courage to back what
still seemed a big gamble. They were J. R. Parten, president
of the Woodley Petroleum Company and then chairman of
the Federal Reserve Board of Dallas; Roland S. Bond, Douglas
W. Forbes, and Guy I. Warren, associated with the Renwar
Oil Company; and three independent operators, C. Andrae,
III, Sylvester Dayson, and E. E. Fogelson. They put up about
$250,000, incorporating Pan American with a million com-
mon shares. They paid 287,500 shares and $82,500 to the
Bradys for their Jáltipan rights. Three Eastern investment
bankers, who had optioned the Jáltipan-Potrerillos concessions hoping to interest some chemical company, were paid
$18,000.[19]

This set-up was subsequently modified. The original
concessionaires, Breceda and Urquidi, obtained by presidential decree 77 amplifications to their exploring rights and
these were also assigned to Pan American's Mexican subsidiary company for 110,082 pesos ($13,760 U. S.) and a
dollar-a-ton royalty. The two groups of concessions aggregate
9443 hectares (approximately 23,300 acres) covering the
Jáltipan and Potrerillos domes and nearby Teterete. The
royalty payable to the Fomento was also fixed, based upon
the similar one initially negotiated by Texas Gulf whereby the
Fomento Minera agreed to pay all export taxes and similar
levies then and in the future payable to the Mexican Government. Pan American only proceeded with their large investment in Mexico with this understanding. In return for this
official obligation of the Fomento, the American companies
agreed to the exceptionally high royalty of 15 per cent for the
first five years of operation and 20 per cent for the remaining
35 years of their concessions.

Pan American also exchanged its stock issued to the Bradys
for a dollar-a-ton royalty on sulphur from Group I and 50

cents-a-ton from Group II concessions, and the Bradys withdrew from the board of directors. A loan of $3,664,000 was
obtained from the Export-Import Bank (later increased to
$4,414,000) for building a plant at Jáltipan which it was esti-
mated would cost $5,500,000. February 4, 1953, a public
offering of stock at $7 per share produced in cash the approxi-
mate amount of $3,500,000.[20]

From the first Pan American was well financed. On its
board sat men trained in big enterprises, experienced in the
oil and gas industry. Parten served as president and later as
chairman when Forbes succeeded him as president. The
group knew they wanted sulphur experts and they found an
exceedingly able active management.

Two years before the company was formally organized, in
1945, they sent to the Isthmus a competent geologist, John C.
Myers. He arrived at the ancient Indian town of Jáltipan
on Easter Sunday, 1947. The cores of Jáltipan No. 1 and Potrerillos No. 1 were at best not very good and the finer sec-
tions had been carried off as samples. Accordingly, Myers
recommended an exploring program which was carried on by
equipment from the Woodley Petroleum organization. In
March 1948, Chris Armstrong, 25 years with Woodley, arrived
to handle the field work. Later J. H. Pollard, a mining engineer with long experience in sulphur, was called in, and in
1954, H. E. Treichler, one of the greatest Frasch sulphur
authorities who had retired from Texas Gulf, was enticed
from retirement to become consultant and director. The Pan
American management believed in expert advice.[21]

For the drilling work, Armstrong found three veterans of
the old oil days, "Tampico gringos," as oil men who stayed
in Mexico after the expropriation are called: Leland Blalock
and True White, drillers, and John E. Sheats, tractor driver;
capable men and real characters. It is still remembered that
"Red" Sheats was only restrained by force from becoming an
archeologist. Outside Jáltipan is a mound where the Indians
believe Cortéz' beautiful Indian slave girl, Marina Malinche,

who was born in Jáltipan, is buried in a golden crown and silver slippers. Sheats was all for borrowing the bulldozer and digging up the Aztec princess.

By March 1949, 45 wells had been drilled. Armstrong was able to maintain unbelievable secrecy in his exploratory work and his excellent core records were invaluable. During negotiations, drilling stopped for about a year, but by April 1952, 69 holes had been cored through the sulphur-bearing zone. All tests were made on the top of the formation, which is the present working field. No exploring was done at Potrerillos or Teterete and practically none has been carried on there. Accordingly, Pan American reserves, estimated by Myers at 7,257,401 tons, are computed on only 285 acres, roughly one-twentieth of its controlled dome area.[22]

For president the Pan American directors found Harry C. Webb, former vice-president of Texas Gulf; an able, energetic executive with 25 years' experience. He became vice-president of Pan American May 1, 1953 and president the following year. He immediately tacked the job of letting a contract for plant construction, which was signed on May 20, with the worldwide engineering firm of Brown & Root, Inc. of Houston.

Webb recruited a staff of able young men. His first assistants were a field man and a chemist: Stephen M. Richards came to Jáltipan in June 1953; Dr. Frederick Gormley, a month later. Richards, a graduate of Georgia Tech with a distinguished World War II record and broad training with Texas Gulf Sulphur, took on the important job of chief engineer—a rugged introduction to work in the Isthmus—and he correlated with the Brown & Root firm the flow of equipment and supplies during the construction of the plant.

Gormley, a Ph.D. chemist from the University of Kentucky, came from an industrial fellowship on sulphur at the Mellon Institute. During construction he kept technical details in order and is now director of research and development. His experience enabled Pan American to become a leader in the production of filtered sulphur when it became evident that the dark sulphur being produced would have to be improved from the viewpoint of quality. Sales were handled by vice-president J. Leonard Townsend who, prior to joining Pan American in 1952, served as counsel for the Federal Reserve Bank in Washington.

Ground was broken in September 1953, and as so often, the big problem was transportation. It ranged literally from airplane to burro back. Most materials came by boat from Houston to Coatzacoalcos or Minatitlán, thence by truck to the plant. Brown & Root engineered and supervised the job and the installation was so laid out that its capacity could be doubled at minimum cost. This was done within eighteen months after the original plant went on-stream.[23]

A dry rainy season helped, but hearty teamwork built the Jáltipan plant ahead of schedule, a unique record among the Frasch plants of the Isthmus, a rare feat anywhere in Mexico. Some of the working force came from the Minatitlán refinery or nearby sugar mills, but most of the men had never handled an axe or a wrench. Scores of Mexicans, whose only tool had been a machete, learned intricate industrial skills: driving a car, even a bulldozer, pipefitting, welding, carpentry, what not. In Mexico, 90 per cent of a plant's workers are required to be Mexicans: less than two per cent of the employees of Pan American are foreigners.

While the plant was being built Harry Webb flew down with a stocky, energetic Louisianian who, since earning M.E. and E.E. degrees at Tulane, had been working domes for Jefferson Lake. The president had picked this experienced operator to manage the plant, but he was anxious that Harold H. Jaquet should sell himself this job. He did. And the splendid production is due largely to Jaquet's personality, experience, and skill. Jaquet became president of the Mexican subsidiary in 1958. Once the plant was on-stream, he brought down as his assistant an engineer graduated from Texas A & M, Richard D. Mills, also from Jefferson Lake, where Jaquet had learned to like him and his work. As general superintendent he has charge of the mining and shipping programs.

September 24, 1954, Jaquet turned the air valves, and after a few minutes of breathless suspense, the molten sulphur poured forth. They began with three wells and during the experimental start-up period surfaced 31,000 tons in three months. By January 1955, some 60 wells had been drilled and equipped. By September 1956, a 50 per cent increase to the plant had been installed. December 10, 1956, the first millionth ton of brimstone had been produced: the second million on April 10, 1957. It is an impressive chronology of success.

At Jáltipan the Azufrera Panamericana, S. A., Pan American's Mexican subsidiary, encountered a Mexican version of the surface rights needed to mine a brimstone deposit. The land where the plant stands has been owned communally and parceled out in strips to families. This Ejido system, which goes back before the coming of the Spaniards, was restored when the great plantations of the large landowners were distributed to the peasants after the 1910 Revolution. It has been surrounded by safeguards, and an Ejido cannot sell, rent or mortgage its lands and its locally elected officers are supervised by a special bureau of the Department of Agriculture. Surface rights had to be acquired on 7500 acres and the company bought 375 hectares from individual owners and exchanged them for Ejido land in the concession area. As a part of this arrangement, the company cleared this new land and built an Ejido building to serve as headquarters, meeting place, and moving picture theatre. It also gave the Ejido a truck and a tractor with farm appliances, barbed wire, and paid two trained agricultural agents for six months each to teach modern farming methods.

Jáltipan veterans like to expound the transformations wrought by this new industry in this old town. Its principal streets have been paved: its historic 17th century church restored. Busses run regularly to "Mina" and "Coatzy." The old market flourishes, but there are new stores where one can buy such unheard of novelties as nylon stockings and sport shirts, bobby pins and ball point pens, instant coffee and canned peaches.

Pesos express more realistically what this new industry means to the Mexican people, their government, and their rapidly developing industrial economy. Pan American's annual payroll in Mexico exceeds 14 million pesos; over a million pesos a month paid in the Isthmus, a lot of pesos in any section of Mexico. Its boilers are fueled by oil bought from Petróleos Mexicanos' recently modernized refinery at Minatitlán, delivered by the railroad which also carries the brimstone to the docks at Coatzacoalcos. Both these agencies are government owned and operated, and during 1956, the record full year of operation, Pan American paid for oil 11,595,000 pesos and its freight bill was 8,522,000 pesos. In addition 2,113,000 pesos went to the Puertos Libres Mexicanos for rent and fees at the port of Coatzacoalcos—a total for supplies and services to federal agencies of over 22 million pesos. Beyond these operating expenses, the company paid in federal, state, and local taxes, 37,719,000 pesos. Finally, royalties to the Fomento Minero were 34,609,000 pesos. All in all—supplies and services, taxes, fees and royalties, the company in 1957 paid directly to the Government 94,582,000 pesos, or more than seven and a half million American dollars.

Up to 1958, the company had made a capital investment of some 132 million pesos in buildings and facilities, much of it for Mexican materials and labor. During the two and a half years of its operations, it shipped 1,232,000 long tons of brimstone to world markets: sales that improved Mexico's balance of international trade and strengthened her foreign exchange. These figures cover operations through 1957.

At the end of a canal leading to the left bank of the Coachapañ above San Cristóbal, the Mezquital dome was brought into production May 3, 1956, by Cia. de Azufre Veracruz, S. A., subsidiary of the Gulf Sulphur Corporation. This company was incorporated by the Bradys in 1951. It took over from their American Sulphur Company the Breceda-Urquidi concessions in this area which they began to develop after the sale of Jáltipan. These aggregate 7414 acres and embrace all of three domes and part of a fourth.

Pearson's Eagle men had drilled this section, and after the dramatic entry into the Salinas territory, Ashton Brady drove an offset to their Amezquite No. 2 and found brimstone at 658 feet. Under Walter Maddox's direction, 37 wells were drilled. Two were water wells: one was on the proposed plantsite to prove the absence of a sulphur-bearing limestone, so eliminating the chance of future subsidence. Of the 34 test wells, 23 were classified as commercial.[24] Maddox estimated the Mezquital reserves at approximately 11 million tons proved and 3.2 additional as probable, based upon the exploration of 70 acres, about 1 per cent of the concession area.

In the Soledad dome, two miles northeast, Eagle had drilled 26 holes, reaching a typical caprock formation, and several reporting sulphur. Here Gulf Sulphur drilled four exploring wells, one showing caprock assaying 14 per cent brimstone. Part of the Vista Hermosa structure is in the concession and here four wells found sulphur-bearing limestone. The Salinas dome, just to the east of Mezquital with a surface radius of a quarter of a mile, has never been drilled, but lime outcroppings indicate brimstone formations.

The purchase and exploration of this promising concession were financed by public sales of securities: first, common stock at $1 a share, then at $3, finally two issues of convertible preferred stock.[25] The plant was designed and constructed by the Hudson Engineering Corporation of Houston and financed by $4.5 million convertible debentures for which the New York Investment house of Baer, Stearns & Co. were underwriters.[26]

Just before the first sulphur was pumped at Salinas, this combination of engineering and financial resources bought all of the Brady's Gulf Sulphur stock and their 15 per cent stock in Mexican Gulf.[27] Included in this deal was a farm-out agreement to explore and eventually to develop the 7000-acre concession held by the Bradys' Pan American Exploration Company. This adjoins Mezquital and embraces the balance of Vista Hermosa dome. The transfer of this concession was subsequently approved by the Fomento.[28]

Having previously sold their minority stock interest in Pan American, the Bradys thus severed their last active connection with the industry they had pioneered and, in the widest sense, promoted. True, the shortage of 1950 encouraged the Export-Import Bank to support a new source of brimstone. Had it not done so, the birth of the Mexican sulphur industry might have been delayed for years for lack of adequate financial backing. But it is doubly true that if Ashton, Lawrence, and William Brady had not proved there is brimstone in the Isthmus of Tehuantepec that can be mined by the Frasch process, there would be no Mexican sulphur industry today. It was their foresight, courage, and persistence—"blood, toil, tears, and sweat"—that brought Mexican sulphur to the world markets.

When the Bradys stepped out, April 27, 1956, Stuart C. Dorman, executive vice-president, was elected president succeeding Lawrence Brady. Harvey D. McLean, of Hudson Engineering and Joseph F. Patten, partner of Baer, Stearns, were named respectively vice-president and secretary. In addition to these, the directors elected were V. Theodore Low and Harrie T. Shea, partners in the investment house, Edward J. Hudson, and V. V. Jacomini of the engineering firm, Jack T. Trotter, attorney and certified public accountant, and Roger H. Van Doren, president of the Douglas Chemical Company. Gerard R. Marlow was named assistant secretary and assistant treasurer.

Gulf Sulphur's plant at Salinas is distinguished for its

automation; its large storage of hot water; the compactness of the entire operation. Automatic control has been carried much further than usual. As an example, instrumentation at the relay station gives a continuous circular chart record of the water, air, and the pressures used in each well. The large stand-by supply of heated water is a precaution against delay, or even a shutdown, if any mishap in the mining operation suddenly changes the water requirements. There are but three miles of road in the operating area. This compactness extends to the plant itself, scrupulously designed to save steps and piping. Cold zeolite water cleaning eliminates the large hot lime-soda tanks and insulation on the pipes.

When the first working crew moved into Salinas to ready the plantsite, they were welcomed by a band of 50 monkeys which lived on a rocky outcrop—known naturally as Monkey Hill. Here now the air conditioned homes of the key personnel command a wonderful view of plant and lakes and distant jungle. With the road builders' first blast of dynamite, the noisy band vanished into the jungle depths. Their hill had been quarried for its limestone by a Mexican of German antecedents named Burger. Other surface rights were purchased from Carlos Almazan, and 339 hectares (about 850 acres) were exchanged with the Salinas Ejido. The company also set aside 250 acres, divided into lots 20 by 30 meters, where it agreed to build 41 houses of brick and concrete blocks, also to provide a playground and school.[29] At first the Salinas people objected to leaving their old village, but when they saw the architect's drawings of their new homes, with glass windows, screens, and porches, they began complaining about the delays in getting the plans and specifications approved and the new houses being built.

Every sulphur deposit has its own individuality: some are easily understood from past experience; some are learned only after trial and error. The original production problems at Mezquital were solved by greatly increasing the original ratio of bleed wells to production wells, and in the prolific, sulphur-bearing limestone areas, concentrating hot water input to very closely spaced producing wells. Original hot water and air capacities have been increased and sulphur production raised to about one thousand tons per day. The area adjacent to the original wells has not been defined by barren wells and further drilling in the immediate area continues to prove additional reserves.[30]

The operations on the Isthmus of the Gulf Sulphur's subsidiary have been under the general supervision of Tom Brown, who carried out the changes from the original operations as planned by the new management. The production department is managed by John J. Redden, a veteran, having spent many years with Freeport Sulphur Company. As in all sulphur plants on the Isthmus, Mexican nationals comprise a large part of the management staff.

When Texas Gulf Sulphur Company entered the Mexican field—its original concession was granted to its Mexican subsidiary, Cia. Exploradora del Istmo, S. A., in August 1949 —its position was far different from that of its contemporaries. The largest brimstone producer in the world had all sorts of resources: experienced men brought up in its own organization and ample available working capital. It did not have to sell stock or secure loans. There was no need for publicity; no pressure to get quickly into production and sales. Accordingly, "T.G.S." quietly and deliberately explored its Texistepec, Nopalapa, and other concessions, and brought its first Mexican producing property on-stream without fanfare.

Headquarters were set up in a large building in Coatzacoalcos, originally built about 1925 by a banana king of those days. The ground floor, now as then, is used as offices while the second story where the family lived, has been converted into guest rooms. In 1950, when Texas Gulf moved in, there was not a single paved street in Coatzacoalcos and only two registered automobiles. Today most streets are paved and parking has already become a problem.

Exploration of the Texas Gulf concessions was thorough. Aerial surveys were followed by geophysical testing, geological checking, finally, by core drilling: more than 450 holes on some 28 structures. The site for development having been determined, a canal was dug from the river to the plant location. The plant itself was built on the Houston ship canal, mounted on two barges, engineered by Brown & Root, and tested at Texas Gulf's Moss Bluff plant on the Trinity River. During June 1956, it was barged across the Gulf of Mexico and up the river to its location. This novel expediency neatly avoided the griefs of plant building in the jungle and the mobile plant has the additional advantage that it can be shifted, if need be, to another operating field.

But the Nopalapa installation was not all beer and skittles. Much of the terrain is low and swampy and before a system of roads had been constructed (in the tropical jungle good gravel is itself a problem) an extraordinarily wet and protracted rainy season turned the working area into a quagmire where even a jeep bogged down. Furthermore, in digging the canal, what appeared to be a low hill turned out to be a ridge of compacted clay agglomerate, almost as hard as granite, through which the canal bed had to be blasted.

To fulfill concession obligations, the Nopalapa plant came on-stream February 8, 1957. It was just at the time when sulphur demand was slackening because of the let-down in the U. S. economy. Therefore, the Texas Gulf management decided to stockpile this new production.

16

Brimstone Today

THE HISTORY of the Frasch sulphur industry in Mexico is just beginning. Despite peculiar hazards and handicaps, by 1958, three out of the four domes mined were producing successfully. This compares well with five successes out of the first seven attempts in Louisiana and Texas.[1] Since there is a potential oversupply of brimstone, it would be foolhardy, at this time, to extend Mexican production, nevertheless exploring will continue. In fact, two other companies have been testing the structures on their concessions.

Texas International Sulphur Company has been indefatigably promoted by Michael A. S. Makris[2] who organized this company in 1953 to exploit a surface sulphur deposit in the State of Baja California. This venture failed and Makris, attracted to Tehuantepec brimstone, took over Central Minera, S. A., with its exploring concessions on 123,550 acres, in exchange for 585,000 shares of TIS stock. Initial exploring on the area west of Texas Gulf's Texistepec property was disappointing: of 16 wells drilled but one showed sulphur. However, beginning January 17, 1956, under the direction of Dr. J. Brian Eby, six out of eight holes drilled in this area found sulphur. By May 1956, 18 holes had been drilled and Dr. Eby estimated reserves at approximately 5 million tons[3] although a subsequent appraisal by De Golyer & MacNaughton, made for Texas International, reduced this to 2.3 million tons. After Mexican Gulf Sulphur closed its San Cristóbal operation in early 1957 arrangements were made to

drill 20 exploratory wells on Texas International's concession, south of Texas Gulf's Nopalapa deposit, with the con-
tingent agreement that if commercial sulphur were found,
the two companies would merge and the San Cristóbal plant
be used to develop this structure.

Behind these various field activities were a series of financial arrangements, revised plans, and complicated international negotiations, and a disagreement among the stockholders that ended in the courts where the Makris management was upheld. Late in 1956 TIS purchased for about
$400,000 cash and stock the assets of the Standard Sulphur
Company at Damon Mound, Texas, with the avowed purpose
of dismantling this mobile plant and moving it to their
Mexican property. To 1959 no sulphur has been produced.[4]

Another concession, 12,401 hectares, granted to Alfonso
G. Gurrea and Angel Orveta, lies around Texas Gulf and
Texas International concessions.[5] These exploring rights
are vested in Azufres de Mexico which in 1954 made an
exploring agreement with the Isthmus Sulphur Company,
a subsidiary of Sulphur Exploration Company. Sulphur Exploration was organized by Messrs. Weaster, Kaplan, and
Spollane, with J. H. Pollard as geologist, to examine and
work small Texas domes. After the failure of their High Island venture in Texas, the two companies were merged to
combine their assets. They drilled 26 wells on this property,
nine of which found some sulphur, and then during 1957-58
Freeport Sulphur Company, under an agreement with Sulphur Exploration, drilled 28 wells and found no commercial
deposit. Later Sulphur Exploration drilled seven more holes,
but as yet no plans for a plant have matured.[6]

Soon after the San Cristóbal plant shut down, the Mexican
Government set up the Consejo de Recursos Naturales No
Renovables (Non-renewable Natural Resources Department), a new, separate agency with funds to conduct mineral
explorations and advise the Mexican Government on min-

eral policies. During the first half of 1958, the Consejo was drilling at Tabaquerno, Hidalgotitlan, and Soledad, in the Sulphur Reserve administered by the Fomento Minero. Up to the end of the year no report had been made and it is understood that results were negative.

Nobody yet knows how large the sulphur reserves of Mexico are. None of the present operating companies has completely explored all of their concessions, and geologists who have prospected in the back country, Weaver, Pollard, Maddox and Salás, agree there are structures in Veracruz and

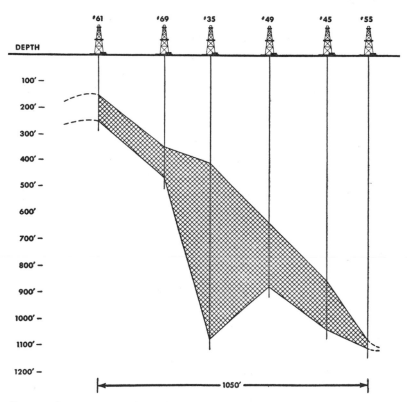

FIG. 9. Cross section of Mexican sulphur structure, based on core data from Mezquital deposit, Gulf Sulphur Corp., Salinas, Veracruz.

Tabasco (especially along the Tonalá River) yet to be tested for sulphur. However, they would present formidable transportation problems.

The sulphur-bearing limestone structures in Mexico are anticlines, that is, folded, stratified ridges, not the regular, rounded salt plugs of Louisiana and Texas.[7] The less regular formations create operating problems. Many of these— tight caprocks, for example, and fissures—are familiar and greater experience will surely teach practical lessons. One feature of the Mexican structures cuts both ways. A single sulphur stratum may show great variations in depth below the surface and in thickness. Six wells drilled in a north-south line 175 feet apart on the Mezquital dome, for example, hit sulphur at the southern end 180 feet down (Figure 8). At the north end, 1050 feet away, sulphur was found 1110 feet below ground. At the southern end the sulphur-bearing limestone is less than 100 feet thick, at the northern end it peters out, but in between, the mineralized zone reaches a thickness of nearly 900 feet.

Millions of gallons of clean water are a requisite of the Frasch process, and in this respect the plants in the Isthmus have some advantage. A network of rivers and lakes furnish a year-round supply of water that is comparatively free of silt so that large settling basins are unnecessary.

In the equally vital matter of fuel, the Mexican industry's position will soon be improved. A new, big gas field, 150 miles away in Tabasco, is being readied for piping. An absorption plant, engineered and built by the Hudson Engineering Company, was completed early in 1958 and the pipeline via Minatitlán to Mexico City, is scheduled for the end of 1959.[8] Natural gas is not only the most efficient fuel, but it eliminates transport of oil by barge or tank car and the maintenance of storage tanks to assure adequate reserves.

The climate of Mexico, not the weather, but the political atmosphere, is not as salubrious as it might be for the growth

Offshore sulphur—construction of Freeport's Grand Isle plant: placing the 650-ton deck section on piling sunk 170 ft. (*above*); a model of the directional system of drilling (*right*) and view (*below*) of the first of the two "Y" arms to be constructed to different mining areas. The plant will be a mile long and will cost $30,000,000.

Photos by Freeport Sulphur Co.

Mexican sulphur—the Brady brothers' historic first rig, drilling the first exploratory hole at what became the San Cristobal mine, the first Frasch operation outside Louisiana and Texas.

Ashton Brady

Pan American at Jáltipan, the third biggest Frasch producer; all Frasch plants run 24 hrs./day; (*below*) the battery of six modern boilers have a capacity of 100,000 gals./hr.

Frank Jo Raymond

Pan American Sulphur Co.

The Mexican plant of Texas Gulf at Nopalapa was built and tested in Texas; barged across the Gulf of Mexico to the head of a canal from the Coachapan River and anchored in place by pumping out the water. The Salinas plant of Gulf Sulphur Corporation is distinguished by its compactness of design and layout—saving time, steps, and piping —and for its advanced automation of operating controls.

Sulphur in France; new and old—the big housing development (*above*) for employees of a new electric power plant and four new chemical companies, all initiated by the supply of gas and sulphur from Lacq, and (*below*) the historic grinding plant—the central unit in the photograph—built by Herman Heockel for Frasch at Marsailles.

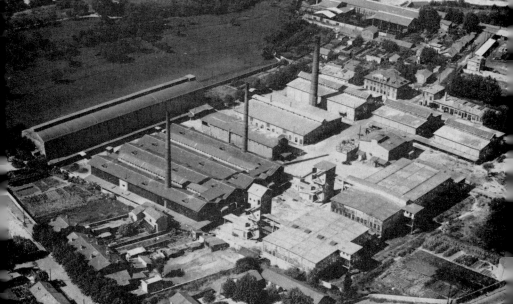

Sulphur recovered from H_2S at Lacq (*above*) the sulphur recovery unit and a general view of this exceptionally attractive and efficient installation, and (*below*) the similar operation of the government-owned Mexican plant at Poza Rico, Veracruz, which has recently been doubled in capacity.

Frank Jo Raymond

Jefferson Lake Petrochemicals Ltd.

Jefferson Lake Petrochemicals' sour gas recovery plant at Taylor Flats, B. C.: exterior taken at −24°F and interior showing the air blowers, and (*below*) the hydrogen sulphide recovery operation of Texas Gulf at Okotoks, near Calgary, Alberta.

Texas Gulf Sulphur Co.

Main St., Sulphur Mine, La., the Union company's employee houses during the Gay Nineties, and the children's wading pool with their parents' homes in the background at Port Sulphur, La., Freeport's townsite, once an uninhabitable swamp, now a community with school and hospital, churches, stores, movies, country club, *et al.*

And always the search goes on—the hunt for new saltdomes, now chiefly in the cedar swamps and marshlands along the Gulf Coast (*left*) and offshore (*below*) where mammoth, mobile drilling rigs probe the sea bottom looking for oil and sometimes strike sulphur. But always, too, other searches are being carried forward, endless researches for improved apparatus, better methods, new applications of this most vital raw material of our key chemical industries.

Freeport Sulphur Co.

Humble Oil and Refining Co.

of this new Mexican industry. This unhealthy smog is generated by self-seeking demagogues, by politicos sniping at the Government, by Communists whose favorite line in Mexico is to rouse distrust of foreign capitalists. These axe-grinders seize upon any newsworthy story, such as the proxy fight among the Mexican Gulf Sulphur Company's stockholders, and twist it to their own propaganda ends.

Lania, a Mexican version of Kiplinger's Letters, edited by R. B. Roberson, a former Texas newspaperman with a reputation for frankness and integrity, under the date of March 21, 1956, vividly described this particular episode:

> The unpleasant, unhealthy, and untrue publicity concerning Mexican sulphur industry carried in the daily press here has continued through this week, dropping from the larger newspapers to the smaller, more vicious sheets with the stories becoming more irresponsible and less logical daily. . . .
>
> The stories tie Texas Gulf with Standard Oil (the latter is supposed to be an enemy-to-the-death of Mexico) saying that the stock in both companies belong to the same stockholders. The stories also accuse former officials of the Mexican Government of being traitors for having issued the concessions to U. S. companies. The irresponsibly written stories have accused the companies of everything from nonpayment of taxes to attempting to put the industry here out of production. The almost million-ton production of this year, none of which was produced by Texas Gulf, was credited all to this firm.

The cheerful disregard of facts in such attacks is illustrated by an article under the byline of Adrian Fernandez de Mendoza, dated Coatzacoalcos, Ver., Mar. 13 (1956) in the Mexico City daily, *Novedades.*

> We were informed that the companies exploiting our sulphur wealth hardly employ 2000 Mexican workers at miserly wages whereas in the refinery in England, they employ 15,000

workers at splendid wages, which indicates the imperious
necessity that a refinery be installed in our country as a protective measure not only as it refers to our economy, but also
to our workers.

The "miserly wages" of the Mexican sulphur plant workers
are in fact twice the legal minimum wage and a chief
advantage of Frasch brimstone is that, aside from filtering to
improve its color, it needs no refining. But the inference
from these misstatements are entirely erroneous. By "refinery" is presumably meant a sulphuric acid plant and the
"English refinery" with 15,000 employees must refer to
Imperial Chemical Industry's Billingham plant. Here, in
addition to making more sulphuric acid in a fortnight than
Mexico consumes in a year, are produced a wide variety of
other chemicals. A modern contact unit to supply all of
Mexico's acid requirements would not employ 100 workers,
and if located in the Isthmus, would be so remote from
the domestic market that it could not economically deliver
acid to the big consumers in the Republic.

Hardened to such wild propaganda, informed Mexicans
are interested chiefly in who paid for its publication and why.
But such false statements and irresponsible attacks damage
Mexico's reputation north of the border: below the Rio
Grande, they hurt good public and labor relations. The
Mexican people are properly proud of their strides forward
in government stability, education, and economic growth.
Their vibrant nationalism is justifiable. Their government
is wrestling with gigantic problems. It desperately needs
funds to maintain the peso against racing inflation; to build
schools, roads, irrigation dams, and hydroelectric plants; to
support public health projects, technical training, modern
agricultural practices. Against this background, demagogic
appeals to prejudice, communistic arguments based upon
unsound economics, politically inspired attacks on sincere

government officials, may all be utterly false and yet they find ignorant or prejudiced readers who give them credence.

The political atmosphere may become more murky. The auction of the Frasch plant of the bankrupt Mexican Gulf Sulphur Company at San Cristóbal having failed to bring a minimum bid of $1,300,000—it was valued by realistic sulphur men at not more than $400,000—it was bought by the Mexican Government. Again, the frank, on-the-spot comments of *Lania* (May 5, 1958) are illuminating:

The Mexican Government had little choice except to buy the plant. The Mexican loan agency, Nacional Financiera, in the case of the Ex-Im Bank loan to Mex-Sul, was the guaranteeing signature, as it is with all other loans made by the U. S. loan agency to private firms in Mexico. Therefore, the cheapest way out for the Mexican Government was to buy the property when it was offered at auction, particularly when the rules called for a low bid of 1,300,000 dollars, a sum higher than any private industry group could pay for the property valued at about one-fourth of the sale price.

The Mexican Government, to explain to the Mexican public why the plant and property had been acquired, issued a press release through the Secretary of Hacienda (Secretary of the Treasury) . . . last month, which stated in effect that the Mexican Government will see that the production of sulphur in this country is doubled, and added that, for the first time since the beginning of this new industry, a few years ago, Mexican capital will enter a field that has been dominated by foreign investments.

This statement could mean anything or nothing. It could mean that the Mexican Government plans to move into the sulphur production in a big way in competition to private enterprise with the Government having all of the rule-makers on its side. Most observers here do not believe that to be the case since the present Administration has repeatedly stated that it believes in private enterprise and has shown that it wants a continued flow of investments into the industry here. On the other hand, should the new acquired plant be turned over to a group of bureaucrats to run, with no taxes to pay and the selection of all the Gulf Coast domes to choose from, it could be the beginning of a second Petróleos Mexicanos— a nationalized industry. Should private enterprise in the sulphur industry have government competition in the future, they will have the Export-Import Bank to thank for this condition.

The Mexican sulphur industry has established itself in an amazingly short time. Sulphur is sold in worldwide markets under particular conditions. Its largest customers, the makers of sulphuric acid, commonly purchase under a year's contract to assure themselves twelve months' supply. In every industrialized nation the acid business is highly competitive. This corrosive chemical is sharply restricted in its shipping area. The profit margin in this standardized, widely used chemical commodity is narrow. The acid manufacturer must be sure his competitors do not buy this raw material more cheaply, and he is concerned that his supplier is able to fulfill his contract deliveries. The Mexican sulphur companies had, therefore, to build up stockpiles before they could hope to sell the big buyers.

But acid makers also sell on yearly contracts: they want to maintain a stable price. While buyers were undoubtedly glad to see a new world source of sulphur in Mexico, nevertheless few were eager to break with their established, dependable suppliers. Under the circumstances, it was only possible for the Mexican companies to break into the world market by offering attractive prices.

In recent years American brimstone for export had been quoted at $3 a ton higher f.o.b. Gulf ports than the price to domestic buyers. The f.o.b. price Gulf port includes a $1.50-a-ton charge for all shipments, domestic and foreign, to cover transportation from mine to port and handling and loading sulphur at the dock. For some years the differential had irked overseas buyers and it provided the opening wedge. In 1955 the Mexican sulphur producers, in order to break into world markets, offered sulphur for export at about $3 below the price charged by the American companies, which at that time was $31 for bright and $30 for dark.[9] At about the same time they offered their sulphur in the United States market at about $2 a ton below the U. S. companies' price. For the first time in 20 years the sulphur price structure was completely upset.

In February 1956, Freeport Sulphur Company lowered its export price by $3 a ton and after several months' delay the other U. S. sulphur producers followed suit, but the price sniping continued.[10] Finally, in September 1957, in order to meet competition, Texas Gulf announced a reduction of $3 on bright and $2.50 on dark material in the domestic market. Immediately, Freeport made the $3-a-ton reduction applicable to both grades of sulphur for domestic and export customers, bringing the f.o.b. dock quotation down to $25 a ton for bright and $24 for dark.[11] Two months later, the Mexican producers, Pan American and Gulf Sulphur, announced an advance of their U. S. price by $1 on new business but not on contract sales, ostensibly reducing by half the differential between their quotation and that of the older companies.[12] U. S. companies shipping to U. S. ports must, by law, ship in U. S. bottoms. Mexican companies may ship in foreign flag vessels at considerably lower cost per ton. Since the distance to East Coast ports from Coatzacoalcos is roughly the same as from Gulf Coast ports, Mexican producers enjoy a built-in freight differential, even though the f.o.b. price is exactly the same.

All this price cutting was tangible and unpleasant but inevitable recognition that Mexican sulphur had become a factor in world trade. It was exaggerated because this new supply appeared after U. S. production, stimulated by the shortage of 1950-52, had been increased just when U. S. consumption was temporarily cut back by the business recession of 1957-58.

The disorganized prices profited no one, not even the acid

manufacturers whose acid sales contracts are usually tied to the price of sulphur. They had been complaining that the acid price was out of line with rising costs, and while they were able to withstand the pressure of their customers for still lower prices, nevertheless, the long expected price advance of sulphuric acid was obviously impossible. As one of the chemical trade papers said, "For the acid makers, the depressed sulphur price in '57 was a 'temporary breather.' " [13]

A stubborn fact of the brimstone market is that lower prices do not increase sales, not by a single ton; but that higher prices encourage consumers to use substitute forms of this chemical element. On the top side, the governor on the price of brimstone has long been the cost of sulphur in pyrite which still supplies between one-third and one-half of the world's sulphur requirements. Today other forms of sulphur are becoming increasingly available, notably, pure elemental sulphur recovered from sour gas which between 1947 and 1957 advanced from 43,000 to 605,000 tons.[14] (See Figure 10.)

These competitive forms of sulphur are a ceiling over the price of Frasch brimstone. The floor beneath is a price that will keep in operation enough high-cost producing units (domes with high water ratios) to supply the market demand. Somewhere between these limits, the price of brimstone is set by competition. For no length of time is it possible to sell in world markets a basic commodity with standardized specifications like brimstone for one price at U. S. Gulf ports and another at Coatzacoalcos. The customers will not permit it. The one thing they cannot tolerate is that their competitors pay less than they do for this raw material.

During the past 25 years the price of sulphur has risen only 30 per cent, and Langbourne M. Williams, chairman of the Freeport Sulphur Company, has pointed out[15] that tin has advanced 140 per cent, zinc almost 150 per cent, petroleum, more than 200 per cent, lead, 235 percent, and copper, nearly 250 per cent. The 30 per cent rise in the sulphur price has not kept up with sulphur production costs which he itemized:

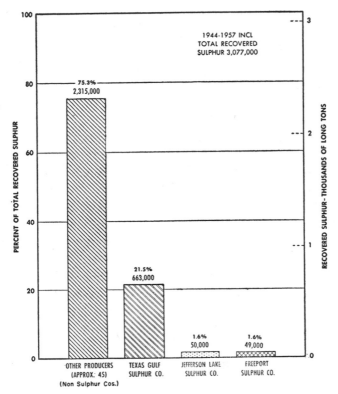

Fig. 10. Sulphur recovered from sour gas (H_2S) U. S. and Canada, 1944-1957 accumulated.

average hourly wages up 330 per cent, pipe, 180 per cent, gas for fuel, over 200 per cent—to say nothing of increases in federal, state, and local taxes.

Because of still higher costs, springing from the world-wide inflationary spiral, the price of brimstone should logically tend higher. It also appears that we have seen the end of the differential export price. When first adopted by Frasch he was selling domestic customers cheaper to discourage imports from Sicily. Later, during the Consortium agreements, a higher price in Europe was a needed bonus to the distressed Sicilian mines. Neither reason holds today. Furthermore, although the consumption of brimstone in Mexico will grow as her industrialization advances, nevertheless, if the sulphur deposits of the Isthmus are to be economically worked, a big tonnage must be sold abroad. From the Mexican point of view, a shipment to Baltimore is as much an export as one to Bombay. The preferential export price now becomes quite illogical.

While the Mexican companies were carving out a niche for themselves, the U. S. companies had been developing new domes, studying the offshore domes, diversifying their activities.

Standard Sulphur Company's operation at Damon Mound in Texas started in November 1953 and after producing 140,000 tons of brimstone shut down in April, 1957. Freeport began production from its Nash property in Texas February 1954 and ceased operations November 1956 after extracting 149,000 tons. Freeport is at present studying a potential underwater operation at Lake Pelto, Louisiana where a substantial deposit has been found. They have no definite plans for producing this dome but will probably move the plant now in operation at Bay Ste. Elaine to Lake Pelto when the former is depleted.

During this period Texas Gulf developed and brought into production two sizable Texas deposits, Spindletop and Fannett. Each has a production capacity of over 400,000 tons a year. Spindletop first produced in May 1952 and through 1957 had yielded 2,111,000 tons. Fannett started up in May 1958 and has produced 195,390 long tons through 1958. Both of these deposits add substantial reserves and production capacity to the Frasch industry. Texas Gulf also explored what appears to be a fairly large deposit at Bully-camp, Louisiana, which can be brought into production when needed.

All four American companies continued to investigate a number of domes during this period of shortage. New domes, opened since 1950, have actually increased the known reserves of Gulf Coast sulphur greatly. Moreover, Garden Island Bay and Bay Sainte Elaine promise that other commercial sulphur deposits may be found alongshore. Then there are the offshore domes in the Gulf of Mexico which belong to the future.

Very real and present, however, is the diversification of the American sulphur companies.[16] All have entered new fields and one, the Duval Sulphur & Potash Company, has changed its name, and properly so, for in 1957, 70 per cent of its sales came from potash.[17] The company began exploring in the Carlsbad, New Mexico area in October 1947, and its two shafts, mill, and refining facilities began operation in March 1952. By 1953 it was producing over 400,000 tons of muriate of potash annually and has already leased other properties near enough to be worked from its present plant. In 1955 Duval began exploring near Tucson, Arizona, in a copper and molybdenum field, and in 1957 began construction of a plant from which it expects to get over 43 million pounds of copper and a million pounds of molybdenum concentrates a year.[18]

Jefferson Lake Sulphur Company has diversified into elemental sulphur recovered from sour gas in British Columbia, Canada, and has announced plans to enter the petrochemical field. In 1955, in association with Socony Mobil Oil Company, a hydrogen sulphide recovery plant was built in the Manderson sour gas field, Wyoming, with a rated capacity of 115 tons of sulphur a day. The Manderson operation produced 15,100 tons in 1955; 19,000 in 1956; 17,000 in 1957,[19] and is reported operating at the rate of "about 20,000 tons during 1958" or about 55 tons per day.[20] In 1956 an Oil and Gas Division was set up with Harold W. Manley as manager in headquarters at Tulsa, Oklahoma. Substantial new gas and oil leases have been secured in Louisiana, Texas, and Oklahoma,[21] and the Rotasorber plant, at Bayou Sale,

St. Mary's Parish, Louisiana, recovering gasoline and lique-
fied petroleum gases from natural gas, has also been placed in
this Division.

January 1, 1957, Jefferson Lake stepped into the petrochemical field by merging the Merichem Company whose
plant at Houston produces cresylic acid and sodium sulphide
by processes developed in its own laboratories, but the
company has chosen not to disclose them through patents.
Facilities here were promptly doubled to a monthly output of
200,000 gallons of cresylic. But Jefferson Lake's major
expansion has been in the Canadian sour gas field through
its subsidiary, Jefferson Lake Petrochemicals of Canada.

Freeport was the first sulphur company to diversify. Having developed a new process to refine manganese from low
grade ores in Oriente Province in Cuba, the company produced 1,500,000 tons of concentrate between 1932 and 1946
when the deposits were exhausted. Freeport thus became, for
a time, the largest manganese producer in the Western Hemisphere. Its output of this indispensable alloying element
for steel was very important during World War II.

For the Government's account, Freeport built and operated a nickel recovery plant at Nicaro, Cuba, in the
war years. By 1946, the plant was producing 25,000,000
pounds a year of nickel in the form of oxide. While the
Nicaro plant was closed down by the Government in 1947,
to be reopened later under the aegis of another company,
Freeport in 1957, had under construction a private project
to recover nickel and cobalt from ores at Moa Bay, some 40
miles east of Nicaro. This Moa Bay project is the most
important advance to date in the diversification and growth
of Freeport. Its subsidiary, Freeport Nickel Company, is
investing $119,000,000 in facilities for mining and concen-
trating the ore at Moa Bay and in a refinery at Port Nickel
below New Orleans. Here nickel and cobalt will be separated as metals. Annual capacity will be 50,000,000 pounds
of nickel and 4,400,000 pounds of cobalt.

Since 1948 Freeport has also conducted extensive exploration for petroleum and gas, and by 1957 had net production and sales of 2,245,000 barrels of oil. While the company sold off important producing properties in the Lake Washington field in Louisiana for $100,000,000 during 1958, the company is continuing its oil and gas program. Further diversification began with the formation in 1955 of National Potash Company, jointly owned by Freeport and Consolidation Coal Company. National Potash began production in early 1957 and is currently shipping to the fertilizer industry from its facilities near Carlsbad, New Mexico. Finally, Freeport has broadened its interest in sulphur. It owns 7,800 acres of pyrites property in Virginia, and since 1950 has operated a sulphur recovery plant in New Jersey using gases from the Texas Company's refinery.

Texas Gulf Sulphur, the largest brimstone producer, has kept close to sulphur. However, in 1952 they became interested in oil and now have production at Boling, Spindletop, and Moss Bluff and are receiving oil royalty payments from other scattered properties. Production in 1957 amounted to over 380,000 barrels of oil.[22] Also now in process is the evaluation of potential oil and gas lands that it controls in Texas and in Canada. New activities, other than Frasch sulphur and oil and gas production, have been in sulphur recovery both from hydrogen sulphide and sulphur dioxide gases, as well as exploration for minerals.

As far back as 1941 Texas Gulf began investigating removal of sulphur from hydrogen sulphide using the Claus process at McKamie, Arkansas. A pilot plant, built in 1942, produced sulphur at the rate of over one ton per day. Although desirous of acquiring the sour gas interest at McKamie, the Southern Acid & Sulphur Company, now a part of Olin Mathieson Chemical Corporation, outbid Texas Gulf for the property because they had a nearby sulphur grinding plant at Bossier City, Louisiana. However, the pioneer work and the information gained later served as a basis for the recovery of sulphur from hydrogen sulphide gas at Texas Gulfs' 400-ton day plant at Worland, Wyoming. This production started April 8, 1950, in time to help relieve the general sulphur shortage during the Korean War. Worland was the first large volume plant for recovery of sulphur from hydrogen sulphide gas in the United States. Through 1957 it had produced over 663,000 long tons of brimstone.

The problem of producing elemental sulphur from sulphur dioxide has also long been under consideration. In 1957 Texas Gulf entered into an agreement with the International Nickel Company and a pilot plant has been constructed at Copper Cliff, Ontario, to extract elemental sulphur direct from sulphur dioxide which International Nickel obtains here by the fluid-bed refining of iron sulphides. This 10-ton pilot plant, designed and operated by Texas Gulf, is an interesting investigation into what may be a valuable process.[23] Direct conversion of sulphur dioxide into sulphuric acid is now being done by several companies, but the process is economical only with a nearby market for acid and where sulphide ore is available far from industrial centers. Texas Gulf will probably use natural gas for the reducing step and an important method of obtaining elemental sulphur from this source may be in the making.

Texas Gulf has also become increasingly active in mineral exploration. In 1936 a property on the Ecstall River, about 50 miles SE of Prince Rupert, B. C. was optioned. Exploration proved the existence of two large bodies of pyritic copper-zinc ore, but World War II interrupted the job. In 1952 work was resumed and reserves have been considerably increased. Geologic work in the general Ecstall region has continued, and in 1957 a large mass of copper-zinc sulphide ore was discovered 10 miles from the original prospect and a third interesting prospect was located in 1958. In 1951 a sulphide prospect was acquired near Petatlan, State of Guerrero, Mexico. Exploration during the next three years revealed a deposit of several million tons of copper pyrite ore.

Another pyrite property, acquired under option near Bathurst, New Brunswick in 1953, was dropped after geophysical surveys and limited drilling. Meanwhile, the geologic program led to claim staking in another part of the district and in 1954 an orebody of several million tons of zinc-lead-pyrite ore was found.

Claims were also staked in 1957 in the northern part of Baffin Island, one of the most northerly exploration jobs for metallic ores in the world. Indications are that an important lead-zinc district may have been discovered. Because of its remoteness and the expense of operations, development may be slow, but this type of work is a valid part of the company's long range exploration program. During the last five years exploration work has also been undertaken by Texas Gulf in Alaska, Ethiopia, Sardinia, Sicily, Egypt, Mexico, Canada, and the United States in its stepped-up search for metals.

Most of these diversification programs have come at a time when the four American sulphur companies were raising the production of Frasch brimstone to an all-time record high. Simultaneously, the new Mexican industry brought an additional tonnage to the world market. The late 1950's certainly provided a resilient springboard from which to leap into the future.

17

—and Tomorrow

LOOMING LARGE on the brimstone horizon, as the 1950's draw to a close, are two new sources of supply: the recovery of elemental sulphur from sour gas in the south of France and in western Canada and production by the Frasch process from the first offshore dome along the Gulf Coast. The sulphur shortage of 1950-51 inspired a worldwide hunt for this essential chemical element, and methods of tapping other sources have been discovered. Under special conditions several are actually in operation. However, they will not, in the near future, contribute importantly to the world market. Ample reserves against future needs have also been found in large bodies of pyrite and sulphide ores. Indeed, though chemical forecasting is dangerously apt to backfire, it is now safe to say that as long as man inhabits this planet he will suffer no lack of sulphur.

Of immediate concern, however, are the consequences arising from these new sources of supply. Sulphur is again in a period of evolutionary change such as has punctuated its history periodically ever since John Roebuck built his first lead-chamber acid plant two centuries ago. Certain aspects of present conditions recall past experience, but the situation is changing so rapidly and is so full of unpredictable possibilities that the best we can do is to examine the present objectively and look to the future rather broadly.

Offshore sulphur, the most spectacular development in the industry since Herman Frasch first pumped molten brimstone to the surface, was discovered when drilling for oil along the Gulf Coast in the late 1940's. Since then over 125 underwater domes have been located.[1] If the dryland average holds, some 15 of them are apt to be commercial prospects.

In 1954, Humble Oil & Refining Company found seven miles off the Louisiana coast and 2000 feet below the floor of the Gulf, a dome of several hundred acres area.[2] Here they conducted an exploratory campaign. By taking carefully recovered cores, in 14 test wells each from 300 to 600 feet through the sulphur-bearing structure, the company's geologists estimated reserves of between 30 and 40 million tons.[3] Apparently they had found one of the largest sulphur domes.

Having decided not to develop this sulphur property, the Humble management selected Freeport. Because Freeport had inaugurated the use of sea-water in sulphur mining and was the first sulphur company to dip into the shallow Gulf waters, it had acquired the greatest experience with underwater operations.[4] Because the project involved novel problems, the agreement, signed September 19, 1956, provided two years for experimental work and two years for building the plant. It must come on-stream in 1960: the two companies will divide the profits.

In the construction of this Grand Isle mining plant, Freeport faced formidable problems: 100-mile-an-hour winds, waves of 40 feet or better, and corrosion which in the open Gulf is extreme. Subsidence could, in this case, dump the plant into the sea. There were also the problems of getting the sulphur ashore and providing for the safety, comfort, and morale of personnel in this isolated, storm-swept location. The answer to these tough questions is a giant Y-shaped structure whose over-all length is roughly that of four "Queen Elizabeths" moored end to end, the biggest permanent structure in the Gulf, dwarfing the offshore platforms of the oil industry. Construction began in June 1958.[5]

Nearly a mile long, 75 feet above sea level, the platform

will support drilling rigs, the sea-water heating plant, living quarters and recreational facilities for 250 men in five-day-on, five-day-off shifts, and a heliport. Five large and 10 smaller steel-pile towers or piers, connected by 200-foot bridge spans, form the basic structure which is pinned to the Gulf floor by steel pilings driven through 17 giant templates. These templates or frameworks will also stiffen the underwater portion of the piling. The vertical members are of 34-inch diameter pipe, through which 237-foot steel piles of 30-inch diameter have been driven deep into the bottom. Once in place, the piles were welded to the template to form a unitized tower. The plant will use 13,000,000 cubic feet of gas every day to heat 5,000,000 gallons of sea water to 325°F. It will also compress large volumes of air used to lift the liquid sulphur, and it will produce electric power to operate drilling rigs and other equipment.

Drilling also presented special problems. The cost of separate platforms for many wells—scattered as they normally are in sulphur mining—would have been prohibitive. Accordingly, drilling activities will be concentrated on two platforms—one at the end of each arm of the "Y"—but wells will be drilled directionally to achieve wide dispersal of bottom hole locations. The platforms are designed to allow wells to reach out a lateral distance of some 800 feet from the wellheads, and even greater deflections may prove economical. In addition to drilling machinery and operating wells, the platforms provide room for a well control or relay station and a pipe reworking shop. All this is packed onto two decks, the upper measuring 110 x 224 feet standing 75 feet off the water, the lower measuring 86 x 200 feet, 60 feet above water.

When subsidence occurs the supporting towers of the structure will tend to slide downward and laterally toward the center of the subsidence area. However, by driving piling only as deep as the clay stratum beneath the Gulf, because of the clay's ability to remold and readjust as the piling moves, the slow, long-term action of subsidence will have no adverse effects on the supporting strength of the piling. There will be considerable sinking of the drilling platform towers and of bridge towers within the mining area. Drilling platforms will be moved to higher "ground" and provision has been made to jack up the bridge towers as subsidence occurs.

Corrosion inherent in a permanent steel structure seven miles at sea has been met in three different ways. The submerged part of the steelwork is cathodically protected with graphite anodes. The splash zone, where the steel is alternately exposed to salt spray and salt air, has an extra coat of copper-alloy steel plate on the piling. Piling entirely above water is coated with a vinyl mastic. The sulphur will be landed through a seven-mile, steam-heated pipeline laid beneath the floor of the Gulf.

Other offshore moves have been made. Some three miles off the Texas coast are a series of domes which both Freeport and Texas Gulf have examined. At San Luis Pass Freeport had five leases and drilled 13 exploratory holes before deciding to abandon this prospect.[6] At Galveston Island, where Texas Gulf had six leases, extensive core drilling failed to find sulphur in commercial quantities.[7]

Offshore sulphur lies in the future. But it opens to the Frasch industry a new future, yet unproven, but extending far beyond the limits of the mainland reserves. It will have novel aspects. Leases must be secured from the States or the Federal Government by competitive bidding which considerably raise the preliminary expenses of exploring. Offshore mining calls for a large capital investment in plant and facilities. However, Freeport's experienced engineers expect confidently that Grand Isle will be one of the world's largest and most efficient Frasch operations.[8]

Sour gas sulphur, on the other hand, is here now. By 1960 it will be a very real factor in world markets. During the next decade it will raise perplexing questions the answers to which, as worked out by the industry in the United States and Mexico, in France and Canada, will be crucial in their effects. Sulphur recovered from natural gas is conspicuously the most significant development of the near future.

Work on the removal of hydrogen sulphide to sweeten hydrocarbon gases and its conversion to elemental sulphur began in the early 1940's by Texas Gulf Sulphur in a pilot plant near McKamie, Arkansas, and simultaneously by Southern Acid & Sulphur Company, cooperating with the Ohio State University Research Foundation at Magnolia, Arkansas. Sour gas was cleaned and concentrated in monoethanolamine and dehydrated in a solution of amines and glycols to an average of 58% hydrogen sulphide, 41% carbon dioxide, and 1% mixed hydrocarbons. This and similar methods had been used for some time to sweeten sour gas. Conversion of hydrogen sulphide to sulphur was by the old Claus method, devised in the early 1880's, to reclaim calcium sulphide waste from the Leblanc soda process. It was based upon carbonizing the calcium sulphide with carbon dioxide and oxidizing the resulting hydrogen sulphide over a ferric oxide catalyst to elemental sulphur vapor: $2H_2S + O_2 = 2H_2O + 2S$.[9]

Following this experimental work, Southern Acid (now absorbed by Olin Mathieson Chemical Company) built a 120-ton-a-day plant at McKamie in 1944 and a second plant two years later at Magnolia. Texas Gulf built a similar plant at Worland, Wyoming, in 1949, with a capacity of 400 tons of recovered sulphur daily, for years the largest in North America.[10]

The Claus process has been modified by (1) using bauxite or alumina as the catalyst, (2) burning some of the hydrogen sulphide gas to sulphur dioxide and mixing it with the original feed gas, and (3) by carrying on the oxidation process in two stages.[11] Other absorbents than the ethanolamines employed in the Girbotol process[12] have been introduced: potassium phosphate, the Shell process;[13] sodium phenolate or sodium carbonate, Koppers' process,[14] and sodium thio-arsenate, the Thylox process.[15]

By 1950 six such recovery plants were operating: Free-port Sulphur at Eagle Point, New Jersey; Hancock Chemical

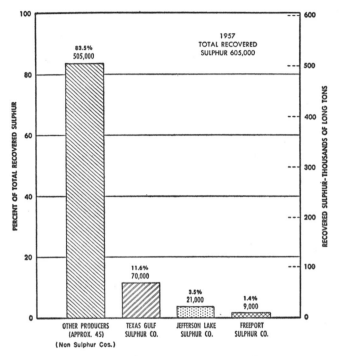

FIG. 11. 1957 production of sulphur recovered from hydrogen sul-phide in U. S. and Canada.

near Los Angeles; Olin Mathieson at McKamie and Mag-nolia, Arkansas; Stanolind, Elk Basin, Wyoming, and Texas Gulf, Worland, Wyoming.[16] Four others were building. Production rose from 32,000 long tons of sulphur in 1940 to 79,000 in 1950 and jumped to 484,000 tons by 1957[17] when some 45 plants were operating and half a dozen others were in the blueprint stage (Figure 11.)

This sensational advance in the United States was but the

first tapping of this new source of sulphur. Throughout the plains flanking the east side of the Rockies from Canada to Mexico may be enormous reserves of sour gas. In West Texas and Wyoming alone, a potential sulphur production of 400 and 500 tons a day respectively is estimated for the next 25 years,[18] and U. S. sour gas reservoirs presently known are less extensive than those in northwestern Canada. The fields in Mexico are just beginning to be explored.

In 1951 at Poza Rica in the State of Veracruz, Petróleos Mexicanos built a sour gas sulphur recovery plant of 120 tons daily capacity (then second in size only to Worland) which is now being enlarged to 200 tons and has planned another.[19] For three years Pemex, being a government agency, delivered free 70 tons of sulphur a day and 5 million feet of gas to the government-owned fertilizer factory, but later was paid $2.65 a ton for the sulphur and 1.7 cents per 1000 cubic feet of gas. Less than half the sulphur recovered was sold to other domestic makers of sulphuric acid. All of the Poza Rica sulphur is delivered in the flake form.[20]

Mexican recovered sulphur has, as yet, had small effect upon the market. It has been sold to domestic acid makers: most of it to the government superphosphate plant at a price that starkly reflects political, not commercial, considerations. But even a government cannot over-ride the basic economics of this by-product operation. Sulphur recovery must await a demand for sweetened sour gas. This becomes effective only if sweet natural gas is either unavailable or insufficient to meet consumers' needs, and only after pipelines from the sour gas field to the consuming area have been laid. These delivery facilities are costly. They are profitable only upon a long-time basis for a big volume of gas and a 24-hour, year-round demand. This usually implies a sizable industrial consumption. Therefore, it is unlikely that the recovery of sour gas sulphur in Mexico will be greatly increased quickly. Of the country's eight known, big gas fields, all are sweet, except those at Poza Rica and in Tabasco, but it is geologically sound to surmise that the oil and sour gas pools in the eastern foothills of the Rockies may extend south of the border. Under the management of the capable, nationalistically minded Antonio Bermudez, Pemex has pushed exploration in this unproved region.

From a different angle, these principles underlying sulphur recovery are exemplified by France, a compact, energy-hungry country anxious to expand her industries. And General Andre Blanchard, the ex-army engineer who heads the French sour gas recovery enterprise, has bluntly expounded the philosophy of such an operation.

In 1939 a shallow sweet gas field was discovered at St. Marcet in the shadow of the Pyrenees, a location strikingly like the Alberta gas fields in the foothills of the Canadian Rockies. In 1948 Hudson Engineering Company of Houston built a gasoline plant here for the French Government. In 1949, drilling with an old German rig, at 1800 feet an oil pool was located. During the war this was developed with German equipment and to date (1958) has produced 12.6 million barrels of crude. However, oil reserves were limited and after the liberation geological logic prompted deeper drilling.

At 8 A.M., December 18, 1951, Lacq No. 3 was blown out when the drill struck gas at 11,000 feet. The well ran wild with a pressure of 9,500 p.s.i. and it was two months before the rush of corrosive, toxic sour gas was brought under control by Myron Kinley, a Texas operator called in to cope with the emergency.[21] Recoverable reserves in the order of 7,000 billion cubic feet of sour gas[22] having been proved, a Girbotol-type recovery plant was engineered by Ralph M. Parsons, Inc., of Los Angeles, and a multi-stage expansion program adopted. In April 1957, the initial unit, handling 37 million cubic feet of gas and producing 200 tons of sulphur a day, came on-stream. By 1959 this production had been increased to 185 million feet of gas and 1000 tons of sulphur. By 1962 annual capacities at Lacq are scheduled to be 1,400,000 barrels of high octane gasoline; 8000 tons each of butane and propane; 1,400,000 tons of sulphur.[23]

Between the first and second stages of this expansion the technical staff of S.N.P.A. (Société Nationale des Pétroles d'Aquitaine) adopted, for the first time in natural gas practice, the water pressure method of scrubbing the gas familiar in the synthetic ammonia process. This is an economy measure. Not only is the plant investment less, but more to the point in France, is the saving in steam, estimated to be 70-80 tons per hour in treating 150 million feet of gas daily. The water scrubbing gets out two-thirds of the H_2S, the final clean-up being with monoethanolamine. On the drawing board are plans for ethylene oxide to be delivered in exchange with the amine manufacturers.[24] The Lacq plant is splendidly laid out for efficient operation and to provide for extensions; its control instrumentation is very advanced; its housekeeping is superb.

Distribution is the only serious problem in the sale of gas. A network of pipelines cover Southeast France, reaching out to Bayonne and Bordeaux, to Nantes and now extending into the Loire Valley. Lyon will be reached during the summer of 1959 and a line to Paris will handle the increased output of 1961. Nor have sulphur sales presented any special difficulties.

Brimstone is recovered in liquid form and vatted. All deliveries have been of lump in bulk, but successful experiments have been completed in making the new pelletized form recently developed in Scandinavia. This might become popular with customers. It is dustless; occupies minimum space for weight; and flows even more freely than the flaked type. Lacq shipments have gone mostly by rail, west 50 miles to Bayonne, thence by small coastwise ships, or east to Marseille, Sète, and other centers where refineries grind it for the large vineyard trade.[25] Only a few shipments, which Claude Bienvenu, in charge of sulphur sales, calls "experimental," have been made to British channel ports, the Netherlands, and West Germany.[26]

The fact remains: France, which has imported some 335,-000 tons of sulphur (200,000 tons of brimstone, most of it from Texas-Louisiana, and 900,000 tons of pyrites, with a sulphur content of about 135,000 tons, from Spain, Portugal, Cypress, and Cuba) was by 1959 ready to export an equal tonnage. By 1961 this exportable surplus will be roughly a million tons. Obviously S.N.P.A. will fill the French demand for brimstone. Although trade treaties with Spain and Portugal provide for an exchange of pyrites for various French products, Lacq sulphur will replace much imported pyrites. The S.N.P.A. management expects the natural increase in acid production, to create a favorable market atmosphere. They point to the new electro-petrochemical center created at nearby Mourenx.[27] Here a gas-fueled electric plant with three 125.000 Kw generators, a Pechiney aluminum plant to take two-thirds this power load, and the Aquitaine-Chemie making ammonia, ammonium sulphate, acetylene, and plastics, will all come on-stream before 1960. Tangible evidence of this gas-sulphur contribution to the French economy is the complex of ultramodern apartments to house the workers in these three new industries which have sprung up in the heart of an exclusively farming district.

General Blanchard, S.N.P.A. president, recently summarized his company's thinking:[28] "We wish we were still in the oil business, but we are now in the gas business and because our gas is sour we are also in the sulphur business. But we are in business to make money. We have borrowed for exploring and construction. We must repay these loans and resume dividend payments, suspended since 1955. We are exploring for oil in the Rhone Valley and in the mountains west of Nancy in France and near Hassi Messaoud in the Sahara, and we are extending our distribution system for gas as fast as is feasible. There are good reasons for these activities: (1) France needs more energy sorely and (2) in twenty years atomic power may be a competitor of both gasoline and gas.

"We will have a lot of sulphur to sell, but we shall not sell a ton for one sou less than competition demands of us. A lot of people wonder what will happen in the sulphur market during the next ten years. Demand for sulphur will increase, we believe, faster than expected. If the sulphur producers do not become panicky; if they respect each others' place in the market and work to increase sulphur consumption, I see no reason why the price of sulphur, already too cheap in comparison with other great chemical commodities, should go lower."

The recovered sulphur situation in Canada appears quite different than in France. The industrial and political environment, the local demand for gas and sulphur, pipeline facilities and the distances from consuming centers, almost every factor, is distinctive to each country. Beneath, however, the same principle holds: timing and output of by-product sulphur depend on the market for sweetened sour gas.

Gas was discovered in Alberta in 1883 and the first commercial production was in 1904 from the field near Medicine Hat to supply the needs of that city.[29] The first Canadian pipeline for oil or gas was laid in 1912, 170 miles of 16-inch pipe to take gas from Bow Island to Calgary, and by the mid-1940's the larger communities throughout Western Canada were supplied with natural gas. During the petroleum boom gas was the tail of the oil kite, but several large gas fields were located. The wells were usually capped and the drilling rigs moved on, but a lot of definite information was accumulated.

It became clear that Northwestern Canada has enormous gas reserves, by billions of cubic feet the largest yet reported. The first official estimate, made in 1947 by the Dominion Geological Survey, set proven reserves at about 1.4 trillion cubic feet with an additional 2.2 trillion listed as probable.[30] A decade later, March 31, 1958, the Alberta Gas & Oil Conservation Board established reserves in that province at 22.5 trillion cubic feet.[31] The Board, as befits its title, is superlatively conservative, and furthermore, since figures reported to it are confidential for one year, this 1958 estimate takes no account of the sensational find of British American Oil and Shell at Berland River. Here are 550 feet of pay with an open flow potential of 1.5 billion cubic feet a day of 16 per cent H_2S gas, the biggest gas field yet found in Canada, one of the biggest in the world, where reserves "might be 10 trillion or more." [32]

Estimates of Canadian reserves vary from 200 to 300 trillion cubic feet. In the 700,000 square miles of the Western Canada Sedimentary Basin are some 789,000 cubic miles of sediments 1000 feet or greater in thickness, considered favorable for prospecting for hydrocarbons.[33] An ultimate recoverable reserve of over 250 trillion cubic feet of natural gas has been calculated for the entire basin.[34] Two-fifths of this is in areas today classified as "inaccessible."

Much has also been learned about the deposits and the properties of the western Canada gas. In the more eastern plains region the gas is generally sweet and dry. It becomes more sour and wet in the foothills. The hydrogen sulphide content of the sour gas reaches over 30% with an average of about 15%. At Panther River, 60 miles northwest of Calgary, Shell found gas in a single well with 87% H_2S and less than 5% hydrocarbons. It flowed 6.2 million cubic feet and, after a 14-hour test, was capped. It is not known whether this is a "freak" or the discovery well of what is in truth a sulphur well. Previous high-record H_2S gas in Canada has been 45.72% at Beddington and 40.68% at Wimborne.[35]

To exploit these gas reserves and their attendant assets of sulphur and raw materials for the petrochemical industry, pipelines to larger markets were needed. For many reasons they have been much delayed. Up to 1959 only two long lines had been laid: (1) Westcoast Transmission's 650-mile, 30-inch pipe with an initial capacity of 400 million cubic feet a day, from the Peace River area via Vancouver to the international boundary where it joins the Pacific Northwest line for delivery to Washington and Oregon; and (2) Trans-Canada's 34-inch pipe from the Alberta-Saskatchewan boundary to the head of the Great Lakes, projected to reach Toronto and Montreal in 1959 and eventually Quebec.

Two export applications are pending: (1) from Westcoast Transmission for 1.3 trillion cubic feet over a period of 25 years from the Savanna Creek-Calgary sour gas fields through Crowsnest Pass to the Pacific Northwest line at the Idaho boundary, and (2) from Alberta & Southern Gas, subsidiary of Pacific Gas & Electric of San Francisco, for 4.2 trillion cubic feet over the next 25 years, chiefly from the sour gas fields of southwestern Alberta, to the Idaho boundary for distribution in Montana and California. These applications have been considered, with public hearings, by the Alberta Conservation Board and a special Royal Commission on Energy, known as the Borden Commission. Both official bodies have issued voluminous reports.[36]

The Alberta Board refused both applications, but gave the companies till December 31, 1958, to file revised, lower gas requests. The Borden Report made a number of regulatory recommendations which raised a cloud of controversies,[37] but it did approve the export of gas. This report went to Parliament for action on its various proposals.

Higher and higher estimates of reserves have won over Canadian opinion to general approval of the sale of gas to American consumers.[38] Both provincial and national agencies controlling gas sales agree to the prompt, reasonable export of these resources. But before this gas can be imported consent of the U. S. Power Commission must be obtained. On both sides of the border, the government attitude inclines towards joint development of these energy sources upon a mutual, continental basis.[39]

In the eastern provinces and western states, greater markets for Northwest Canadian gas are coming. Just how quickly and for exactly how many billion feet of gas is not now precisely predictable. But the increased demand will be filled mainly by sweetened sour gas, and knowledgeable experts agree that probably by 1961 the output of by-product recovered sulphur may reach over a million tons; by 1965, at least 2 million, by 1970, 2.5 million.[40]

At the end of 1958 six recovery plants were producing at the rate of about 290,000 tons of sulphur a year. The largest, is British American Oil at Pincher Creek, south of Calgary. It came on-stream in 1956 with 225 tons daily capacity and its second stage was completed October 1958, raising the capacity to 450 tons daily, actual production being about 400 tons. Shell Oil's plant at Jumping Pound, which to 1959 produced some 100,000 tons, has a capacity of 100 tons a day, but is producing at the rate of 75 tons. Imperial Oil at Redwater and Royalite at Turner Valley are rated at 10 and 40 tons a day, respectively. The former had produced to October 1958, a total of 2880 tons. Royalite's total production at this date was 58,563 tons of which 8462 tons was recovered during 1958. These four plants are all in Alberta. At Taylor Flats in British Columbia, Jefferson Lake Petrochemicals of Canada is believed to produce 425 tons daily to process the sour gas from the large, prolific Peace River gas area. At Steelmans in Saskatchewan, Provo Gas Producers are recovering 40 tons a day.

Seven additional plants are planned for 1959. At Okotoks Texas Gulf Sulphur will bring its 350-ton plant on-stream in June. Also slated for summer production are Standard Oil of California in the Homeglen-Rimbey field, 190 tons; British American and Standard of California at Nevis, 100 and 65 tons respectively. Late in 1959, possibly not till early 1960, a 150-ton plant is planned at Dick Lake, either by British American or Standard of California. Both are active in this field where the gas has been committed to Alberta &

Southern or, if the export program is delayed, to Trans-Canada. The largest projects for 1959 are two by Jefferson Lake: a 320-350-ton-a-day installation at either Savanna Creek or Coleman and a 900-ton plant at East Calgary. If these new enterprises all come through on schedule, they will add 1805 tons to Canada's daily output of sour gas sulphur. This would increase the Canadian yearly capacity by 595,650 tons, bringing the 1960 total to roughly 886,000 tons.[41]

Even larger sulphur recovery projects are in the offing. These big gas fields could not be tapped for the Trans-Canada pipeline, even if this company's application for an additional line to Minneapolis were granted (as is considered likely) and their development definitely awaits the allocation of gas for export to Westcoast Transmission and Alberta & Southern. Accordingly, these plans are tentative and the capacities announced only approximate, but the total projected daily tonnage of 2600 would virtually double the 1960 total to 1,744,000 tons.

These if-and-when projects are Imperial Oil at Joffre, 200 tons/day; Canadian Oil at Innisfail, 200 tons; Shell and/or Hudson's Bay Oil & Gas at Olds, 100 tons minimum; Mobile and/or British American at Wimborne, 100; in the Edson area, 120 miles northwest of Edmonton, comprising three big fields, Pine Creek, Beaver Creek, and Windfall, three big oil companies, Pan American (Stanolind), Hudson's Bay, and the Belgian owned Canadian Fina, are reported drawing up a joint proposal to all the sulphur companies for a recovery plant of 2000 tons minimum capacity.

To date, Canadian sulphur has been consumed nearby. But the local market is small: the increased output must be exported. The production area is landlocked—600 miles to the Pacific; 1200 miles to the Great Lakes—so freight rates are critical costs. The present rate from Alberta points to Vancouver is 44¢ cwt. or $9.85 per long ton. This is lower than the all-rail rate of $14.78 from Worland, Wyoming, the

U. S. production nearest to the pulp and paper market in the Northwest. It is not, however, competitive with U. S. Gulf ports or Coatzacoalcos for export to the Far East.[43] By an 1897 agreement between the Canadian Pacific Railway and the Dominion Government, the freight rate in perpetuity, unless abrogated by an act of Parliament, on wheat for export to Pacific ports and the head of the Great Lakes is 20¢ and 26¢ per cwt. respectively. The rate on domestic grain, not subject to this agreement, is 54¢ to both the West Coast and the Lakes, and sulphur, being a big-tonnage bulk commodity, is in the same category. The railroad could insist on trainloads to be stockpiled at export points; thus sulphur would give them a much needed year-round traffic.

There is a possible alternative solution to the delivery costs problem. The cheapest overland shipment of liquids is by pipeline, so companies are studying the practicability of liquefying hydrogen sulphide and piping it to consuming centers where sulphur would be recovered by the Claus process. This method of delivery has its own problems, notably those of corrosion and toxicity, and no conclusions have been reached.[44]

Production costs as between the Frasch and the H_2S recovery processes are not believed to be seriously out of line. Operating costs and obsolescence seem to favor the Frasch installation. Drilling costs, both for development and production, are less in a sour gas operation. American experience indicates that the overall costs of the two processes are at least reasonably comparable.

How this new supply of sulphur is sold, and by whom, may become important. Many oil companies show reluctance to embark in this new and unfamiliar business which calls for additional investment and makes heavy demands on personnel. Two of the old-line sulphur companies, Texas Gulf Sulphur and Jefferson Lake, have already moved into Canada. Freeport and Pan American have had men in the field, keeping in close touch with developments. A third type of sulphur recovery set-up is the proposal of the International Sulphur Company of Canada, subsidiary of the Continental Ore Corporation, to finance small gas producers by building 50-ton plants in several locations, taking the sulphur, condensate, and liquefiable petroleum gases in exchange for the sweetened pipeline gas. The terms and conditions of any deal between sulphur and oil companies are as yet not standardized. They frequently hinge upon whether the oil company shall sweeten its own gas and deliver hydrogen sulphide to the sulphur company or whether the sulphur company takes in raw gas and carries on both the amine separation and catalyst recovery operations.

With the big plant at Worland and the new one building at Okotoks, Texas Gulf, the largest brimstone producer, evidently does not intend that sour gas sulphur shall jeopardize its present position. Their Canadian plant embodies the results of their pioneering experience and will be run under the eye of trained, practical supervisors. Already they are testing the water-pressure scrubbing methods recently adopted at the French plant.

Jefferson Lake, which operates through its 69%-owned subsidiary, Jefferson Lake Petrochemicals of Canada, Ltd.,[45] brought its British Columbia plant into production November 1957 and made its first carload shipment to paper mills in the Pacific Northwest, the following August.[46] This plant has first call on the hydrogen sulphide extracted by Westcoast Transmission Company from the gas it collects from 70 per cent of the proved reserves in the Peace River area and it is deemed reasonable that all the hydrogen sulphide produced in this area will be processed in this plant. The Canadian subsidiary also has natural gas leasehold interests in some 80,000 acres in the Calgary area and a conditional agreement with Westcoast Transmission to sweeten the sour gas collected by Westcoast in the Savanna Creek area for the proposed pipeline to the Idaho boundary. The plants projected for 1959 at East Calgary and Savanna Creek or Coleman are based upon these reserves.

Another source of recovered sulphur looms in the future from the Middle East where there are extensive sour gas fields and the oil is often contaminated with sulphur.[47] Production is chiefly of acid for intraplant consumption and much of it is from petroleum and sludge acid.

In Iran, for example, the big Abadan refinery produced in 1957 77,000 tons of virgin and 30,000 tons of regenerated acid; 7000 tons of sulphur having come from refinery operations and 11,000 tons from gas cleaning.[48] In Iraq, the new 300 ton/day H_2S recovery unit, now being built by Ralph M. Parsons, will clean 80 million cubic feet of gas daily for delivery to a nearby plant to produce 250,000 tons of ammonium sulphate and 21,000 tons of 100% acid annually. In Saudi Arabia, both Bahrein and Arabian-American Oil, and in Egypt, Anglo-Egyptian, all have acid plants ranging in output from 20 to 35 tons daily, and the new refinery in Syria will include a sulphur recovery unit of 80 tons daily capacity.

Akin to these Middle East projects, hundreds of all types of by-product recovery operations are spotted over North America and Europe. Each is governed by its own peculiar conditions, economic and geographic, financial and chemical. They exert on the brimstone market chiefly a negative effect by eliminating the sulphur consumption of a certain amount of acid-making capacity, an inconspicuous, but not insignificant tonnage. The percentage of acid contributed by all these sources is estimated to be 19 per cent of the world total while brimstone supplies 70 per cent and pyrites 11 per cent.[49] With elemental sulphur in abundant supply, such by-product projects are less attractive and over the years many may become unattractive as commercial enterprises.

Although the facts are dubious, other possible foreign sources of supply deserve at least passing mention. Russia has evidently met the increasing sulphur requirements of her expanded industries, and it is believed that production of the element in all forms approaches 2 million tons. Of this, possibly 175,200,000 tons is elemental sulphur; native, from the Orkla pyrite process, and recovered, chiefly, no doubt, from Banku oil. Japan and China have of late been exporting brimstone. As their domestic needs are growing and in the future native sulphur is hardly expected to be competitive with Frasch and recovered elemental sulphur, neither country is to be very seriously reckoned with in the present world market.

That sulphur will be in oversupply for the next few years nobody doubts. But it is also indubitably certain that the demand for this chemical raw material will grow greatly and at an accelerated rate. The law of supply and demand (which, despite private interferences and government controls, still functions) will eventually re-establish a reasonably balanced market.

The economic characteristics of brimstone are as unusual and distinctive as its chemical and physical properties. They must be reckoned with. First, sulphur is an essential industrial raw material. While the demand for this chemical commodity is remarkably stable and has been steadily increasing, it is also a demand over which the producers have almost no control. So long as sulphuric acid remains "the king of chemicals," the future of brimstone is as secure as Gibraltar.

However, all the uses of sulphur depend upon the activities of a multitude of industries which buy no more nor less than they need as a chemical tool in their own manufacturing operations. A lower price may tempt a buyer to switch from one supplier to another, but it will not induce him to increase his order a single ton beyond his requirements. Likewise, a consumer may prefer the molten or flake form to lump brimstone, but whatever reasons prompt this choice, they will not lead him to buy more. Nor can the brimstone producer employ the customary sales appeals to widen his market. He cannot add any "miracle ingredient." It would do no good to package his product in cellophane and tie it with a pink bow. There is no "impulse buying" of brimstone.

The second distinctive characteristic of this chemical commodity is that it can be stored indefinitely without appreciable loss of weight or deterioration. Accordingly, no sulphur will be dumped to salvage stock. On the other hand, a mounting stockpile, while disturbing to shareholders, embarrassing to management, inconvenient and expensive, is by no means ruinous, that is, if the producer has the courage and financial strength to carry a heavy load of frozen assets. The ability to hold sulphur in stock thus discourages the debacle of distressed sales. It also encourages an unhappy delay in bringing a potential oversupply in balance with effective demand. Therefore, the balanced market, essential to the good health of the entire sulphur industry, is going to come chiefly from increased demand.

By 1975 U. S. consumption of sulphur will reach 10,115,-000 long tons, a 110 per cent increase over the 1950 consumption of 4,806,000 tons. That is the conclusion reached in *Resources for Freedom,* the closely reasoned, well considered report of the Materials Policy Commission appointed by the President, January 22, 1951, and supported by a staff of the best economists and statisticians.

This 25-year projection of sulphur demand by Arnold C. Harberger of John Hopkins University, was predicated upon an estimated percentage increase in the use of sulphur in acids: for chemicals and ammonium sulphate at 200 per cent increase for each; for superphosphate, 130 per cent; for rayon and film, and miscellaneous, 100 per cent each; petroleum, and paints and pigments, 50 per cent each; and for iron and steel, 40 per cent. The increase in the non-acid uses were estimated: for rayon, rubber, and chemicals at 100 per cent each; for pulp and paper, 20 per cent; and for pesticides, zero.[50]

These figures are derived from many factors, the pre-
dominant one being the expansion of American industries
grounded on the growth of our population. Their validity
is attested by the long-standing, close correlation existing

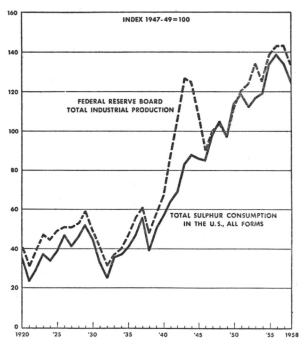

FIG. 12. Correlation between U. S. consumption of sulphur and U. S.
industrial production: 1920-58.

between sulphur consumption and industrial production.
(Figure 12.)   Leibig's axiom that the economic welfare of a
nation can be most accurately measured by its consumption
of sulphuric acid holds universally. The United States is
incomparably the greatest consumer of sulphur, nevertheless
the rate of growth, because of both greater increase in population and the more rapid advance of their under-developed
industries, promises to be faster in many other countries.

World consumption of sulphur, in all forms, according to
Eugene H. Walet, Jr., president of Jefferson Lake, will reach

24 million long tons by 1965. Consumers, he believes, will seek additional quantities of elemental sulphur in preference to other forms. The overall, long-term worldwide view of the sulphur situation cannot be pessimistic.

Everyone forecasts that the greatest increase in sulphur consumption will be in fertilizers and chemicals. With half the people on earth undernourished and living in lands where population is growing with extraordinary rapidity, greater use of artificial plantfoods is the inevitable solution to one of man's oldest, most persistent problems, starvation. With chemists inventing new products and engineers perfecting improved processes, progress in the chemical field is extraordinarily rapid and often unpredictable. In other words, the greatest demands for more brimstone in the immediate futue will arise from imperious need and dynamic progress.

There will be changes in the sulphur market. New uses will appear, but they will be found, as they always have been, not by the sulphur industry, but by its customers, often by new customers. A current example is the use of sulphuric acid in leaching uranium from its ores.

Ample stocks of pure sulphur at four widely separated points—Frasch brimstone at both ends of the Gulf of Mexico crescent and elemental sulphur in southern France and western Canada—will tend to localize what has been a one-world market, and freight rates will become a potent element in competition. An acid maker, anywhere on earth, need no longer hesitate to tie to sulphur for fear of being dependent upon a single source of supply. It is hard to conceive that any new acid plant will be designed for pyrites: the market for brimstone will be further increased at the expense of its old rival.

In the first edition of this book, published in 1942, it was stated that "it appears unlikely that we shall again see such spectacular annual increases in acid consumption as were recorded between 1880-99 when a 375 per cent increase was scored in 19 years. What is to be expected rather is the restoration of a steady annual growth, an increase proportional to the nation's annual growth in population and manufacturing activities."[51]

During the past 19 years, the increase in our sulphuric acid consumption has been 305 per cent, much closer to that old record than to the average increase in industrial activity or in population. During these years, American per capita annual consumption of this acid increased from 68 to 206 pounds—another way of saying that sulphur is still a key element in our exceedingly chemical civilization.

Notes and References

Chapter 1: PRELUDE TO A NEW ERA

[1] Bernal Diaz del Castillo, *Discovery and Conquest of Mexico* (N. Y., 1956) 62, 68; Wm. H. Prescott, *Conquest of Mexico* (Everyman's Ed., N. Y., 1909) I, 40.

[2] M. Alcala, *Min. y Revis. Soc. Sient. Antonio Alzate* **13**, 311, 1900, abst. in *Mining Mag.* **11**, 86, 1905; T. L. Laguerenne, *ibid.*, **17**, 128, 1902.

[3] *Eng. & Mining J.* **77**, 777, 1900; Paul Weaver, interview, Houston, Tex., July 12, 1956; J. H. Pollard, *ibid.*, July 14, Dec. 10, 1956.

[4] Best primary sources in English on geology and exploration of the Isthmus salt domes are A. H. Redfield, *Eng. & Mining J.* **111**, 510, 1921; B. Hartley, *Econ. Geol.* **12**, 581, 1917; and S. Huntley, *Trans. Am. Inst. Mining Met. Engrs.* **69**, 1150, 1923; in Spanish, J. R. Villarello, *Bol. Inst. Geol. Mex. No. 26*, 1916, abst. in *Mining Mag.* **85**, 609, 1909; *Bol. Petrol* **2**, 10, 1916; and W. A. Ver Viebe, *Panam. Geologist* **44**, 121, 1925. See also Alcala, *op. cit.*; A. Barroso, *Anal. Minist. de Formento, Repub. Mex.* **3**, 273, 1897; F. W. Moon, *Trans. Inst. Mining & Met.* (London) **20**, 259, 1910; P. Baud, *Rev. Scient.* (Paris) **2**, 260, 1912; R. Arnold, *Proc. 2nd Panam. Sci. Cong., 1917*, III, 222; E. de Golyer, *Trans. Am. Inst. Mining & Met. Engrs.* **61**, 456, 1919; J. Santalla, *Excelsior* (Mexico, D. F.) Jan. 4, 1927, 5.

[5] Jas. A. Clark and Michel T. Halbouty, *Spindletop* (N. Y., 1952); C. W. Warner, *Texas Gas and Oil Since 1543* (Houston, 1939) 37; *Texas Almanac*, 1939-40, 215; Max W. Ball, *This Fascinating Oil Business* (Indianapolis, 1940) 61, 354. For A. F. Lucas see B. S. McBeth, *Pioneering the Gulf Coast* (N. Y., 1908); *Dict. Am. Biog.* XI, 482; *Who Was Who I*, 751; obits. in *Trans. Am. Inst. Mining & Met. Engrs.* **65**, 421, 1921 and *Mining & Scient. Press*, Sept. 17, 1921, 414.

[6] J. V. Harrison, *Quart. J. Geol.* (London) *No. 344*, 463, 1930; *J. Inst. Petrol. Geol.* **17**, 300, 1931.

[7] In this enormous technical literature two of the best general descriptions of the saltdomes are G. D. Harris, *U. S. Geo. Survey Bull. No. 429* (Washington, 1910) and *La. State Geol. Surv. Bull. No. 7* (Baton Rouge, 1908). Especially useful are also R. Owen, *Trans. St. Louis Acad. Sci.* **2**, 250, 1868; E. V. Hopkins, *La. State Geol. Surv. Ann. Rept. 1869*, 77; *1870*, 1; *1871*, 163; A. C. Veatch, *Preliminary Report on Geology of Louisiana* (Baton Rouge, 1899); Alex. Deussen, *U. S. Geol.*

Surv., Prof. Paper No. 128 (Washington, 1924); Williams Haynes, *Stone that Burns* (N. Y., 1942) 49; hereinafter cited as Haynes, *Stone.* Important journal articles are A. F. Lucas, *Trans. Am. Inst. Mining Engrs.* **57,** 1034, 1918; E. de Golyer, *Econ. Geol.* **13,** 616, 1918; L. Hager, *Eng. & Mining J.* **79,** 137, 180, 1904; A. G. Wolf, *ibid.,* **112,** 606, 1921; J. B. Eby, *Bull. Am. Assoc. Petrol. Geol.* **29,** 210, 1945; *Geophysics 8,* 348, 1955; M. T. Halbouty and G. C. Hardin, Jr., *Bull. Am. Assoc. Petrol. Geol.* **40,** 737, 1956; popular summary, *J. Chem. Educat. 12,* 19, 1935.

8 de Golyer, *op. cit.*

9 *Union Sulphur Co. vs Freeport Sulphur Co.; U. S. Circuit Court of Appeals for 3rd Circuit,* I, 512, 544; hereinafter cited as *Union vs Freeport.*

10 Luigi Delabretoigne, *L'industria mineraria solfifera Siciliana* (Torino, 1925); Caesar Vannutelli, *Solfio d'industria solfifera Siciliana* (Palermo, 1893); Haynes, *Stone,* 70.

11 F. Deschamps, *Revista Mex. Ingen y Arquit.* **15,** 665, 777, 1936.

12 Haynes, *Stone,* 313.

13 *Ibid.,* 315.

14 Account of exploring and financing Mexican deposits based on interviews with Lawrence B., Wm. C. and Ashton G. Brady, Eugenio de Anzorena, C. L. Basland, Gen. Alfredo Breceda, Enrique Carstens, L. N. J. Creel, J. H. Kearney, E. O. Mason, R. B. Roberson, G. P. Salas, David Segura, Jos. Sperling, in Mexico, D. F., Mar. 20 to Apr. 6, Apr. 23 to May 4, July 15-21, 1956; Mar. 15 to Apr. 28, 1957; C. E. Armstrong, Wm. P. Barnard, J. B. Brannan, Jose A. Gallegos, Luis A. Iturbide, H. H. Jaquet, S. M. Richards, W. H. Maddox, Eugene Rossi, Jos. Soper, Robt. M. Stoy, and Jas. Woodburn at operations in Isthmus, Apr. 5-22, 1956; Jan. 5 to Feb. 3, 1957; Claude Crockett, J. B. Eby, H. W. Haines, Jr., K. H. Johnson, Douglas Johnston, G. R. Marlow, Dwight Morrow, Geo. P. Murrin, John C. Myers, J. H. Pollard, Ralph Taylor, M. E. Weaster, Paul Weaver, Harry C. Webb, Houston, Tex., March 12-19, July 10-25, 1956; May 7-20, 1957; Gilbert Ebarb, Sr., Rosenberg, Tex., Apr. 11, 1957; Chris Elliott, Wharton, Tex., Apr. 11, 1957; Paul Nachtman, New York, June 8, 1956; Fred Nelson, New York, July 11, 1956; Newgulf, Tex., Dec. 6, 1956.

15 Mex. Gulf Sulphur Co., *SEC Prospectus,* Ap. 3, 1946, 1.

16 J. H. Kearney, *Eng. & Mining J.* **136,** 37, 1955.

17 W. L. Lundy, *Ind. Eng. Chem.* **42,** 2199, 1950; J. C. Carrington, *Mining Cong. J.* **37,** 53, 1951; *Chem. Engr.* **59,** 165, 1952; popular resume, *Fortune,* **44,** 37, 1951.

18 *Julius Caesar,* Act IV, Sc. 3.

Chapter 2: THE WORKHORSE OF CHEMISTRY

1 Ralph K. Strong, ed., *Kingsett's Chemical Encyclopaedia,* 6th ed. (N. Y., 1940) 945. For use of sulphur in chemical industries: H. C. Lint, *Chem. Met. Eng.* **22,** 9, 1925; W. A. Cunningham, *J. Chem. Educat.* **12,**

17, 1935; P. E. Hattinger, *Am. Dye. Rptr.* **25**, 609, 1936; R. F. Bacon, *Chem Ind.* **40**, 465, 1937; E. R. Riegel, *Quart. J. Econ.* Feb. 1934, 4; W. W. Duecker & E. W. Eddy, *Chem. Ind.* **50**, 174, 1942.

2 Chas. D. Hodgman, ed., *Handbook of Chemistry & Physics* (Cleveland, 1957) 382, 3126.

3 For data and statistics on various sulphur-bearing materials see current issues of Bur. of Mines, *Minerals Yearbook.*

4 *Odyssey*, XXII, 481.

5 A. Lucas, *Ancient Egyptian Materials and Industries*, 2nd ed. (London, 1924); Chas. H. La Wall, *Four Thousand Years of Pharmacy* (Phila., 1927).

6 *Exodus*, III, 1-20.

7 Kenneth C. Bailey, *Elder Pliny's Chapters on Chemical Subjects*, 2 vols. (London, 1932); for early sources of sulphur: C. G. W. Lock, *Sci. Am. Suppl.*, Aug. 30, 1884, 1171.

8 Li Ch'iao-p'ing, *Alchemical Arts of Old China* (Easton, Pa., 1948) 114.

9 Prescott, *op. cit.* I, 326; F. J. M. Rhodes, *Eng. & Mining J.* **77**, 730, 1904; N. J. Harrar, *J. Chem. Educat.* **11**, 640, 1934.

10 Good introductions to alchemy are E. J. Holmyard, *Alchemy* (Pelican ed., Balto., 1957); John Read, *Prelude to Chemistry*, 2nd ed. (London, 1939); A. J. Hopkins, *Alchemy, Child of Greek Philosophy* (N. Y., 1934); F. Sherwood Taylor, *The Alchemists* (N. Y., 1949).

11 Georg Lunge, *Manufacture of Sulphuric Acid and Alkali*, 2 vols. (London, 1823); Sheridan Muspratt, *Chemistry Applied to the Arts and Manufactures*, 2 vols. (Glasgow, 1862).

12 Best account of early sulphuric acid in England is W. H. Dickinson, *Trans. Newcomen Soc.* (London) **18**, 43, 1951; see also J. Mactear, *Proc. Glasgow Phil. Soc.* **13**, 409, 1881; O. Guttman, *J. Soc. Chem. Ind.* (London) **20**, 5, 1901; Saml. Parks, *Chemical Essays*, 4 vols. (London, 1814) III, 398; Archibald and Nan Clow, *The Chemical Revolution* (London, 1952) chap. 6.

13 C. C. Concannon and F. M. Hofheims, *Chem. Eng. News* **26**, 1074, 1948; Appendix XXI.

14 Dickinson, *op. cit.*

15 J. Leander Bishop, *History of American Manufactures*, 3 vols. (Phila. 1868) II, 567; Edwin T. Freedley, *Philadelphia and Its Manufacturers* (Phila., 1858) 206; Williams Haynes, *American Chemical Industry*, 6 vols. (N. Y., 1941) I, 177; hereinafter cited as Haynes, *History*.

16 More detailed account in Haynes, *Stone*, chaps. 4 and 5; Delabretoigne, *op. cit.;* Vannutelli, *op. cit.;* Ludovico Bianchini, *Storia economica della Sicilia* (Naples, 1841); Jules Brunfaut, *L'exploitation des soufres* (Paris, 1874); Riccardo Travaglia, *Por l'industria solfifera Siciliana* (Palermo, 1895). For description and geology of Sicilian deposits: Lunge, *op. cit.*, I, 17; A. d'Achiardi, *Mineralogia della Toscana*, 2 vols. (Pisa, 1872) I, 18; W. C. Phalen, *Mineral Industries 1910*, II, 785; Walter F. Hunt, *Origin of Sulphur Deposits in Sicily* (Lancaster,

Pa., 1918); *Chemiker Zeitung* 6, 1389, 1405, 1421, 1882; *J. Soc. Chem. Ind.* 9, 118, 1890.

[17] Muspratt, *op. cit.*, II, 1010.

[18] Good discussion in Theo. J. Kreps, *Economics of the Sulfuric Acid Industry* (Stanford, Calif., 1938) 78; Andrew M. Fairlie, *Sulfuric Acid Manufacture* (N. Y., 1936) 564.

[19] For appearance of powdery mildew and early control methods see *Gardener's Chronicle* (London) for years 1846-49; P. Rozouls, *Rev. Agr. Fance* 66, 199, 1954.

[20] Historical literature of rubber is enormous, for vulcanization see: Chas. Goodyear, *Gum-Elastic and Its Varieties* (New Haven, 1853); Howard and Ralph Wolf, *Rubber* (N. Y., 1936) bk. 4, chaps. 1 and 2; Williams Haynes and Ernst A. Hauser, *Rationed Rubber* (N. Y., 1942) chap. 6; Chas. M. Wilson, *Trees and Test Tubes* (N. Y., 1943) chap. 3.

[21] Haynes, *History, op. cit.*, I, 254.

[22] *Ibid.* I, chaps. 11 and 16.

[23] Kreps, *op. cit.*, 22.

[24] *Ibid.* 105; Haynes, *Stone, op. cit.*, 87.

[25] Lunge, *op. cit.*, I, 1264; Wm. M. Grovesnor in *Roger's Manual of Industrial Chemistry* 4th ed. (N. Y., 1925) I, 175.

Chapter 3: SULPHUR IN A SWAMP

[1] John Henning, interview, Lake Charles, La., June 13, 1940.

[2] U. S. Geol. Survey, *Ann. Rept., 1883,* III, 509.

[3] E. W. Hilgard, *Eng. & Mining J.*, Sept. 28, 1869, 196.

[4] *Louisiana Ann. Rept.*, XXII, 280.

[5] A. Granet, *Engineer's Rept. Property of Calcasieu Sulphur & Mining Co.*, New Orleans, May 27, 1871, 12.

[6] *Union vs Freeport*, Plaintiff's Brief, Feb. 7, 1918, I, pp. 24.

[7] Granet, *op. cit.*, 36, 44.

[8] U. S. Bur. Mines, *Mineral Resources, 1883-84,* 864.

[9] H. Frasch, *Chem. Met. Eng.* Feb. 1912, 77.

[10] Records of these various companies are incomplete, but for further details of them and their activities, see Haynes, *Stone,* 10-13.

[11] For American Sulphur Co. best firsthand sources are R. P. Rothwell, *Rept. of Progress* to Alex. H. Tiers, treas., Am. Sulphur Co., N. Y., Oct. 13, 1890, printed as Plaintiff's Exhibit No. 45; *Union vs Freeport, op. cit.*, III, 291; E. J. Schmitz, *Rept. to A. H. Tiers,* Plaintiff's Exhibit No. 46, *ibid.*, III, 297; testimony of Dr. Raymond and Jacques Toniette, *ibid.*, I, 463, 358.

[12] Schmitz, *op. cit.*

[13] *Ibid.*, 351.

[14] Frasch, *op. cit.*

[15] U. S. Pats. 461, 429, 431.

[16] Allen Nevins, *Study in Power*, 2 vols. (N. Y., 1953) II, 30, 98.
[17] *Union vs Freeport, op. cit.*, I, 456, 477.
[18] *Ibid.*, testimony of Cornelius Tiers, I, 475.

Chapter 4: FRASCH AND HIS PROCESS

[1] Allan Nevins has pointed out that "a biography of Frasch yet remains much needed." C. F. Chandler's Perkin Medal presentation address, *J. Ind. & Eng. Chem.*, Feb. 1912, 132, and *Dict. Am. Biography* VI, 602, are best published sources. See also Haynes, *Stone*, 17; *Union vs Freeport, passim;* obits. *World's Work*, July 1914, and *N. Y. Times*, May 2, 1914.
[2] Nevins, *op. cit.*, II, 98, 101.
[3] H. Frasch, *Chem. & Met. Eng.*, 10, 78, 1912.
[4] Firsthand accounts of these early events are in the testimony of Toniette and Hoffman, *Union vs Freeport* I, 358, 487, respectively. I am indebted to John Henning, interview, Lake Charles, La., June 13, 1940. See also for account of Union Sulphur Co. mine D. A. Welley, *Eng. & Mining J.* 84, 1107, 1908, and S. H. Lebowitz, *J. Chem. Educat.* 8, 1630, 1931; C. E. Weaver, *ibid.*, 10, 304, 1933; for Frasch process W. W. Duecker, *Chem. & Met. Eng.* (flow sheet) Mar. 1941, 104.
[5] Frasch, *op. cit.*

Chapter 5: DOUBLE TROUBLE

[1] John Henning, interview, Lake Charles, La., June 13, 1940.
[2] *Union vs Freeport, op. cit.*, I, 202.
[3] Geo. M. Wells, interview, New York, Aug. 20, 1941.
[4] *Handbook of Chemistry, op. cit.*
[5] *Union vs Freeport*, II, 1003, 1185, 1223.
[6] *Ibid.*, I, 505.
[7] For physical properties of sulphur see Appendix I; also *Kingslett, op. cit.*, 913.
[8] L. C. Nettleton, *Bull. Am. Assoc. Petr. Geol.* 18, 1175, 1934.
[9] *Union vs Freeport*, testimony of F. H. Browning, I, 565.
[10] *Ibid.*, Plaintiff's Exhibit No. 54, III, 378.
[11] *Ibid.*, I, 508.
[12] *Ibid.*, testimony of C. A. Snider, I, 339.
[13] *Ibid.*, I, 512, 544.
[14] U. S. Gcol. Survey, *Ann. Rept., 1898-99*, 641; *Mineral Industry, 1896*, 514; *1898*, 643.
[15] *Union vs Freeport*, testimony of A. F. Lucas, I, 543.
[16] *Ibid.*, Plaintiff's Exhibit No. 25, III, 271.
[17] G. M. Wells, *op. cit.*
[18] *Union vs Freeport*, testimony of J. Toniette, I, 373.
[19] Haynes, *History* I, 171, 242.

[20] McBeth, *op. cit.; Trans. Am. Inst. Mining & Met. Engrs., 1921,* 421; *Mining & Scien. Press,* Sept. 17, 1921, 414; J. B. Eby and M. T. Halbouty, *Bull. Am. Assoc. Petrol. Geol.* **21,** 475, 1937.

[21] *Union vs Freeport,* testimony of Lucas, I, 536.

[22] Henning, *op. cit.*

[23] *Union vs Freeport,* testimony of Snider, I, 336, 354.

Chapter 6: COMPETITION ABROAD

[1] For detailed accounts of the Sicilian sulphur crisis of the early 1890's, see Riccardo Travaglia, *Per l'industria solfifera Siciliana* (Palermo, 1895); Prof. Bresciani-Turroni, *Annali del Seminario Guiridico della R. Universita de Palermo,* III, 1896; also Delabretoigne, *op. cit.,* Vannutelli, *op. cit., Union vs Freeport,* testimony of C. A. Snider, I, 336, 354.

[2] For this classical case of chemical interprocess competition see Maill, *op. cit.,* 19; Morgan and Pratt, *op. cit.,* 15; Haynes, *History* I, 76; D. A. Pritchard, *Chem. Met. Eng.* **33,** 330, 1926; **34,** 262, 1927; C. G. Fink, *Ind. Eng. Chem., News Ed.* **19,** 194, 1941.

[3] Detailed data on production and sales are in the statistics of the Italian Mining Dept., quoted by Vannutelli in *L'industria mineraria, op. cit.;* figures on stocks in hand are from Anglo-Sicilian *Ann. Repts.*

[4] H. Frasch, *Chem. & Met. Eng.* **10,** 79, 1912.

[5] Delabretoigne, *op. cit.,* 357.

[6] L. Baldacci, *Il giacimento de solfa della Louisiana* (Rome, 1906).

[7] *La valorization du Cafe an Bresil* (Rio de Janeiro, 1910) quoted by Delabretoigne, *op. cit.,* 359.

[8] The German potash monopoly has striking similarities to the Sicilian sulphur industry: see Geo. W. Stocking, *Potash Industry* (N. Y., 1931), especially chaps. 2, 3, and 4.

[9] The best account of the Consortium's activities is in Vannutelli, *op. cit.,* chaps. 5, 6, and 7.

[10] *Italian Parliamentary Record XXII. Legislature, 1st session, 1904-06,* portions of which are translated and filed as Plaintiff's Exhibits Nos. 57, 58, and 61, *Union vs Freeport, op. cit.,* II, 406, 407, 413.

[11] P. Di Fratta, Enrico Barone, L. Baldacci, and Ettore Candiani, *Sulla limitazione della produzione solfifera,* Rept. to Ministry of Agriculture, Industry, & Commerce (Rome, 1909).

[12] *Union vs Freeport,* testimony of W. R. Keever, I, 410, 430.

[13] John Henning, interview, Lake Charles, La., June 13, 1940.

[14] C. F. Chandler, *Chem. & Met. Eng.* **10,** 74, 1912; Clarence A. Snider, interview, New York, June 2, 1940.

[15] Henning, *op. cit.*

[16] Delabretoigne, *op. cit.,* 380.

[17] Henning, *op. cit.*

[18] Robt. H. Ridgeway, *Sulphur, U. S. Bur. Mines Infor. Cir. No. 6329* (Washington, 1916; reprinted 1934) 22, 40.

[19] F. H. Pough, interview, St. Louis, Mo., June 20, 1940.

Chapter 7: COMPETITION AT HOME

[1] Brazoria County Abstract Co., *Abstract of Bryanmound*, certified Sept. 16, 1920. All following references to options, leases, and sales at Bryanmound, unless otherwise noted, are from this *Abstract* which is in the Freeport Sulphur Co. Bryanmound Depletion File.

[2] Wm. Kennedy, *The Bryan Heights Salt Dome* in Moore, ed., *Geology of the Salt Dome Oil Fields* (Houston, 1926) 678.

[3] E. H. Thaete, *Rept. to Freeport Sulphur Co.*, based on interviews with old residents of Brazoria County, Mar. 1, 1939, in Company files.

[4] Geo. Hamman, interview, Houston, Tex., June 13, 1940.

[5] F. Zambonini, *Cenni sulla cupole solfifera della coastal plain* (Torino, 1914) 13.

[6] Brazoria County Abst. Co., *op. cit.*

[7] For vivid picture of early life in the Brazos Valley see Laura Lettie Krey's novel, *And Tell of Time* (Boston, 1938).

[8] Kennedy, *op. cit.*, 679.

[9] Robt. C. Marony, memo to author, Feb. 11, 1932. Marony was Pemberton's confidential clerk, Oct. 1892 to May 1916, when the investment firm of Pemberton & McAdoo was dissolved. This firm handled the financing of the Detroit Street Railways, the Philadelphia Co., and the Hudson Tunnel. See also Wm. G. McAdoo, *Crowded Years* (Boston, 1931) chaps. 5 and 6.

[10] Hamman, *op. cit.*

[11] S. C. Browne, interview, New York, June 4, 1940.

[12] Bernard M. Baruch, *My Own Story* (N. Y., 1957) 234, see also Margaret L. Coit, *Mr. Baruch* (N. Y., 1957) 124.

[13] Browne, *op. cit.*

[14] Baruch, *op. cit.*, 235.

[15] Hamman, *op. cit.*; Browne, *op. cit.*

[16] Browne, *op. cit.*

[17] Lewis Mims, interview, Houston, Tex., June 10, 1940.

[18] Hamman and Mims, *op. cit.*

[19] The voluminous records of this case, *Union vs Freeport*, U. S. Dist. Court, Delaware, In Equity No. 336; U. S. Circuit Court of Appeals, 3rd Circuit, Nos. 2391 and 2392, Oct. Term 1918, are a veritable mine of all sorts of information, historical, technical, financial, and legal on the Frasch process and the industry based upon it. See also *J. Ind. & Eng. Chem.* 11, 374, 1919.

[20] This contract is printed as Plaintiff's Exhibit A1, *American Sulphur Royalty Co. vs Freeport Sulphur Co.*, Dist. Court Brazoria County, Texas, No. 16005, Feb. term, 1924.

[21] *Record of Deeds,* Brazoria County, Texas, **113,** 70; **116,** 65, 67, 69; **117,** 240, 242; **118,** 225; **119,** 218, 227, 617.

[22] For details and personalities of the early days at Bryanmound, I am indebted to interviews with Browne, Hamman, and Simms, *op. cit.;* P. George Maercky, Houston, Tex., June 12, 1940; Homer S. Burns, New Orleans, June 17, 1940; Roy Johns, New York, July 15 1940.

[23] Benj. Andrews, *Rept. on Examination and Investigation of Sulphur Deposits at Bryan Heights, Texas, as Conducted by the Brazoria Syndicate, Aug. 1910 to Apr. 1911,* printed as Plaintiff's Exhibit A-28, *Am. Sulphur Royalty vs Freeport, op. cit.*

Chapter 8: FROM PYRITES TO BRIMSTONE

[1] John M. Corbett, memo to author, Bay City, Tex., Dec. 9, 1941; A. G. Wolf, *Big Hill Salt Dome, Matagorda Co., Texas,* in Moore, ed. *Geology of Salt Dome Oil Fields, op. cit.;* C. A. Warner, *Texas Oil and Gas Since 1543, op cit.,* 193.

[2] My chief sources on the early development of the Matagorda Big Hill Dome have been MS histories by Albert G. Wolf and H. E. Treichler, Apr. 15, 1921, and Jas. W. Schwab, Jan. 27, 1941, in files of Texas Gulf Sulphur Co; Wolf, *op. cit.;* personal interviews with H. E. Treichler, Newgulf, Tex., June 11, 1940; Walter H. Aldridge and Henry F. J. Knobloch, New York, July 15, 1940; Spencer C. Browne, New York, July 10, 1940.

[3] Gulf Sulphur Co. *Minutes, Incorporators Meeting,* Dec. 23, 1909.

[4] *Eng. & Mining J.,* June 19, 1926, 1026.

[5] *Matagorda Co. Records,* XXI, 15.

[6] *Ibid.,* XXIV, 274; XXV, 68, 414, 497.

[7] A. R. Brunker, *Final Rept. Acid & Heavy Chems. Sect., Chem. Div., War Ind. Bd.* (Washington, 1919).

[8] Theodore E. Kreps, *Economics of the Sulfuric Acid Industry, op. cit.,* 105.

[9] Haynes, *Stone,* Appendix XVIII.

[10] A. E. Wells and D. E. Fogg, *U. S. Bur. Mines, Bull. 184* (Washington, 1920) 7.

[11] Figures from annual statistics, *Mineral Resources.*

[12] Charles H. MacDowell, memo to author, Washington, June 23, 1940.

[13] A. E. Wells, *Rept. to War Ind. Bd., Supply of Raw Materials for Manufacturers of Sulfuric Acid,* Mar. 14, 1918.

[14] *Ibid.*

[15] R. H. Ridgeway, *Bur. Mines Inform. Circ. No. 6329,* 1930, 22; *Eng. & Mining J.* **95,** 96, 1913.

[16] *Mineral Industries, 1912,* 786.

[17] Obits: *N. Y. Times,* May 2, 1914; *J. Ind. Eng. Chem.* **6,** 506, 1914; *O.P.D. Reptr.,* May 11, 1914, 11.

[18] J. Park Channing, *Confidential Sulphur Rept. to Bur. Mines,* New

Orleans, La., Nov. 4, 1917, transmitted to War Ind. Bd., Dec. 17, 1917.
[19] Freeport Sulphur Co., *Minutes, Directors Meeting*, Apr. 24, 1917.
[20] *Ibid.*, June 26, 1917.
[21] *Ibid.*, Aug. 28, 1917.
[22] H. S. Burns, interview, New Orleans, La., June 17, 1940.
[23] Lewis Mims, interview, Houston, Tex., June 10, 1940.
[24] *Tax Appraisal Hearing, Estate of Herman Frasch,* Surrogate Court, N. Y. County, testimony of Henry D. Whitton, June 1915, certified copy, 72.
[25] Wells, *op. cit.*
[26] W. G. Woolfolk, *Final Rept. Div. Chiefs to War Ind. Bd.*, Washington, Dec. 18, 1918; Horace Bowker, *The Chemical Alliance* (N. Y., privately printed, 1919).
[27] Wells and Fogg, *op. cit.*, 32. For western deposits: W. T. Lee, *U. S. Geol. Surv. Bull. No. 315, 1906,* 485; E. G. Woodruff, *ibid., Bull. No. 340, 1907,* 451; R. W. Richards and J. H. Bridges, *ibid., Bull. No. 470, 1910,* 499; F. L. Hess, *ibid., Bull. No. 530, 1911,* 347; E. S. Larson and J. F. Hunter, *ibid.,* 363; D. F. Hewett, *ibid., Bull. No. 540, 1912,* 477; E. L. Porch, Jr., *Univ. Texas Bull. No. 22, 1917,* 57.
[28] W. H. Aldridge letter to Capt. W. H. Gelshenen, Feb. 16, 1918, and interview, New York, July 15, 1940.

Chapter 9: THE THIRD COMPETITOR

[1] C. H. MacDowell, memo to author, *op. cit.;* W. H. Aldridge, interview, July 15, 1940, New York. In an article reviewing the sulphur situation during the war MacDowell wrote "Early in 1918 permission was granted the Texas Gulf Sulphur Co. to develop at their expense a sulphur . . ." (*Chem. Met. Eng.* 33, 321, 1926). In quoting this sentence Kreps inserted in brackets "(government) expense," thus changing the entire meaning (*Economics of the Sulfuric Acid Industry, op. cit.,* 95). The company's willingness and ability to develop Big Hill without financial aid from the Government was a major reason prompting MacDowell to extraordinary efforts to secure the necessary priorities.
[2] Wolf, *op. cit.*, 706.
[3] Treichler, *op. cit.*
[4] Haynes, *History, op. cit.*, III, Appendix VIII, 437.
[5] Haynes, *Chemical Economics* (N. Y., 1933) 115.
[6] F. H. Pough, interview, St. Louis, Mo., June 20, 1940.
[7] John Henning, interview, Lake Charles, La., June 13, 1940.
[8] Compiled by Edward H. Hempel.
[9] Delabretoigne, *op. cit.*
[10] Vannutelli, *op. cit.*
[11] Delabretoigne, *op. cit.*
[12] *Ibid.;* interviews, New York, C. A. Snider, June 2, 1940; Wilber Judson, June 5, 1940.
[13] *Mineral Industries, 1923,* 632; Haynes, *History, op. cit.,* IV, 78;

Victor S. Clark, *History of Manufactures in the U. S.,* 3 vols. (N. Y., 1929) III, 326.

[14] Snider, *op. cit.*

[15] *Fertilizer Rev.* 13, 18, 1938.

[16] W. H. Waggaman and H. W. Easterwood, *Phosphoric Acid, Phosphates, and Phosphoric Fertilizers* (N. Y., 1927) 122.

[17] Am. Petrol. Inst., *Petroleum Facts & Figures,* 5th ed. (N. Y., 1937) 122.

[18] Emil R. Reigel, *Industrial Chemistry,* 2nd ed. (N. Y., 1933) 368.

[19] Allen Abrams, Marathon Paper Co., memo to author, Apr. 16, 1941.

[20] Bjorne Johnson in *Manufacture of Pulp and Paper* 2nd. ed. (N. Y., 1927); Louis Tellotson Stevenson, *Background and Economics of American Papermaking* (N. Y., 1940) 24; John A. Guthrie, *Economics of Pulp and Paper* (Pullman, Wash., 1950) 3, 28.

[21] Increase in U. S. production of various sulphur chemicals 1919-29, in 1000's units: barium sulphate, 13,636 to 26,050 lbs.; carbon bisulphide, 15,470 to 71,010 lbs.; copper sulphide, 35,288 to 78,669 lbs.; iron sulphate, 29 to 56 tons; magnesium sulphate, 29 to 36 tons; sulphur chloride, no data to 17,827 lbs.; sulphur dioxide, 856 to 17,601 lbs.; zinc sulphate, 7,326 to 24,904 lbs.—From *U. S. Census Mfrs., 1919 and 1929.*

Chapter 10: ADDITIONAL DOMES

[1] Geo. M. Bevier, in Moore ed. *Geology of the Salt Dome Oil Fields, op. cit.,* 613; Warner, *Texas Oil and Gas Since 1543,* op. cit., 46, 117.

[2] Bevier, *op. cit.,* 640.

[3] Geo. Santella, *Bull. Am. Assoc. Petr. Geol.* 20, 726, 1936; R. E. Taylor, *La. Geol. Survey, Geol. Bull. No. 11,* 1938.

[4] C. L. Thompson, *Oil* 1, 42, 1941.

[5] A. H. Marx, *Bull. Am. Assoc. Petr. Geol.* 20, 156, 1936; U. S. Bd. of Tax Appeals, *Texas Pipe Line Co. vs Commr. Internal Revenue,* testimony of H. H. Ford, Apr. 11-12, 1933, Houston, Tex.

[6] Jas. L. Darnell, *Valuation Rept., Hoskins Mound Sulphur Deposit,* in the Hoskins Mound Depletion File, 1926-29, Freeport Sulphur Co.

[7] *Brief of Texas Co. and Freeport Sulphur Co.* on Application for Depletion Allowance, Nov. 19, 1929, 4.

[8] For early history of Hoskins Mound I have again drawn on personal interviews with Spencer C. Browne, W. T. Lundy, P. George Maercky, Homer S. Burns, and Lewis Mims, all of whom were active in the development of this property and upon the *MS History Freeport Sulphur Co.* by J. C. Carrington in company library. Recognized authorative source on the geology of the dome is Marx, *op. cit.,* see also *Mfrs. Record,* June 7, 1926, 19.

[9] Darnell, *Valuation Report, op. cit.*

[10] Roy Johns, interview, New York, July 15, 1940.

11 *Ibid.*

12 Homer S. Burns, interview, New Orleans, June 17, 1940.

13 Freeport Sulphur Co., *Ann. Rept., 1923,* 4.

14 W. T. Lundy, *Rept. on Estimated Ore Reserves at Hoskins Mound,* Jan. 18, 1927, 10.

15 Marx, *op. cit.,* 159; Carrington, *MS History, op. cit.;* R. T. Kenworthy, *Oil 1,* 14, 1941.

16 Kenworthy, *op. cit.*

17 Lundy, *op. cit.,* 23.

18 *Ibid.,* 25.

19 Freeport Sulphur Co., *Ann. Rept., 1928,* 1.

20 Warner, *Texas Oil and Gas, op. cit.,* 204, 208, 219; Jas. W. Schwab, *MS History Texas Gulf Sulphur Co.: Mining Operations,* Jan. 27, 1941, in company files; for early history of Boling I have again relied largely on personal interviews with the pioneers at this plant: H. E. Treichler and H. A. Swem, Newgulf, Texas, June 11, 1940; Wilber Judson, New York, Nov. 10, 1941.

21 H. A. Swem, *op. cit.*

22 Texas Gulf Sulphur Co., *Application to List Additional Shares,* N. Y. Stk Exch., A-10246, Sept. 4, 1934.

Chapter *11:* TWO NEW COMPANIES

1 H. E. Treichler, interview, Newgulf, Tex., June 11, 1940.

2 Jas. W. Schwab, *MS History, op. cit.,* 14.

3 Donald C. Barton in Moore, ed., *op. cit.,* 718.

4 For early development of Palangana, personal interviews: V. J. Thornhill, Houston, June 10, 1940; Geo. F. Zoffman, New York, Dec. 4, 1940; Wilber Judson, New York, Nov. 10, 1941; see D. C. Barton, *Econ. Geol. 6,* 497, 1920.

5 A. T. Drachenberg, quoted by W. Haynes, *Chem. Ind. 34,* 499, 1934.

6 Roy Johns, interview, New York, June 15, 1940.

7 *Ibid.*

8 Drachenberg, *op. cit.*

9 Warner, *Texas Oil and Gas, op. cit.,* 205, 218.

10 X. T. Stoddard, interview, Orchard, Tex., April 13, 1957.

11 Geo. F. Zoffman, interview, New Orleans, La., Dec. 10, 1956.

12 Duval Sulphur & Potash Co., *SEC Prospectus,* Mar. 15, 1957.

13 United Oil & Gas Synd. Circular, New Orleans, 1926.

14 A. S. Park, *Compressed Air Mag. 39,* 4526, 1923; Haynes, *op. cit.,* 499.

15 A. A. Mayer, interview, New Orleans, La., June 14, 1940.

16 Drachenberg, *op. cit.,* 499.

17 L. O'Donnell and J. M. Todd, *Southern Power J.,* Dec. 1932, 10; Park, *op. cit.* 4528.

18 Jefferson Lake Oil Co., *Ann. Rept., 1938,* 9.

[19] P. Geo. Maercky, interview, Newgulf, Tex., June 11, 1940.

[20] Interviews: Chas. J. Ferry, New Orleans, La., Nov. 29, 1956; Harvey A. Wilson Brazoria, Tex., Dec. 5, 1956.

[21] *Abstract No. 92.* John McNeal League, Brazoria County, Tex.

[22] Ferry, *op. cit.*

[23] Co. memo to author, Dec. 1, 1956.

[24] *Ibid.:* data for Dec. 31, 1957.

[25] Jefferson Lake Oil Co., *Ann. Rept., 1939,* 7.

[26] *Ibid.,* 8.

[27] C. A. Snider, interview, New York, June 2, 1940.

Chapter 12: WEB-FOOT MINING

[1] Earl Dissinger, *Rept. to Freeport Sulphur Co.,* Oct. 2, 1928.

[2] C. A. Jones, letter to Lewis Mims, Freeport, Tex., Nov. 1, 1927.

[3] F. H. McConnell, *Barron's,* May 6, 1940, 9.

[4] Firsthand sources on development of Grande Ecaille are Monroe B. Lanier and W. T. Lundy, *Rept. to L. M. Williams, Jr., ex. vice-pres. Freeport Sulphur Co.,* Nov. 12, 1932; W. T. Lundy, *Trans. Am. Inst. Min. & Met. Engrs.* 109, 354, 1934; J. C. Carrington, *MS Hist. Freeport Sulphur Co., Pt. 3, Grande Ecaille,* in Co. files, supplemented by personal interviews: W. T. Lundy and H. S. Burns, New Orleans, June 17, 1940.

[5] Lanier and Lundy, *op. cit.*

[6] Lundy, *Trans., op. cit.,* pp. 357-59.

[7] Quoted by W. Haynes, *Chem. Ind.* 34, 496, 1934.

[8] H. S. Burns, *Chem. Ind.* 34, 503, 1934.

[9] *Ibid.*

[10] *Chem. & Met. Eng.* 46, 762, 1939.

[11] Lundy, interview, *op. cit.*

[12] Freeport Sulphur Co., *Ann. Rept., 1935.*

[13] Lundy, interview, *op. cit.*

[14] R. F. Bacon and R. Fanelli, *Ind. Eng. Chem.* 34, 1043, 1942; J. A. Lee, *Chem. Eng.,* Ap. 1948, 119.

[15] *Union Sulphur Co. vs H. A. Reid, Sheriff, Calcasieu Parish, et al.,* U. S. Dist. Court, West Dist. La., No. 45 in Equity, May-June 1920.

[16] Lundy, letter to Lanier, Mar. 19, 1932.

[17] J. T. Claiborne, Jr., letter to Gov. Saml. Houston Jones, May 31, 1940.

[18] *Chem. Ind.* 42, 386, 1938.

[19] Best account of this legislation is in *Eng. & Min. J.,* Sept. 1956.

Chapter 13: WAR AND POSTWAR

[1] For year-by-year figures see Appendix IX.

[2] J. C. Carrington, memo to author, Aug. 30, 1950; interviews: Mar-

shall B. Sheldon, New Orleans, La., Nov. 26, 1956; Paul D. Bybee, Port Sulphur, La., Nov. 28, 1956.

[3] W. T. Lundy, *Ind. Eng. Chem.* **42,** 2199, 1950; W. A. Jordan, *Chem. Wk.,* June 3, 1951, 2; J. C. Carrington, *Mining Cong. J.* **37,** 53, 1951.

[4] E. J. Reigel, *Quart. J. Econ.,* Feb. 1939, 4.

[5] J. E. Teeple, *Chem. Mkts.* **21,** 37, 1927; D. P. Morgan, *Ind. Eng. Chem.* **30,** 943, 1938; E. P. Stevenson, *Chem. Eng. News* **31,** 2954, 1953; Williams Haynes, *This Chemical Age* (N. Y., 1942); L. F. Haber, *Chemical Industry during 19th Century* (Oxford, 1958).

[6] Figures from Fed. Res. Bd., *Index of Industrial Production, 1950.*

[7] For detailed figures see Appendix XIX.

[8] W. W. Duecker, *Chem. & Met. Eng.,* Mar. 1941, 74.

[9] Year-by-year figures in Appendix XI.

[10] W. W. Duecker and E. W. Eddy, *Mining Cong. J.* **36,** 47, 1950; *Chem. Ind.* **67,** 718, 1950; *Chem. Eng. News* **29,** 2126, 1951; *Chem. Eng.* **59,** 165, 1952; popular review *Fortune,* July 1951, 87.

[11] A. M. Fairlie, *Chem. Eng.* July 1948, 109; E. M. Jones, *Ind. Eng. Chem.* **42,** 2208, 1950.

[12] Haynes, *History,* I, chap. 16; III, chap. 3.

[13] *Fertilizer Rev.* Jan-Feb. 1940, 6; D. B. Ibach, *J. Plant Food Council,* Jan. 1955, 17.

[14] *Chem. Wk.,* Dec. 20, 1952, 55; V. Sauchelli, *Soil Sci.* **70,** 1, 1950; K. D. Jacob, *Fertilizer Technology and Resources in U. S.* (N. Y., 1953).

[15] E. M. Crowther, *Chem. & Ind.* (London) Nov. 13, 1954, 1400.

[16] M. F. Crass, Jr., *Ind. Eng. Chem.* **44,** 1193, 1952.

[17] Detailed figures, Appendix XX.

[18] *Textile Organon* **23,** 120, 1952.

[19] Williams Haynes, *Cellulose: the Chemical that Grows* (N. Y., 1953) 338.

[20] Year-by-year figures in Appendix XX.

[21] *Chem. Ind.* **67,** 718, 1950.

[22] The sulphur shortage was front-page news during 1951-53; among the most valuable articles and reviews are *Chem. Eng. News* **29,** 2126, 3094, 1951; **30,** 3094, 1952; **31,** 1968, 1953; *Chem. Wk.* Apr. 29, 1951, 9; June 30, 1951, 33; Sept. 27, 1952, 77; *Chem. Eng.* Jan 1952, 165; *Business Wk.* Oct. 25, 1952, 186.

[23] For shortage in Great Britain and its effects see W. A. Parks, *Chem. Age* (London) **63,** 577, 1950; *64,* 679, 1951; *Economist* (London) Nov. 25, 1950, 159; May 26, 1951, 1250; *Chem. Eng. News* **29,** 212, 302, 1951; *Chem. & Ind.* (London) June 7, 1952, 511.

[24] *Chem. Eng. News* **29,** 3021, 1951.

[25] Good summaries of new sources of sulphur: *Chem. Wk.,* June 30, 1951; *Chem. Eng. News 30,* 3095, 1952.

[26] Co. memo to author, Dec. 15, 1957; interviews: Chas. J. Ferry, New Orleans, La., Nov. 29, 1956; Harvey A. Wilson, Brazoria, Tex., Dec. 5, 1956.

[27] Interviews with Sheldon, *op. cit.;* De Witt Morris, Wm. S. Donner, Douglas King, and Richard Wormat, Garden Island Bay, La., Nov. 27-28, 1956; also *Chem. Eng. News* **28**, 3618, 1951; **30**, 4468, 1952; I. E. Hanson and W. S. Nelson, *Offshore Operations,* Feb. 1955, 15; *New Orleans Chamb. Com. Bull.,* July 1955, 6.

[28] Interviews with A. B. Axelrad and Sam Muery, Bay Ste. Elaine, La., Nov. 26, 1956; K. T. Price, New Orleans, La., Nov. 27, 1956; also *Chem. Wk.* Aug. 23, 1952, 34; Oct. 18, 1952, 68.

[29] Freeport Sulphur Co., *Ann. Rept. 1954, 1955; Times-Picayune* (New Orleans) May 26, 1955.

[30] E. J. McNamara, interview, Chacahoula, La., Nov. 28, 1956; *Wall St. J.* (N. Y.) Jan. 26, 1955; *Chem. Eng. News* **33**, 1416, 1955.

Chapter 14: BIRTH OF THE MEXICAN INDUSTRY

[1] *Mexican Herald* (Mexico, D. F.) *1904,* No. 178, 2.

[2] *Eng. & Mining J.* **77**, 1777, 1904.

[3] Paul Weaver, interviews, Houston, Tex., July 12, Dec. 8, 1956.

[4] For early oil explorations in the Isthmus: Weaver, *op. cit.;* interviews: J. H. Pollard, Houston, Tex., July 14, Dec. 10, 1956; G. P. Salas, Mexico, D. F., Mar. 15, 1957.

[5] In addition to refs. 6, 7, and 8, see also *Ministera Fomento Mex., Annales 1897,* III 273; *Inst. Geol. Mex. Par.* I, 95, 1904; F. W. Moon, *Trans. Inst. Mining & Met.* (London) **20**, 250, 1910; P. Baud, *Rev. Scient.* (Paris) **2**, 260, 1912; M. H. Aymé, *Bull. Soc. Geol. Com. de Paris 1916,* 410; R. Arnold, *Proc. 2nd Pan-Am. Sci. Cong.* III, 222, 1917; C. S. Casillas, *Bol. Petrol.* **2**, 423, 1916; **3**, 125, 1917; **7**, 268, 1919; L. J. Lajous, *ibid.* **13**, 150, 1922; S. E. Sotelo, *ibid.* **25**, 322, 1928; G. S. Rogers, *Econ. Geol.* **13**, 464, 1918; E. de Golyer, *Trans. Am. Inst. Mining & Met. Engrs.* **61**, 456, 1919; Ordóñez, *Bol. Soc. Geol. Mex. No. 5,* 32, 1936; B. J. Gibson, *ibid.,* 9; J. Santaella, *Excelsior* (Mexico, D. F.) Jan. 4, 1937, 5; G. P. Salas, *Bol. Assoc. Mex. Geol. Petro.* **7**, 81, 1955.

[6] J. D. Villarello, *Par. Inst. Geol. Mex.* I, 94, 1904; *Bol. Inst. Geol. Mex. No. 26,* 1908.

[7] W. A. Ver Wiebe, *Panam. Geologist* **44**, 121, 1925; **45**, 358, 1926.

[8] B. Hartley, *Econ. Geol.* **12**, 581, 1917; A. H. Redfield, *Eng. & Mining J.* **111**, 510, 1921; S. Huntley, *Trans. Am. Inst. Mining & Met. Engrs.* **69**, 1150, 1923.

[9] F. Deschamps, *Rev. Mex. Ingen. y Arquit.* **15**, 665, 777, 1936.

[10] *Cf.* Villarello, Ver Wiebe, Huntley, *op. cit.*

[11] A. Breceda, interviews, Mexico, D. F., July 20, 1956; Feb. 15, 1957.

[12] Antonio Acevedo Escobedo, *Azufre en Mexico* (Mexico, 1950) 15. The concessions on (1) San Cristobal and amplifications, (2) Jáltipan and Portrerillos and their amplifications, (3) Teterete and amplifications, (4) Mesquital and Almagres were all made by the Secretaria de Economica, prior to setting up the Fomento.

[13] *Ibid.,* 16; decree published in *Diario Oficial,* July 12, 1943.

[14] Interviews with David Segura of the Fomento, Mexico, D. F., July 14, 1956, Apr. 6, 1957; José Campillo, secty., Mex. Mining Chamb., Mexico, D. F., Apr. 26, 1957.

[15] Rafael Martinez de Escobar, interview, Mexico, D. F., Apr. 27, 1956; M. G. Vidal, letter to Texas International Sulphur Co., Sept. 24, 1953.

[16] For the Brady explorations, interviews in Mexico City with L. B. Brady, July 16, Dec. 18, 20, 1956; A. G. Brady, July 17, Dec. 18, 1956; Apr. 9, 1957; W. C. Brady, July 16, 19, 1956; Eugene Rossi and W. H. Maddox, Salinas, Ver., Apr. 14-15, 1956, Mexico, D. F., Dec. 18, 1957.

[17] Chris Armstrong, interview, Jáltipan, Ver., Apr. 17, 1956, Jan. 17, 1957; C. L. Basland, Mexico, D. F., Apr. 23, 1956.

[18] A. G. Brady, op. cit.

Chapter 15: THREE WINS: ONE LOSS

[1] David Segura, interviews, Mexico, D. F., July 14, 1956; Apr. 6, 1957.

[2] A. Breceda, ibid., July 20, 1956; Feb. 15, 1957.

[3] For beginning of the Mexican industry: Chem. Eng. 45, 165, 1952; 46, 128, 1953; Chem. Wk. Jan. 3, 1953, 12; Jan. 25, 1954, 16; Wall St. J., Aug. 9, 1954, 1; Economist (London) Feb. 5, 1955, 168; J. H. Kearney, Eng. Mining J., 156, 37, 1955.

[4] Interviews: Chas. J. Ferry, New Orleans, La., Nov. 29, 1956; Harvey A. Wilson, Brazoria, Tex., Dec. 5, 1956.

[5] Geo. F. Zoffman, interview, New Orleans, La., Dec. 3, 1956.

[6] Interviews: Ralph Taylor and Robt. Johnson, Houston, Tex., Dec. 10 and 6, 1956; R. B. Roberson and J. H. Kearney, Mexico, D. F., July 21 and 28, 1956; J. T. Claiborne, Jr., New York, July 9, 1956.

[7] Escorbedo, Azufre en Mexico, op. cit., 20.

[8] Chris S. Elliott, interview, Wharton, Tex., Apr. 11, 1957.

[9] Mexican Gulf Sulphur Co. SEC Registration Statement No. 2-11223, Dec. 7, 1954, 3; hereinafter cited as Mexsul Regist. Stmt.

[10] For early operations and plant at San Cristóbal: Kearney, Eng. Mining J., op. cit.; Chem. Wk., Jan. 23, 1954, 16; interviews: Claiborne, Elliott, Kearney, Roberson, op. cit., also W. H. Maddox and E. de Anzorena, Mexico, D. F., July 17 and 29, 1956; Wm. P. Barnard, San Cristóbal, Ver., Apr. 16, 1956; New York, July 19, 1956; Paul Natchtman, New York, June 6, July 9, 1956.

[11] Mexsul Regist. Stmt., op. cit.

[12] Ibid., for details of this stock offering and various royalty and stock option agreements, stock ownership, etc.

[13] Letters to stockholders of Mexican Gulf Sulphur Co.: Geo. W. Myer, chm., Stockholders Com., Jan. 14, Feb. 28, Mar. 21, Apr. 5, 1957; J. T. Claiborne, Jr., pres. Co., Feb. 28, Mar. 7, Mar. 27, Apr. 2, 1957.

[14] Wall St. J. and N. Y. Times, Apr. 17, 1957.

[15] De Golyer & MacNaughton, Inc., Appraisal of Sulphur Deposits of San Cristóbal Dome, Veracruz, Mex., Mar. 26, 1957.

[16] Wm. P. Barnard, memo to author, Mar. 12, 1958.

17 *Lania* (Mexico, D. F.) *10*, Apr. 4, 1958.

18 Pan American Sulphur Co., *Ann. Rept., 1955.*

19 *Ibid., 1953; SEC Prospectus*, Feb. 4, 1953, 3, 13.

20 *Ibid.*, interviews: Harry C. Webb, Houston, Tex., Apr. 12, 1957; R. S. Bond, Sylvester Dayson, D. W. Forbes, and Raymond Devine, Dallas, Tex., Apr. 15, 1957.

21 For early development of Pan Am. operations interviews at Jáltipan, Ver., Chris E. Armstrong, Fredrico Engels, Frederick Gormley, Jaimie Pavón, Stephen S. Richards, Ernesto Webber, Apr. 12-17, 1956; Jan. 9-16, 1957; John C. Myers and J. H. Pollard, Houston, Tex., Apr. 12 and 15, July 16 and Dec. 10, 1956; Carl L. Basland, Mexico, D.F., Apr. 23, 1956.

22 J. C. Myers, *Rept. on Jáltipan Sulphur Deposit*, Nov. 25, 1952.

23 For Jáltipan plant: Pan American Sulphur Co., *Ann. Repts., 1954, 1955; Chem. Eng. News 32*, 1200, 1955; interviews at Jáltipan, Ver., Harold H. Jaquet, Apr. 10, 1956, Jan. 18, 1957, and Richard D. Mills, Apr. 11, 1956, Jan. 16, 1957; Charles Currion Arrivillaga, Coatzacoalcos, Ver., Apr. 15, 1956.

24 W. H. Maddox, *Geologic Rept. on Mezquital Concession*, Aug. 23, 1954, printed in Gulf Sulphur Corp., *SEC Prospectus*, Nov. 3, 1954 and July 13, 1955.

25 Details in Gulf Sulphur Corp., *SEC Prospectus*, Dec. 18, 1951, Oct. 24, 1952, Feb. 19 and Nov. 3, 1954.

26 Gulf Sulphur Corp., *SEC Prospectus*, July 13, 1955.

27 Stuart C. Dorman, letter to Gulf Sulphur Corp. stockholders, May 21, 1956; W. Haynes, *Chem. Eng. News*, May 14, 1956, 2412.

28 *Chem. Wk.*, May 19, 1957, 24.

29 This agreement set forth in a presidential resolution, Sept. 14, 1955; published in *Gaceta Official Veracruz*, Oct. 25, 1955.

30 Kearney, *op. cit.; Chem. Eng. News*, May 14, 1956; 2412; interviews Jas. P. Berling, J. B. Brannan, José A. Gallegos, Aldolfo Mendoza, Archibaldo G. Pratt, Wm. J. Ridden, and Jos. L. Soper, Salinas, Ver., Apr. 14-16, 1956; Jan. 5-9, 1957: with Stuart C. Dorman, Houston, Tex., July 25, 1956; Mexico, D. F., Dec. 10, 1956; New York, May 16, 1958; V. V. Jacomini, Houston, Tex., Apr. 12, 1956; Jas. Woodburn, Mexico, D. F., July 20, 1956, Jan. 24, 1957.

31 For Texas Gulf activities in Mexico, interviews with Edward O. Mason, Mexico, D. F., July 20, 1956, Jan. 25, 1957; Robt. M. Stoy and S. E. Staffa, Nopalapa, Ver., Apr. 17, 1956; Jan. 16, 1957; Luis A. Iturbide, Coatzacoalcos, Ver., Jan. 14, 1958.

Chapter 16: BRIMSTONE TODAY

1 For the Mexican sulphur development: Harold H. Jaquet, *Address*, Am. Inst. Mining & Met. Engrs. Chicago, Feb. 15, 1955; J. H. Kearney, *Eng. & Mining J.* 156, 118, 1955; Lic. J. Campillo, *Mining Chamb.*

Mex., Memo. 07962, Apr. 26, 1956; *Brit. Sulphur Corp. Quart. Bull. No. 13,* 27, 1956; R. B. Roberson, *Mex. Am. Rev.,* Dec. 1956, 41; *Punto* (Mexico, D. F.) Apr. 7, 1956; *Chem. Eng.,* Jan. 1953, 128; *Chem. Wk.,* Jan. 13, 1953, 12; Jan. 23, 1954, 16; Aug. 27, 1955, 17; *Wall St. J.,* Aug. 9, 1954, Oct. 23, 1956; for current news stories, *Chem. Eng. News* **31,** 5375, 1953; **32,** 3628, 1954; **33,** 458, 1140, 1200, 1269, 1440, 1855, 2376, 2566, 3152, 3778, 4956, 5233, 5305, 1955; **34,** 3246, 3680, 4082, 4942, 5808, 6161, 1956; Jan. 7, 1957, 19; Jan. 21, 162; Feb. 4, 20; Mar. 25, 61; May 13, 26; July 15, 78; Sept. 30, 19; Oct. 7, 40; Oct. 14, 98; Dec. 9, 42: for background of Mexican chem. ind., Jos. Sperling, *ibid.,* **32,** 3628, 1954; *Ibid.,* April 21, 1958, 88.

[2] *Business Wk.,* Sept. 18, 1954, 64.

[3] J. B. Eby, *Rept. to Texas Interntl. Sulphur Co.,* Houston, Tex., Apr. 13, 1956.

[4] For TIS exploring and financing, interviews at Houston, Tex., M. A. S. Makris and J. B. Eby, May 7, 1956; at Mexico, D. F., Rafael Martinez de Escobar, Apr. 29, July 10, 1956 and G. P. Salas, Mar. 15, 1957; *Chem. Eng. News* **34,** 2270, 3737, 4082, 1956; Jan. 21, 1957, 62; *Chem. Wk.,* May 25, 1957, 23; Oct. 12, 1957, 49.

[5] Alfonso G. Gurrea and Angel Orveta, interviews Mexico, D. F., Apr. 27, 1957; Houston, Tex., J. H. Pollard, July 14 and Dec. 10, 1956; Marvin Weaster, Dec. 3, 1956.

[6] *Chem. Eng. News* **31,** 215, 1953.

[7] Nelson Steenland and L. L. Nattleton, interview, Houston, Tex., Apr. 11, 1957; M. I. Goldman, *Geol. Soc. Am., Memoir No. 50,* 1952.

[8] *Lania* (Mexico, D. F.) **8,** Feb. 10, 1956.

[9] *Chem. Eng. News* **33,** 1140, 3152, 1955.

[10] *Barron's,* Feb. 20, 1956; *Ind. Eng. Chem.,* Aug. 1956, 16A; *Chem. Wk.,* Oct. 12, 1956, 145.

[11] *Chem. Eng. News,* Oct. 7, 1957, 40; *Chem. Wk.,* Sept. 28, 1957, 85; Oct. 19, 80.

[12] *Ibid.,* Dec. 14, 1957, 92.

[13] *Ibid.,* Dec. 28, 1957, 82.

[14] Year-by-year statistics, Appendix V.

[15] L. M. Williams, address, N. Y. Soc. Security Analysts, Mar. 17, 1958.

[16] *Chem. Eng. News,* Nov. 15, 1954, 4346.

[17] Duval Sulphur & Potash Co., *SEC Prospectus,* March 15, 1957, 2, 10.

[18] *Ibid.,* 14.

[19] Chas. J. Ferry, interview, New Orleans, Nov. 29, 1956; *Chem. Eng. News,* May 7, 1956, 2223; *Duval Co. Ann. Repts.,* 1956, 1957.

[20] Co. memo to author, June 10, 1958.

[21] *Co. Ann. Repts., op. cit.*

[22] Texas Gulf Sulphur Co., *Ann. Rept.,* 1957, 8.

[23] *Chem. Wk.,* Dec. 29, 1956, 31; Feb. 2, 1957, 65; *Chem. Eng. News,* Feb. 11, 1957, 54.

Chapter *17*: ———— AND TOMORROW

[1] Interviews at Houston, Texas, with Morgan J. Davis and Harry W. Haines, July 13, 1956; Robt. H. Johnson, Dec. 6, 1956; H. H. Meridith and Paul Weaver, Dec. 9, 1956; Ralph Taylor and Hunter Yarborough, Dec. 10, 1956; J. B. Carsey, *Bull. Am. Assoc. Petrol. Geol.* 34, 3, 1950; I. Cram, address Houston Geol. Soc., Mar. 1955; T. B. Goodicke, *Texas J. Sci.* 1, 149, 1955.

[2] *Mining Cong. J.*, Nov. 1954, 71; *Oil & Gas J.*, Oct. 3 and 24, 1955, 49, 69; *Chem. Eng. News* 34, 3325, 4752, 5361, 5615, 1956.

[3] M. J. Davis, quoted in *Brit. Sulphur Corp. Quart. Bull.* No. 8, 27, 1955.

[4] *Chem. Wk.*, Sept. 29, 1956, 21; *Chem. Eng. News*, Oct. 1, 1956, 4752.

[5] For details of Grand Isle plant design and construction I am indebted to Co. memo, Sept. 9, 1958; *Chem. Eng.*, July 28, 1958, 60.

[6] *Chem. Eng. News* 34, 4752, 5361, 5615, 1956.

[7] *Ibid.* 33, 4908, 1955; Texas Gulf Sulphur Co., *Ann. Rept., 1957.*

[8] Co. memo to author, *op. cit.;* B. A. Axelrad and K. T. Price, interviews, Bay Ste. Elaine, La., Nov. 26-27, 1957.

[9] J. A. Lee, *Chem. Met. Eng.*, June 1942, 80; *Chem. Ind.* 65, 598, 1949; *Petrol. Refiner.* 29, 225, 1950 (with flow sheet); F. G. Sawyer and R. N. Hader, *Ind. Eng. Chem.* 42, 1942, 1950; *Chem. Eng.*, Apr. 1951, 181; Oct. 1952, 210 (with flow sheet) Feb. 1953, 138; A. L. Kobl and E. D. Fox, *ibid.*, Oct. 22, 1952, 154; G. Wilson, *Oil & Gas J.*, Aug. 23, 1951, 130; F. E. Hixon, *Chem. & Ind.*, Mar. 26, 1955, 322; *Chem. Wk.*, Jan. 14, 1956, 66.

[10] *Ibid.*, Mar. 19, 1951, 22; *Chem. Eng.*, Apr. 1951, 181; *Oil & Gas J.*, July 19, 1951, 78.

[11] G. A. Cain, *U. S. Dept. Comm. FIAT, Final Rept.*, 1013, 1947.

[12] R. M. Ree, *Oil & Gas J.* 44, 219, 1946.

[13] T. W. Rosenbaugh, *Refiner & Nat. Gas. Mfr.* 17, 245, 288, 1938.

[14] A. R. Powell, *Ind. Eng. Chem.* 31, 789, 1939.

[15] H. A. Gollmar, *ibid.*, 26, 130, 1934.

[16] *Oil & Gas J.*, Feb. 25, 1952, 15.

[17] Appendix IX.

[18] R. H. Epach, *Ind. Eng. Chem.* 42, 2235, 1950; W. A. Chamberlain, *ibid.*, 2238.

[19] Victor Gama Arrederrdo and Cabaré Azuna Pavón, interviews, Poza Rica, Ver., May 1, 1956 and Antonio Bermudez, Mexico, D. F.; Mar. 1, 1956, Feb. 20, 1957; *Chem. Age* (London) Feb. 21, 1953; S. Schwartz, *Petrol. Refiner.* 32, 95, 1953, *N. Y. Herald-Tribune*, Jan. 8, 1956; A. Bravo, *Frontera* (Mexico, D. F.) Aug.-Sept. 1957, 41.

[20] For early hist. and development at Lacq, interviews, Gen. A. Blanchard, Paris, Oct. 28, and Nov. 20, 1956; Claude Bienvenu and Raoul Guillo, Lacq, Nov. 12, 1959.

[21] Analysis of Lacq gas: H_2S, 15.3%; CO_2, 9.6%; CH_4, 69.5%; C_2H_6, 3.2%; C_3H_8, 1.4%; C_4H_{10}, 0.4%; other hydrocarbons, 0.48%; CS_2, 0.03%; COS, 0.03%; various mercaptans, 0.01% *L'Usine de Lacq*, co. booklet, 10.

[22] *Chem. Wk.*, May 11, 1957; *Chem. Eng.*, Apr. 7, 1956, 58; May 11, 1958, 72.

[23] Oliver Serard, interview, Paris, Nov. 20, 1958.

[24] *Ibid.*

[25] Raffineries de Soufre Reunies, largest of these refiners, with five plants in France (including the one at Marseille built by Hoeckle for Frasch in 1909 and taken over in 1936) and two in Algiers, has been buying some 75,000 tons a year of brimstone, roughly two-thirds from the U. S. This important firm has gone over completely to Lacq sulphur. (Jean Roubaud, interview, Marseille, Nov. 7, 1958.)

[26] Bienvenu, *op. cit.*

[27] *Chem. Eng. News*, Feb. 19, 1958, 88.

[28] Blanchard, *op. cit.*

[29] Eric J. Hanson, *Dynamic Decade* (Toronto, 1958) Chaps. 19 and 20.

[30] *Ibid.*, p. 225; see also for Canadian sour gas-sulphur development, *Chem. Wk.*, Oct. 8, 1955, 23; Feb. 5, 1955, 16; Oct. 8, 1955, 8; July 7, 1956, 22; Nov. 23, 1956, 23; Dec. 29, 1956, 31; *Oilweek*, Sept. 27, 1957, 15.

[31] Alberta Oil & Gas Conserv. Bd., *Rept. to Lt-Gov. in Council*, Calgary, Sept. 15, 1958, 20.

[32] *Oil Wk.*, Sept. 12, 1958, 8.

[33] Brit. Am. Oil Co., brief to Royal Comm. on Energy, Feb., 1958.

[34] J. G. Stabbach, *Oil & Gas J.*, Oct. 27, 1958, 69.

[35] *Oil Wk.*, Oct. 3, 1958, 10.

[36] Alberta Gas & Oil Conserv. Bd., *op. cit.;* Royal Comm. on Energy, *1st Rept.*, Ottawa, Oct. 29, 1958.

[37] For discussion of Borden Comm. proposals, *Albertan* (Calgary) Oct. 27, 1958; *Herald* (Calgary) Oct. 27, 1958, Nov. 28, 1958; *Oil in Canada*, edit., Nov. 3, 1958; *Petrol. Wk.*, Nov. 14, 1958, 28.

[38] Carl O. Nickle, *Daily Oil Bull.* (Calgary) edit., Aug. 21, 1957.

[39] *Ibid.*, July 2, 1958.

[40] Elgin D. Bell, A. D. Insley, Carl O. Nickle, J. E. Peary, J. T. Stabbach, interviews, Calgary, Dec. 15-19, 1958; H. W. Manley, memo to author, Tulsa, Okla., Jan. 5, 1959.

[41] Estimates based on figures from various companies, taking accepted average of 330 operating days per year.

[42] Manley, *op. cit.*

[43] W. J. Mickle, address, Can. Chem. Engrs. Assoc., Calgary, Sept. 23, 1958.

[44] Manley, *op. cit.*

[45] Jeff. Lake Petrochems., *SEC Prospectus*, June 2, 1958.

[46] *Oil Wk.*, Aug. 18, 1958, 16.

[47] Jeff. Lake Petrochems., *Prospectus, op. cit.*

[48] Average S Content of oil from principal fields: Kuwait, 2.5%; Iraq, 1.9%; Arabian, 1.5%. (F. E. Hixon, *Chem. & Ind.,* Mar. 26, 1955, 332.)

[49] For Middle East plants and figures I am indebted to J. M. Lancaster, ed. *Brit. Sulphur Corp. Quart. Bull.,* memo to author, London, Oct. 20, 1958.

[50] Estimated current figures; these percentages have repeatedly shifted over the years, see Appendix XIX.

[51] Matls. Policy Comm., Rept. to President, *Resources for Freedom* (Washington, D. C., 1952) II, 126.

[52] Haynes, *Stone,* 263.

Appendix

I. THE PROPERTIES OF SULPHUR

State. Normally solid. Melts at about 114°C (238°F); sublimes in a closed tube; boils at 444.6°C (832.3°F).

Color. Sulphur-yellow, varying with impurities to yellow shades of green, gray, and red.

Luster. Resinous, transparent to translucent.

Crystalline Form. Naturally orthorhombic dipyramidal commonly in irregular masses. Also massive reniform, stalactitic, as incrustations, earthy. Changes to monoclinic crystals above 95.5°C (203.9°F).

Fracture. Conchoidal to uneven, brittle to imperfectly sectile.

Cleavage. Imperfect.

Streak. White.

Combustibility. Ignites in air at about 260°C (500°F). Burns with a blue flame, evolving sulphur dioxide gas.

Thermal. Poor conductor of heat. Crystals emit a crackling noise when warmed by the hand.

Electrical. Non-conductor of electricity. Electrifies negatively upon friction.

Hardness. 1.5.2.5 on Mohs' scale.

Density. 2.07 g/ml (129 lb/cu ft), in the form of rhombic crystals.

Solubility. Insoluble in water and acids; attacked by alkalies. Very soluble in carbon disulphide; various solubilities in organic liquids, generally increasing with temperature.

Viscosity of Molten Sulphur. Fairly limpid at the melting point, becoming extremely viscous as the temperature approaches 188°C (370°F), and decreasing in viscosity at still higher temperatures.

Atomic Number. 16.

Atomic Weight. 32.066.

Natural Isotopes. 95.1%S^{32}, 0.74%S^{33}, 4.2%S^{34}, 0.016%S^{36}.

Chemical Valences. 2, e.g., H_2S; 4, e.g., SO_2; 6, e.g., SO_3.

IIA. WORLD PRODUCTION OF SULPHUR IN ALL FORMS—1938[a]
(Thousands of Long Tons Sulphur Equivalent)

	TOTAL SULPHUR	ELEMENTAL SULPHUR BRIMSTONE FRASCH	BRIMSTONE OTHER	RECOVERED ELEMENTAL[c]	PYRITE	SULPHUR IN GASES[d]	SULPHATE MINERALS
Total World	8,465	2,389	659	263	4,308	769	77
North America	2,872	2,389	4	30	239	210	—
United States	2,772	2,389	4	4	219	156	
Canada	100			26	20	54	
South America	25	—	25	—	—	—	—
Bolivia	2		2				
Chile	21		21				
Peru	2		2				
Europe	4,203	—	385	233	3,048	460	77
Austria	4				4		
Belg.-Lux.	177			2		175	
Cyprus	233				253		
Finland	44				44		
France	111				66	45	
Germany	368			70	173	125	
Greece	117				117		
Italy	764		384[b]		380		
Norway	418			109	309		
Portugal	239			11	228		
Spain	1,271		1	23	1,247		
Sweden	101			18	83		
U. K.	194				2	115	77
Yugoslavia	67				67		
Others	75				75		
Africa	46	—	—	—	46	—	—
Algeria	21				21		
So. Rhodesia	11				11		
Union of So. Africa	14				14		
Asia	1,270	—	245	—	950	75	—
Indonesia	17		17				
Israel	1		1				
Japan	1,196		223		898	75	
Korea	52				52		
Turkey	4		4				
Oceania	49	—	—	—	25	24	—
Australia	49				25	24	

[a] Excludes U.S.S.R. and China.
[b] Includes 9,300 tons of ground sulphur rock.
[c] Elemental production of Norway, Portugal and Spain is from sulphide ores.
[d] Includes sulphur in acid produced from smelter gases, hydrogen sulphide and the roasting of spent oxide. Sulphur equivalent is included in the country in which the acid is produced whether from domestic or imported materials.

IIB. WORLD PRODUCTION OF SULPHUR IN ALL FORMS—1950[a]
(Thousands of Long Tons Sulphur Equivalent)

| | TOTAL SULPHUR | ELEMENTAL SULPHUR | | RECOV- ERED ELEMEN- TAL[c] | PYRITE | SULPHUR IN GASES[d] | SULPHATE MINERALS |
| | | BRIMSTONE | | | | | |
		FRASCH	OTHER				
Total World	11,002	5,192	372	354	3,842	985	257
North America	6,277	5,192	12	143	527	403	—
United States	5,987	5,192	1	143	393	258	
Canada	269				134	135	
Mexico	21		11			10	
South America	36	—	31	—	—	5	—
Argentina	13		8			5	
Bolivia	4		4				
Chile	15		15				
Colombia	2		2				
Peru	2		2				
Europe	3,570	—	227	191	2,455	448	249
Austria	4				3	1	
Belg.-Lux.	103			2		101	
Cyprus	294				294		
Finland	86				69	17	
France	178		6		105	35	32
Germany, W.	310			30	189	91	
Greece	42				41		1
Italy	646		214[b]		408	24	
Netherlands	18					18	
Norway	306			95	202	9	
Portugal	258			14	244		
Spain	682		7	31	644		
Sweden	213			14	199		
U. K.	376			5	5	150	216
Yugoslavia	54				52	2	
Africa	41	—	—	1	32	8	—
Algeria	10				10		
Belgian Congo	8					8	
Egypt	1			1			
Fr. Morocco	1				1		
So. Rhodesia	5				5		
Tunisia	1				1		
Union of So. Africa	15				15		
Asia	979	—	102	19	775	75	8
India	8						8
Iran	21		2	19			
Japan	938		91		775	72	
Taiwan	3		3				
Turkey	9		6			3	
Oceania	99	—	—	—	53	46	—
Australia	99				53	46	

[a] Excludes U.S.S.R., East Europe and China.
[b] Includes 4,500 tons ground sulphur rock.
[c] Elemental production of Norway, Portugal and Spain is from sulphide ores.
[d] Includes sulphur in acid produced from smelter gases, hydrogen sulphide and the roasting of spent oxide. Sulphur equivalent is included in the country in which the acid is produced whether from domestic or imported materials.

IIC. WORLD PRODUCTION OF SULPHUR IN ALL FORMS—1956[a]
(Thousands of Long Tons Sulphur Equivalent)

ELEMENTAL SULPHUR

	TOTAL SULPHUR	BRIMSTONE FRASCH	OTHER	RECOVERED ELEMENTAL[c]	PYRITE	SULPHUR IN GASES[d]	SULPHATE MINERALS
Total World	16,937	7,177	661	923	5,929	1,664	583
North America	9,309	7,177	65	559	848	660	—
United States	7,818	6,424	60	465	432	437	
Canada	628			33	384	211	
Cuba	32				32		
Mexico	797	753	5	27		12	
Netherlands							
W. Indies	29			29			
Trinidad	5			5			
South America	100	—	72	—	14	14	—
Argentina	36		27			9	
Bolivia	3		3				
Brazil	2					2	
Chile	37		37				
Colombia	5		5				
Peru	3					3	
Venezuela	14				14		
Europe	5,287	—	257	337	3,494	736	463
Austria	86					8	78
Belg.-Lux.	148					148	
Cyprus	530				530		
Finland	153				128	25	
France	227			2	126	76	23
Germany, W.	484		4	77	253	150	
Greece	121		1		102	1	17
Italy	932		246[b]	5	634	47	
Netherlands	30			12		18	
Norway	354			95	235	24	
Portugal	280			17	263		
Spain	951		6	46	869	30	
Sweden	282			30	239	13	
U. K.	594			53	2	194	345
Yugoslavia	115				113	2	
Africa	224	—	—	3	175	46	—
Algeria	3				3		
Belgian Congo	38					38	
Egypt	3			3			
Fr. Morocco	1				1		
So. Rhodesia	16				8	8	
Union of So. Africa	163				163		
Asia	1,877	—	267	24	1,310	156	120
India	110						110
Iran	20		2	18			

IIC. WORLD PRODUCTION OF SULPHUR
IN ALL FORMS—1956[a] (Continued)
(Thousands of Long Tons Sulphur Equivalent)

	TOTAL SULPHUR	ELEMENTAL SULPHUR BRIMSTONE FRASCH	OTHER	RECOVERED ELEMEN- TAL[c]	PYRITE	SULPHUR IN GASES[d]	SULPHATE MINERALS
Japan	1,685		243	6	1,280	156	
Pakistan	10						10
Taiwan	19		8		11		
Turkey	33		14		19		
Oceania	140	—	—	—	88	52	—
Australia	140				88	52	

[a] Excludes U.S.S.R., East Europe and China.

[b] Italian statistics include: 68,900 tons mining waste used to manufacture acid and 6,700 tons ground sulphur rock.

[c] Includes elemental produced from sulphide ores as follows:

Canada	3,500 Long Tons
Norway	95,400 Long Tons
Portugal	16,900 Long Tons
Spain	42,000 Long Tons

[d] Includes sulphur in acid produced from smelter gases, hydrogen sulphide and the roasting of spent oxide. Sulphur equivalent is included in the country in which the acid is produced whether from domestic or imported materials.

IIIA.   COMPARATIVE IMPORTANCE OF SULPHUR AND OTHER MATERIALS IN THE CHEMICAL INDUSTRY*

	ALL FORMS OF SULPHUR LONG TONS	GROSS SULPHURIC ACID 100% NET TONS	CHLORINE NET TONS	CAUSTIC SODA NET TONS	LIME NET TONS	SALT NET TONS
Alcohols.............	(inc.)	650,000				
Aluminum Sulphate....	(inc.)	360,000				
Ammonium Sulphate....	430,000	1,236,000				
Chemicals (other than listed)....	1,755,000	1,420,000	3,000,000	1,155,000	1,892,000	16,273,000
Dyes.....	(inc.)	150,000	(inc.)			
Hydrochloric Acid.....	(inc.)	128,000	(inc.)			
Hydrofluoric Acid.....	(inc.)	135,000				
Industrial Explosives....	20,000	375,000			5,000	
Inorganic Pigments....	450,000	1,249,000				
Insecticides.....	130,000	130,000			70,000	
Iron and Steel.....	380,000	856,000			1,497,000	158,000
Metallurgical.....	80,000	200,000			674,000	
Petroleum Catalysts.....	(inc.)	155,000				135,000
Petroleum Refining.....	170,000	1,882,000		284,000	36,000	135,000
Phosphate Fertilizers....	1,270,000	4,053,000				
Pulp and Paper.....	459,000	634,000	563,000	285,000	857,000	126,000
Rayon and Cellulose....	250,000	110,000		640,000		100,000
Rubber.....	80,000	225,000			2,000	
Synthetic Detergents....	(inc.)	28,000	(inc.)			
Textile Finishing.....	10,000		(inc.)	135,000		192,000
Miscellaneous......	383,000	668,000	217,000	1,711,000	5,544,000	7,233,000
Totals...........	5,858,000	14,644,000	3,780,000	4,210,000	10,577,000	24,216,000

* Sulphuric acid is gross consumption in 1952 as reported in BDSA release BD 123, February 19, 1954; Sulphur Chlorine, and caustic soda are 1956 figures as estimated by *Chemical Engineering*, with sulphur calculated from reported acid uses with allowance for any recycled acid used in each industry and new acid from sludge treated as recycled acid, lime and salt for 1956 as reported in *Minerals Yearbook*.

IIIB. UNITED STATES CONSUMPTION OF SULPHUR AND SELECTED COMMODITIES

Commodity	ESTIMATED 1956 CONSUMPTION (*Thousands of Long Tons*)	RATIO OF SULPHUR TO EACH	PER CAPITA (*Pounds*)
Petroleum[a]	391,000	0.015	5,200
Steel[b]	102,871	0.056	1,370
Salt	21,651	0.3	288
Phosphate Rock	11,536	0.7	115
SULPHUR[c]	5,768	1.0	77
Potash	3,132	1.8	42
Rubber	1,707	3.4	23
Aluminum	1,658	3.5	22
Copper	1,309	4.4	17
Nickel	114	50.6	2

[a] Crude Runs to Stills.
[b] Ingot Production.
[c] Sulphur in all forms.

IV. SULPHUR IN AGRICULTURE

A. Sulphur Removed per Acre by Crops[1]

CROP	DRY WEIGHT OF CROP Pounds	WEIGHT OF SULPHUR REMOVED Pounds
Wheat, grain, 30 bushels.....	1,530	2.6
Wheat, straw..............	2,653	3.7
Total crop..............	4,183	6.3
Corn, grain, 30 bushels......	1,500	2.6
Corn, stalks...............	1,877	2.2
Total crop..............	3,377	4.8
Beans, grain, 30 bushels......	1,613	3.8
Beans, straw..............	1,838	2.0
Total crop..............	3,451	5.8
Turnips, roots.............	3,126	23.1
Turnips, tops.............	1,531	13.8
Total crop..............	4,657	36.9
Potatoes..................	3,360	4.6
Alfalfa hay...............	9,000	26.0
Cabbage..................	4,800	39.2

B. U. S. Agricultural Sulphur Balance[2]

	ANNUAL REMOVALS Short Tons	ANNUAL ADDITIONS Short Tons
Cultivated crops...........	711,400	....
Drainage..................	4,998,000	....
Precipitation..............	....	2,499,000
Fertilizers................	....	653,000
Total..................	5,709,400	3,152,000
Total deficit............................		2,557,400

[1] Hart and Peterson, "Sulphur Requirements of Farm Crops," *Wisc. Agr. Exp. Station Bull.* No. 14 (1911).

[2] Lipman and McLean, "Agricultural Aspects of Sulphur and Sulphur Compounds," *Chem. & Met. Eng.*, XXXVIII, pp. 394-396 (1931).

V. UNITED STATES PRODUCTION OF SULPHUR IN ALL FORMS
(Thousands of Long Tons Sulphur Equivalent)

YEAR	BRIMSTONE		ELEMENTAL SULPHUR		SULPHUR CONTAINED IN PYRITES[3]	SULPHUR IN BY-PRODUCT H_2SO_4 FROM SMELTER GASES[4]	SULPHUR IN H_2S CONVERTED TO H_2SO_4 AND LIQUID SO_2	TOTAL SULPHUR[1]
	FRASCH[2]	OTHER	RECOVERED ELEMENTAL	TOTAL				
1880	—	(a)	—	(a)	—	—	—	(a)
1885	—	(a)	—	(a)	20	N.A.	—	N.A.
1890	—	(a)	—	(a)	40	N.A.	—	N.A.
1895	(a)	2	—	2	40	N.A.	—	N.A.
1900	(a)	3	—	3	82	10[e]	—	95
1905	219	1	—	220	101	40[e]	—	361
1910	247	(a)	—	247	97	100[e]	—	444
1915	517	4	—	521	158	217	—	896
1920	1,255	—	—	1,255	124	291	—	1,670
1925	1,409	—	—	1,409	77	235	—	1,721
1930	2,558	(a)	—	2,559	124	211	—	2,895
1935	1,627	5	—	1,633	203	137	—	1,973
1940	2,726	6	4	2,736	262	191	16	3,205
1941	3,130	9	5	3,144	270	208	21	3,644
1942	3,456	5	5	3,466	307	218	19	4,010
1943	2,539	N.A.	5	2,544	337	279	18	3,177
1944	3,218	N.A.	19	3,237	333	263	22	3,855
1945	3,753	N.A.	25	3,778	296	246	19	4,340
1946	3,860	2	35	3,897	338	209	18	4,462
1947	4,441	1	43	4,486	392	212	21	5,111
1948	4,869	(a)	44	4,914	388	187	26	5,515

V. UNITED STATES PRODUCTION OF SULPHUR IN ALL FORMS (Continued)

(Thousands of Long Tons Sulphur Equivalent)

| | ELEMENTAL SULPHUR | | | | SULPHUR CONTAINED IN PYRITES[3] | SULPHUR IN BY-PRODUCT H_2SO_4 FROM SMELTER GASES[4] | SULPHUR IN H_2S CONVERTED TO H_2SO_4 AND LIQUID SO_2 | TOTAL SULPHUR[1] |
| | BRIMSTONE | | RECOVERED ELEMENTAL | TOTAL | | | | |
YEAR	FRASCH[2]	OTHER						
1949	4,745	2	57	4,804	378	167	38	5,387
1950	5,192	1	142	5,336	393	216	42	5,986
1951	5,278	1	184	5,464	433	241	60	6,197
1952	5,293	2	251	5,546	418	253	67	6,284
1953	5,155	38	342	5,535	380	253	80	6,248
1954	5,515	64	359	5,938	405	259	73	6,675
1955	5,739	61	399	6,199	410	325	94	7,027
1956	6,424	60	465	6,949	432	348	89	7,818
1957	5,491	87	511	6,089	436	390	89	7,004

a Less than 1,000 tons.
e Estimated.
N.A.—Not available.
[1] Totals may not add due to rounding.
[2] Includes a small amount of other native for the years 1905-1925.
[3] Sulphur content for 1905-1915 estimated at 40% and calculated from gross pyrites statistics. Years 1925-1930 adjusted for flotation concentrates.
[4] Years 1915-1948 derived from calculating sulphur content of acid production from nonferrous metal smelters. Years 1925-1930 adjusted for flotation concentrates. Years 1915-1920 from U. S. Bureau of Census.
Source: U. S. Bureau of Mines except where noted.

VI. UNITED STATES APPARENT CONSUMPTION OF SULPHUR IN ALL FORMS

(Thousands of Long Tons Sulphur Equivalent)

YEAR	ELEMENTAL SULPHUR[1]	SULPHUR CONTAINED IN PYRITES			SULPHUR IN GASES[3]	TOTAL SULPHUR
		DOMESTIC[2]	IMPORTS	TOTAL		
1880	89	N.A.	4	4	—	93
1885	98	20	20	40	—	138
1890	163	40	54	94	—	257
1895	124	40	85	125	—	249
1900	171	82	146	228	10[e]	409
1905	236	101	230	331	40[e]	607
1910	251	97	328	425	100[e]	776
1915	287	158	380	538	217	1,042
1920	1,040	124	150	274	291	1,605
1925	1,229	77	124	201	235	1,665
1930	1,397	124	166	290	211	1,898
1935	1,240	203	179	382	137	1,759
1940	1,850	262	183	445	207	2,502
1941	2,389	270	177	447	229	3,065
1942	2,499	307	144	451	237	3,187
1943	2,555	337	123	460	297	3,312
1944	2,933	333	87	420	285	3,638
1945	2,943	296	90	386	265	3,594
1946	2,944	338	88	426	227	3,597
1947	3,582	392	61	453	233	4,268
1948	3,806	388	52	440	213	4,459
1949	3,484	378	58	436	205	4,125
1950	4,276	393	100	493	258	5,027
1951	4,005	433	106	539	301	4,845
1952	3,989	418	142	560	320	4,869
1953	4,313	380	91	471	333	5,117
1954	4,071	405	134	539	332	4,942
1955	4,660	410	172	582	419	5,661
1956	4,724	432	175	607	437	5,768
1957	4,502	436	169	605	479	5,586

[e] Estimated.
[1] See table "Elemental Sulphur in the United States."
[2] Domestic production.
[3] Includes total sulphur equivalent of H_2SO_4 produced directly from smelter gas and H_2S, plus by-product liquid SO_2.
Source: *Mineral Resources of the United States*, 1885-1930, and thereafter *Mineral Yearbook*.

VII. ELEMENTAL SULPHUR IN THE UNITED STATES
(Thousands of Long Tons)

YEAR	APPARENT FRASCH SALES[1]	NATIVE SULPHUR[2]	RE-COVERED[3]	IMPORTS[4]	EXPORTS[5]	APPARENT CON-SUMPTION[6]
1880	—	(a)	—	88	—	89
1885	—	(a)	—	97	—	98
1890	—	(a)	—	163	—	163
1895	—	2	—	122	—	124
1900	(a)	3	—	168	—	171
1905	162	1	—	84	12	236
1910	251	(a)	—	31	31	251
1915	294	4	—	26	37	287
1920	1,518	—	—	(a)	477	1,040
1925	1,858	—	—	(a)	629	1,229
1930	1,990	(a)	—	(a)	593	1,397
1935	1,635	5	—	2	402	1,240
1940	2,559	6	4	28	746	1,850
1941	3,076	9	5	29	729	2,389
1942	3,032	5	5	26	568	2,499
1943	3,191	N.A.	5	17	657	2,555
1944	3,580	N.A.	7	(a)	654	2,933
1945	3,850	N.A.	12	(a)	919	2,943
1946	4,094	2	37	(a)	1,189	2,944
1947	4,840	1	40	(a)	1,299	3,582
1948	5,015	(a)	54	(a)	1,263	3,806
1949	4,871	2	42	(a)	1,431	3,484
1950	5,637	1	79	(a)	1,441	4,276
1951	5,095	1	194	2	1,288	4,005
1952	5,062	2	225	5	1,304	3,989
1953	5,202	38	314	1	1,242	4,313
1954	5,309	64	342	1	1,645	4,071
1955	5,786	61	380	35	1,601	4,660
1956	5,670	60	432	212	1,651	4,724
1957	5,005	87	473	499	1,562	4,502

a Less than 1,000 Tons.
N.A.　Not available.
[1] Years 1900-1940 Frasch shipments; years 1941-1957 apparent sales of Frasch.
[2] Native sulphur production.
[3] Recovered sulphur shipments.
[4] All grades of sulphur including refined and ore; 1880 and 1885 are years ending June 30th.
[5] Crude sulphur only. The U. S. also exports 10,000 to 50,000 long tons of refined grades annually.
[6] Data may not add, due to rounding.

Source: *Mineral Resources of the United States*, 1885 through 1930, and thereafter *Mineral Yearbook*.

VIII. FRASCH SULPHUR PRODUCTION BY MINES THROUGH 1957

DEPOSIT	COMPANY	PRODUCTION DATES	LONG TONS PRODUCED
United States			
Sulphur Mine, La.	Union	12/28/95—12/23/24	9,400,000
Bryanmound, Tex.	Freeport	11/12/12— 9/30/35	5,001,000
Gulf (Big Hill), Tex.	Texas Gulf	3/19/19— 9/19/32 and	
		1/ 1/36— 8/10/36	12,346,000
Hoskins Mound, Tex.	Freeport	3/31/23— 5/26/55	10,865,000
Damon, Tex.	Union	(a)	—
Big Creek, Tex.	Union	3/ 6/25— 2/24/26	2,000
Palangana, Tex.	Duval	10/27/28— 3/10/35	238,000
Boling, Tex.	Union	11/14/28— 8/30/29	8,000
Boling, Tex.	Texas Gulf	3/20/29—operating 1958	49,993,000
Boling, Tex.	Duval	3/23/35— 4/25/40	571,000
Boling, Tex.	Baker-Williams	6/ 2/35—12/ /35	2,000
Long Point, Tex.	Texas Gulf	3/19/30—10/19/38	402,000
Lake Peigneur, La.	Jefferson Lake	10/20/32— 6/ 7/36	431,000
Grand Ecaille, La.	Freeport	12/ 8/33—operating 1958	19,791,000
Clemens, Tex.	Jefferson Lake	5/ 3/37—operating 1958	1,988,000
Clemens, Tex.	Texas Gulf	5/ 3/37— 4/18/49	746,000
Orchard, Tex.	Duval	1/29/38—operating 1958	3,735,000
Long Point, Tex.	Jefferson Lake	6/ 7/46—operating 1958	1,198,000
Long Point, Tex.	Texas Gulf	6/ 7/46—operating 1958	1,198,000
Moss Bluff, Tex.	Texas Gulf	6/24/48—operating 1958	2,604,000
Starks, La.	Jefferson Lake	6/15/51—operating 1958	586,000
Spindletop, Tex.	Texas Gulf	5/12/52—operating 1958	2,111,000
Bay Ste. Elaine, La.	Freeport	11/19/52—operating 1958	817,000
Damon, Tex.	Standard	11/11/53— 4/20/57	140,000
Garden Island Bay, La.	Freeport	11/19/53—operating 1958	2,318,000
Nash, Tex.	Freeport	2/ 5/54—11/21/56	149,000
Long Point, Tex.	Lone Star	6/ 8/54— 7/15/54	(b)
Long Point, Tex.	Admiral	6/19/56— 9/23/56	(b)
Fannett, Tex.	Texas Gulf	5/16/58—operating 1958	—

TOTAL U. S. PRODUCTION   126,931,000

Mexico			
San Cristobal	Mexican Gulf	3/ 4/54— 5/ 5/57	152,000
Jaltipan	Pan American	9/26/54—operating 1958	1,767,000
Amezquite	Gulf Sulphur	5/ 3/56—operating 1958	285,000
Nopalapa	Texas Gulf	2/ 8/57—operating 1958	90,000

TOTAL MEXICAN PRODUCTION   2,294,000

TOTAL FRASH PRODUCTION   129,225,000

a Union constructed a plant in 1923, but the project was abandoned without attempting production.
b Lone Star produced only 2 or 3 tons. The mine was later acquired by Admiral who produced about 200 tons before abandoning the property.

IX. WORLD'S ELEMENTAL SULPHUR PRODUCTION BY SOURCE: 1939-1956
(Long Tons)

	1939	1940	1941	1942	1943	1944
Frasch						
Mexico...............	0	0	0	0	0	0
United States..........	2,090,979	2,732,088	3,139,253	3,460,686	2,538,786	3,218,158
Totals............	2,090,979	2,732,088	3,139,253	3,460,686	2,538,786	3,218,158
Recovered						
Belgium-Luxembourg[1]..	4,000*	4,000*	0	0	0	0
Canada...............	0	0	0	0	0	0
Egypt................	0	0	0	0	0	0
France...............	0	0	0	0	0	0
Germany[2]............	90,000*	150,000*	—	—	—	—
Iran.................	5,000	5,000	5,000	5,000	5,000	6,500
Italy.................	0	0	0	0	0	0
Mexico..............	0	0	0	0	0	0
Netherlands..........	0	0	0	0	0	0
Netherlands Antilles (Aruba).............	0	0	0	0	0	0
Sweden..............	0	0	0	0	8,762	14,218
Trinidad.............	0	0	0	0	0	0
United Kingdom (Total)	0	0	0	0	0	0
From Spent Oxide ...	0	0	0	0	0	0
From Refinery Gases .	0	0	0	0	0	0
United States..........	4,307	3,942	5,493	5,125	5,101	19,096
Totals............	103,307	162,942	10,493	10,125	18,863	39,814
From Sulphide Ores						
Canada...............	33,988	35,871	34,850	34,914	11,694	0
Norway..............	95,433	75,657	77,426	77,423	90,410	65,237
Portugal.............	11,218	11,036	11,158	11,843	10,882	11,533
Spain................	22,818	25,762	19,457	23,343	26,705	23,459
Sweden..............	20,572	18,161	9,520	0	0	0
Totals............	184,029	166,487	152,411	147,523	139,691	100,229
From Sulphur Ores						
Argentina............	—	—	367	2,148	10,649	11,092
Bolivia...............	2,126	4,065	2,315	3,626	7,079	6,151
Chile................	26,999	32,440	28,745	29,570	32,360	30,250
China................	1,874	2,062	2,082	1,949	2,460	2,229
Colombia.............	0	0	0	0	0	0
France...............	689	309	575	703	1,000	1,021
Greece...............	—	2,239	1,585	4,685	6,373	1,860
Iran.................	1,500	1,500	1,500	1,500	1,500	600
Italy (Total Equivalent Sulphur).........	356,078	330,173	299,588	232,610	145,256	85,681
Crude Sulphur Production...........	350,208	325,473	294,288	223,410	135,756	76,081
Sulphur Ore for Agriculture........	5,870	4,700	5,300	9,200	9,500*	9,600
Sulphur Ore for Acid Manufacturing.....	0	0	0	0	0	0
Japan................	202,562	192,357	198,056	160,917	145,368	75,339
Mexico..............	—	—	—	3,000*	4,400	5,100
Peru.................	571	610	935	1,126	564	1,316
Philippines...........	0	0	0	0	0	0
Spain................	3,770	3,560	6,230	5,000	5,511	6,280
Taiwan (Formosa).....	500*	442	280	124	863	230
Turkey..............	2,560	2,600	2,600	2,695	3,326	3,348
United States..........	0	0	0	0	0	—
Totals............	599,229	572,357	544,858	449,653	366,709	230,497
World Total (all sources)..	2,977,544	3,633,874	3,847,015	4,067,987	3,064,049	3,589,698

[1] Produced from spent oxide.
[2] Partially produced from spent oxide. West Germany from 1947-1956.
* Estimated.

IX. WORLD'S ELEMENTAL SULPHUR PRODUCTION BY SOURCE: 1939-1956 (Continued)
(Long Tons)

Frasch	1945	1946	1947	1948	1949	1950
Mexico	0	0	0	0	0	0
United States	3,753,188	3,859,642	4,441,214	4,869,210	4,745,014	5,192,184
Totals	3,753,188	3,859,642	4,441,214	4,869,210	4,745,014	5,192,184

Recovered	1945	1946	1947	1948	1949	1950
Belgium-Luxembourg[1]	2,000 *	3,000 *	2,500 *	2,000 *	400	400
Canada	0	0	0	0	0	0
Egypt	0	0	0	0	0	1,000 *
France	0	0	0	0	0	0
Germany[2]	—	—	12,000 *	20,000	20,000	30,000
Iran	16,000	19,000	19,000	19,000	19,000	19,000
Italy	0	0	0	0	0	0
Mexico	0	0	0	0	0	0
Netherlands	0	0	0	0	0	0
Netherlands Antilles (Aruba)	0	0	0	0	0	0
Sweden	21,136	21,389	14,000	11,815	13,000 *	14,256
Trinidad	0	0	0	0	0	0
United Kingdom (Total)	0	0	0	5,000	5,000	5,000 *
From Spent Oxide	0	0	0	5,000	5,000	5,000
From Refinery Gases	0	0	0	0	0	0
United States	25,184	34,990	43,427	44,369	56,781	142,475
Totals	64,320	78,379	90,927	102,184	114,181	212,131

From Sulphide Ores	1945	1946	1947	1948	1949	1950
Canada	0	0	0	0	0	0
Norway	21,061	71,937	80,415	77,685	79,879	94,634
Portugal	12,753	12,399	7,520	9,668	10,703	14,198
Spain	13,604	18,348	15,781	26,462	26,750	30,709
Sweden	0	0	0	0	0	0
Totals	47,418	102,684	103,716	113,815	117,332	139,541

From Sulphur Ores	1945	1946	1947	1948	1949	1950
Argentina	9,072	10,070	10,871	8,388	10,048	7,622
Bolivia	640	468	2,275	2,685	4,398	4,307
Chile	28,617	8,979	11,659	13,124	7,599	15,228
China	3,000 *	5,000 *	7,278	—	—	—
Colombia	0	0	0	592	793	1,461
France	2,672	2,083	8,427	6,648	5,201	5,571
Greece	1,500 *	1,000	—	—	—	—
Iran	600	600	600	600	1,500	1,500
Italy (Total Equivalent Sulphur)	81,890	144,565	151,910	175,504	204,074	214,467
Crude Sulphur Production	73,990	140,765	146,310	170,904	198,274	209,767
Sulphur Ore for Agriculture	7,900	3,800	5,600	4,600	5,800	4,700
Sulphur Ore for Acid Manufacturing	0	0	0	0	0	0
Japan	37,333	21,046	28,670	40,120	61,414	90,940
Mexico	7,100	5,000 *	3,200	2,100	5,400	11,000
Peru	1,197	363	779	971	248	1,461
Philippines	0	0	0	0	0	0
Spain	4,840	4,000	3,600	3,100	5,620	6,531
Taiwan (Formosa)	34	280	508	1,578	362	2,657
Turkey	4,088	2,970	2,620	2,556	3,046	5,911
United States	—	—	—	—	2,092	1,072
Totals	182,583	206,424	232,397	257,966	311,795	368,365
World Total (all sources)	4,047,509	4,247,139	4,868,254	5,343,175	5,288,322	5,912,221

[1] Produced from spent oxide.
[2] Partially produced from spent oxide. West Germany from 1947-1956.
* Estimated.

IX. WORLD'S ELEMENTAL SULPHUR PRODUCTION BY SOURCE: 1939-1956 (Continued) (Long Tons)

	1951	1952	1953	1954	1955	1956
Frasch						
Mexico..............	0	0	0	75,404	475,351	753,415
United States.........	5,278,249	5,293,145	5,155,342	5,514,640	5,738,978	6,423,883
Totals...........	5,278,249	5,293,145	5,155,342	5,590,044	6,214,329	7,177,298
Recovered						
Belgium-Luxembourg[1]..	400	400	200	400	400 *	400 *
Canada..............	0	7,975	16,340	19,932	25,980	29,883
Egypt..............	2,360	2,800	3,250	3,640	3,800	3,000 *
France..............	0	0	0	3,700	2,850	2,300
Germany[2]...........	38,300	51,100	59,600	67,800	70,800	76,965
Iran................	10,000	6,000	10,000	17,000	18,000	18,000
Italy...............	0	0	0	4,000 *	5,000 *	5,000 *
Mexico..............	15,000	36,500	27,588	26,800	20,061	25,700
Netherlands..........	600	3,000	11,713	9,252	6,900	12,200
Netherlands Antilles (Aruba)............	0	3,800	11,900	19,703	29,476	29,022
Sweden..............	14,149	17,788	23,426	27,416	28,434	30,342
Trinidad.............	0	1,600	3,000 *	4,300	5,000 *	5,000 *
United Kingdom (Total)	4,700	14,800	25,600	40,200	45,200	52,200
From Spent Oxide....	4,700	8,900 *	5,900 *	8,700	7,800	8,900
From Refinery Gases .	0	5,900 *	19,700 *	31,500	37,400	43,300
United States.........	184,013	251,198	341,660	359,271	398,780	464,758
Totals...........	269,522	396,961	534,277	603,414	660,681	754,770
From Sulphide Ores						
Canada..............	0	0	0	0	0	3,700
Norway..............	96,826	103,104	101,675	99,058	98,834	95,387
Portugal.............	13,902	15,376	16,727	16,076	15,425	16,877
Spain................	32,400	34,550	33,445	31,300	34,500	46,100
Sweden..............	0	0	0	0	0	0
Totals...........	143,128	153,030	151,847	146,434	148,759	162,064
From Sulphur Ores						
Argentina............	7,560	15,000	16,000	17,000	17,651	27,298
Bolivia..............	9,100	5,497	2,458	2,565	3,975	3,418
Chile................	29,672	47,821	32,275	43,100	56,338	37,272
China................	—	—	—	—	—	—
Colombia............	2,479	2,974	2,657	5,118	5,413	4,921
France..............	10,905	17,692	10,710	0	0	0
Greece..............	—	—	1,200	2,507	3,600	1,200
Iran.................	1,500	1,500	1,500	1,500	250	1,500 *
Italy (Total Equivalent Sulphur)..........	246,282	275,206	272,161	243,064	247,129	245,694
Crude Sulphur Production..........	197,382	232,706	224,161	194,064	181,629	170,094
Sulphur Ore for Agriculture........	6,600	6,400	5,100	6,800	6,500	6,700
Sulphur Ore for Acid Manufacturing.....	42,300	36,100	42,900	42,200	59,000	68,900
Japan...............	140,181	176,652	186,556	184,745	199,676	243,312
Mexico..............	11,375	11,784	5,900	5,000	5,000	5,000
Peru................	2,251	5,066	4,916	5,000	2,000	2,000
Philippines...........	0	0	1,089	761	3,700	—
Spain................	6,510	5,400	6,287	5,400	6,500	5,900
Taiwan (Formosa).....	2,732	5,001	3,423	5,873	4,854	7,864
Turkey..............	7,273	8,232	9,626	9,862	11,318	13,681
United States.........	1,365	2,197	38,257	64,333	60,902	60,402
Totals...........	479,185	580,022	595,015	595,828	628,306	659,394
World Total (all sources)..	6,170,084	6,423,158	6,436,481	6,935,720	7,652,075	8,753,526

[1] Produced from spent oxide.
[2] Partially produced from spent oxide. West Germany from 1947-1956.
* Estimated.

X. WORLD'S ELEMENTAL SULPHUR PRODUCTION
BY COUNTRIES: 1939-1956
(Long Tons)

Elemental Sulphur Production	1939	1940	1941	1942	1943	1944
Argentina.................	—	—	367	2,148	10,649	11,092
Belgium-Luxembourg....	4,000	4,000	0	0	0	0
Bolivia.................	2,126	4,065	2,315	3,626	7,079	6,151
Canada.................	33,988	35,871	34,850	34,914	11,694	0
Chile..................	26,999	32,440	28,745	29,570	32,360	30,250
China.................	1,874	2,062	2,082	1,949	2,460	2,229
Colombia..............	0	0	0	0	0	0
Egypt.................	0	0	0	0	0	0
France.................	689	309	575	703	1,000	1,021
Germany..............	90,000	150,000	—	—	—	—
Greece.................	—	2,239	1,585	4,685	6,373	1,860
Iran..................	6,500	6,500	6,500	6,500	6,500	7,100
Italy..................	356,078	330,173	299,588	232,610	145,256	85,681
Japan.................	202,562	192,357	198,056	160,917	145,368	75,339
Mexico................	—	—	—	3,000	4,400	5,100
Netherlands...........	0	0	0	0	0	0
Netherlands Antilles (Aruba)............	0	0	0	0	0	0
Norway...............	95,433	75,657	77,426	77,423	90,410	65,237
Peru.................	571	610	935	1,126	564	1,316
Philippines............	0	0	0	0	0	0
Portugal..............	11,218	11,036	11,158	11,843	10,882	11,533
Spain.................	26,588	29,322	25,687	28,343	32,216	29,739
Sweden...............	20,572	18,161	9,520	0	8,762	14,218
Taiwan (Formosa)......	500	442	280	124	863	230
Trinidad..............	0	0	0	0	0	0
Turkey...............	2,560	2,600	2,600	2,695	3,326	3,348
United Kingdom.......	0	0	0	0	0	0
United States.........	2,095,286	2,736,030	3,144,746	3,465,811	2,543,887	3,237,254
Totals............	2,977,544	3,633,874	3,847,015	4,067,987	3,064,049	3,588,698

Summary						
Frasch................	2,090,979	2,732,088	3,139,253	3,460,686	2,538,786	3,218,158
Recovered[1]...........	103,307	162,942	10,493	10,125	18,863	39,814
From Sulphide Ores.....	184,029	166,487	152,411	147,523	139,691	100,229
From Sulphur Ores.....	599,229	572,357	544,858	449,653	366,709	230,497
Totals............	2,977,544	3,633,874	3,847,015	4,067,987	3,064,049	3,588,698

[1] Excludes Germany from 1941-1946.
Sources: Frasch and Sulphur Ore data mostly obtained from U. S. Bureau of Mines Publications. Recovered and Sulphide Ore data from International Materials Conferences, O.E.E.C. Publications, British Sulphur Corporation *Quarterly Reports* and other trade publications.

X. WORLD'S ELEMENTAL SULPHUR PRODUCTION BY COUNTRIES: 1939-1956 (Continued) (Long Tons)

Elemental Sulphur Production	1945	1946	1947	1948	1949	1950
Argentina	9,072	10,070	10,871	8,388	10,048	7,622
Belgium-Luxembourg	2,000	3,000	2,500	2,000	400	400
Bolivia	640	468	2,275	2,685	4,398	4,307
Canada	0	0	0	0	0	0
Chile	28,617	8,979	11,659	13,124	7,599	15,228
China	3,000	5,000	7,278	—	—	—
Colombia	0	0	0	592	793	1,461
Egypt	0	0	0	0	0	1,000
France	2,672	2,083	8,427	6,648	5,201	5,571
Germany	—	—	12,000	20,000	20,000	30,000
Greece	1,500	1,000	—	—	—	—
Iran	16,600	19,600	19,600	19,600	20,500	20,500
Italy	81,890	144,565	151,910	175,504	204,074	214,467
Japan	37,333	21,046	28,670	40,120	61,414	90,940
Mexico	7,100	5,000	3,200	2,100	5,400	11,000
Netherlands	0	0	0	0	0	0
Netherlands Antilles (Aruba)	0	0	0	0	0	0
Norway	21,061	71,937	80,415	77,685	79,879	94,634
Peru	1,197	363	779	971	248	98
Philippines	0	0	0	0	0	0
Portugal	12,753	12,399	7,520	9,668	10,703	14,198
Spain	18,444	22,348	19,381	29,562	32,370	37,240
Sweden	21,136	21,389	14,000	11,815	13,000	14,256
Taiwan (Formosa)	34	280	508	1,578	362	2,657
Trinidad	0	0	0	0	0	0
Turkey	4,088	2,970	2,620	2,556	3,046	5,911
United Kingdom	0	0	0	5,000	5,000	5,000
United States	3,778,372	3,894,632	4,484,641	4,913,579	4,803,887	5,335,731
Totals	4,047,509	4,247,129	4,868,254	5,343,175	5,288,322	5,912,221

Summary						
Frasch	3,753,188	3,859,642	4,441,214	4,869,210	4,745,014	5,192,184
Recovered[1]	64,320	78,379	90,927	102,184	114,181	212,131
From Sulphide Ores	47,418	102,684	103,716	113,815	117,332	139,541
From Sulphur Ores	182,583	206,424	232,397	257,966	311,795	368,365
Totals	4,047,509	4,247,129	4,868,254	5,343,175	5,288,322	5,912,221

[1] Excludes Germany from 1941-1946.
Sources: Frasch and Sulphur Ore data mostly obtained from U. S. Bureau of Mines Publications. Recovered and Sulphide Ore data from International Materials Conferences, O.E.E.C. Publications, British Sulphur Corporation *Quarterly Reports* and other trade publications.

X. WORLD'S ELEMENTAL SULPHUR PRODUCTION BY COUNTRIES: 1939-1956 (Continued)
(Long Tons)

Elemental Sulphur Production	1951	1952	1953	1954	1955	1956
Argentina.............	7,560	15,000	16,000	17,000	17,651	27,298
Belgium-Luxembourg....	400	400	200	400	400	400
Bolivia................	9,100	5,497	2,458	2,565	3,975	3,418
Canada................	0	7,975	16,340	19,932	25,980	33,583
Chile.................	29,672	47,821	32,275	43,100	56,338	37,272
China.................	—	—	—	—	—	—
Colombia..............	2,479	2,974	2,657	5,118	5,413	4,921
Egypt.................	2,360	2,800	3,250	3,640	3,800	3,000
France................	10,905	17,692	10,710	3,700	2,850	2,300
Germany..............	38,300	51,100	59,600	67,800	70,800	76,965
Greece................	—	—	1,200	2,507	3,600	1,200
Iran..................	11,500	7,500	11,500	18,500	18,250	19,500
Italy.................	246,282	275,206	272,161	243,064	247,129	245,694
Japan.................	140,181	176,652	186,556	184,745	199,676	243,312
Mexico...............	26,375	48,284	33,488	107,204	500,412	784,115
Netherlands...........	600	3,000	11,713	9,252	6,900	12,200
Netherlands Antilles (Aruba).............	0	3,800	11,900	19,703	29,476	29,022
Norway...............	96,826	103,104	101,675	99,058	98,834	95,387
Peru..................	2,251	5,066	4,916	5,000	2,000	2,000
Philippines...........	0	0	1,089	761	3,700	—
Portugal..............	13,902	15,376	16,727	16,076	15,425	16,877
Spain.................	38,910	39,950	39,732	36,700	41,000	52,000
Sweden...............	14,149	17,788	23,426	27,416	28,434	30,342
Taiwan (Formosa)......	2,732	5,001	3,423	5,873	4,854	7,864
Trinidad..............	0	1,600	3,000	4,300	5,000	5,000
Turkey................	7,273	8,232	9,626	9,862	11,318	13,681
United Kingdom.......	4,700	14,800	25,600	40,200	45,200	52,200
United States.........	5,463,627	5,546,540	5,535,259	5,938,244	6,198,660	6,949,043
Totals............	6,170,084	6,423,158	6,436,481	6,935,720	7,652,075	8,753,526

Summary

	1951	1952	1953	1954	1955	1956
Frasch................	5,278,249	5,293,145	5,155,342	5,590,044	6,214,329	7,177,298
Recovered[1]..........	269,522	396,961	534,277	603,414	660,681	754,770
From Sulphide Ores.....	143,128	153,030	151,847	146,434	148,759	162,064
From Sulphur Ores.....	479,185	580,022	595,015	595,828	628,306	659,394
Totals............	6,170,084	6,423,158	6,436,481	6,935,720	7,652,075	8,753,526

[1] Excludes Germany from 1941-1946.
Sources: Frasch and Sulphur Ore data mostly obtained from U. S. Bureau of Mines Publications. Recovered and Sulphide Ore data from International Materials Conferences, O.E.E.C. Publications, British Sulphur Corporation *Quarterly Reports* and other trade publications.

XI. MEXICAN PRODUCTION AND SHIPMENTS OF SULPHUR IN ALL FORMS

(Thousands of Long Tons Sulphur Equivalent)

PRODUCTION	1954	1955	1956	1957
Frasch	75.4	475.5	753.4	990.1
Native	5.9	4.0[e]	5.0	6.9
Recovered	19.9	28.0	26.8	21.7
Sulphur in Gases	12.0[e]	12.0[e]	12.0[e]	12.0[e]
Total	113.2	519.5	797.2	1,030.7
SHIPMENTS	1954	1955	1956	1957
Domestic				
Frasch	15.0[e]	10.0	40.0	23.0[e]
Other	31.9[e]	37.0[e]	39.0[e]	60.7[e]
Total	46.9	47.0	79.0	83.7
Exports				
U.S.A.	—	33.8	241.1	464.0
Other	—	146.2	234.7	394.2
Total	—	180.0	475.8	858.2

[e] Estimated.

Source: Production: Year 1954, British Sulphur Corp.; year 1955, Bureau of Mines; year 1956, 1957, BDSA U. S. Dept. of Commerce, Shipments: Frasch exports, BDSA U. S. Dept. of Commerce; Frasch domestic shipments, British Sulphur Corp. except where noted.

XII. EXPORTS OF FRASCH SULPHUR
(Thousands of Long Tons)

DESTINATION	1938 U.S.A.	1950 U.S.A.	1957 U.S.A.	1957 MEXICO[a]	1957 TOTAL
Total	579	1,441	1,562	394	1,956
North America	101	392	368	—	368
Canada	83	354	348		348
Cuba		13	19		19
Mexico	6	2			
West Indies	9	23			
Other	3		1		1
South America	20	86	151	—	151
Argentina	16	24	45		45
Brazil	4	60	100		100
Columbia		2			
Uruguay			4		4
Venezuela			2		2
Europe	273	651	663	227	890
Austria		24	19		19
Belgium	6	57	85	19	104
Finland	4		32		32
France	99	95	148	72	220
West Germany	33	25	68	12	80
Netherlands	22		6	43	49
Spain		5			
Sweden	6	8	12		12
Switzerland		16	34		34
United Kingdom	99	420	246	81	327
Other Europe	4	1	13		13
Africa	25	112	103	48	115
Algeria	14	16			
Egypt		4	3		3
French Morocco		5	7		7
Tunisia		10	13	18	31
Union of So. Africa	11	77	80	30	110
Asia	9	53	133	24	157
India	1	45	102		102
Indonesia	5	5	2		2
Iran	2		15		15
Iraq					
Israel				24	24
Japan					
Pakistan			2		2
Philippines			8		8
Other Asia	1	3	4		4
Oceania	151	147	144	95	239
Australia	108	68	80	59	139
New Zealand	43	79	64	36	100

[a] Excludes 464,000 tons exported to U. S.
Source: U. S. Department of Commerce.

XIII. SULPHUR IN CANADA: 1940-1957

(Short Tons of Sulphur Content)

YEAR 19—	PYRITES SHIPPED	SMELTER GASES UTILIZED	RECOVERED SULPHUR SHIPPED	TOTAL	PYRITES EXPORTED	SULPHUR EXPORTED	SULPHUR IMPORTED	APPARENT CANADIAN CONSUMPTION
40	63,230	107,400[b]		170,630	40,380		215,597	345,847
41	149,130	110,130[b]		259,260	129,629		235,271	364,902
42	182,780	120,930[b]		303,710	166,451		290,121	427,380
43	139,450	118,060[b]		257,510	104,509		218,527	371,528
44	121,770	126,320		248,090	90,836		235,955	393,209
45	110,200	139,910		250,110	75,479		248,846	423,477
46	96,540	138,230		234,770	68,045		273,502	440,227
47	82,637	139,144		221,781	56,336		361,424	526,869
48	87,126	142,337		229,463	50,243		354,622	533,842
49	117,581	144,290		261,871	90,553		280,557	451,875
50	150,487	150,685		301,172	111,652		390,333	579,853
51	215,363	156,427		371,790	178,039		395,928	589,679
52[a]	253,241	170,547	4,225	428,013	197,897		415,185	645,301
53[a]	172,650	186,200	16,072	374,922	129,608		359,928	605,242
54[a]	297,159	235,247	18,665	551,071	188,608		310,127	672,590
55[d]	387,986	240,457	25,976	654,419	225,000[c]	3,051	373,373	799,741
56[d]	473,605[b]	236,088	34,784	744,477	330,000[b]	4,331	474,117	884,263
57[d]	569,000[b]	246,337	98,172	913,509	400,000[c]	12,364	416,930	918,075

[a] Estimated sulphur equivalent of the zinc sulphide roasted at Arvida, Quebec, subtracted from reported pyrites totals and added to smelter gas totals where it is currently reported.

[b] Includes some sulphur produced from smelter gases and sulphide ores.

[c] Estimates based on the reported values, and reported gross weight of pyrites 1,239,606 N. T. in 1957.

[d] The production of pyrrhotite by the International Nickel Company at Copper Cliff, Ontario is reported as valued at $759,000 in 1956 and $1,240,000 in 1957. This ore was used only for iron, nickel and other metal values so total sulphur consumption is over stated by an estimated 35,000 N. T. in 1956 and 55,000 in 1957.

XIV. PYRITES IN THE UNITED STATES
(Long Tons)

	PRODUCTION	IMPORTS	APPARENT CONSUMPTION
1880	NA	8,000	8,000
1885	49,000	45,000	94,000
1890	99,854	120,000	219,854
1895	99,549	190,435	289,984
1900	204,615	322,484	527,099
1905	253,000	511,946	764,946
1910	241,612	803,551	1,045,163
1915	394,124	964,637	1,358,761
1920	310,777	332,606	643,383
1925	193,642	276,385	470,027
1930	347,512	368,114	715,626
1935	519,497	397,113	916,610
1940	626,640	407,004	1,033,644
1941	645,257	368,838	1,014,095
1942	720,363	300,140	1,020,503
1943	802,384	256,308	1,058,692
1944	788,530	180,763	969,293
1945	722,596	186,507	909,103
1946	813,372	182,893	996,265
1947	940,652	126,553	1,067,205
1948	928,531	107,411	1,035,942
1949	888,388	120,937	1,009,325
1950	931,163	208,766	1,139,929
1951	1,017,769	221,487	1,239,256
1952	994,342	296,047	1,290,389
1953	922,647	190,474	1,113,121
1954	908,715	279,569	1,188,284
1955	1,006,943	358,165	1,365,108
1956	1,069,904	365,816	1,435,720
1957	1,067,396	353,032	1,420,428

Source: 1880 to 1940—The Stone That Burns, page 320, with revisions, 1941 to date—United States Bureau of *Mines*, Mineral Yearbook.

XV. WORLD PYRITES PRODUCTION
(Gross Weight in Metric Tons)

| | AMERICA | | | | EUROPE | | | | | | | | | |
	CANADA	CUBA	UNITED STATES	VENE-ZUELA	FINLAND	FRANCE	EAST GERMANY	WEST GERMANY	GREECE	ITALY	NORWAY	POLAND	PORTUGAL	SPAIN
1900	36,316		207,889			304,991		169,402		71,597	16,166		345,351	355,922
1905	29,706		257,048			267,129		185,378		117,674	25,569		352,500	179,089
1910	48,871		245,478			250,447		215,721	33,293	135,636	79,680		393,762	294,201
1915	269,355		400,430			196,666		641,600	12,113	369,320	67,536		236,692	2,282,795
1920	158,524		315,749			140,375		436,271	3,239	321,589	138,499	264	274,972	1,355,047
1925	14,157		196,740			212,559		223,293	65,000	533,737	312,627	11,217	217,296	3,359,240
1930	48,619		353,072			196,320		289,741	177,808	717,270	561,400	11,046	400,224	3,416,465
1935	26,494		527,809		83,023	150,130		290,188	175,000	833,405	1,311,468	732	214,754	2,286,113
1940	116,000		636,666		250,000	210,000		894,000	16,000	1,061,000	762,000		394,000	962,000
1941	275,202		655,581		290,000	201,000		1,185,000	10,000	1,023,000	933,000		172,759	575,000
1942	344,268		731,889		288,000	218,420		1,215,977	7,000	970,624	822,207		128,280	627,005
1943	258,162		815,262		110,490	207,260		1,397,065	3,860	465,253	808,779		109,994	881,150
1944	226,859		801,186		127,660	112,908			4,380	229,000	750,405		130,131	512,294
1945	206,595		734,194		110,320	146,625		73,000	6,510	102,508	247,465	8,900	170,967	899,760
1946	183,191		826,427		126,310	218,510		238,700	80,140	400,519	539,850	28,253	314,976	1,175,976
1947	161,718		955,479		153,268	196,180		321,000	58,185	642,445	720,015	39,659	388,727	1,217,442
1948	166,985		943,434		177,512	181,683	65,000	383,100	60,236	835,027	735,422	58,100	561,136	1,463,912
1949	227,227		905,746		180,040	205,909		431,963	15,785	866,179	745,367	81,000	622,925	1,559,044
1950	283,596		946,108		162,050	247,615	92,000	535,196	87,678	900,912	748,793	99,400	613,522	1,653,699
1951	403,648		1,034,104		232,546	280,558	102,000	533,530	180,120	898,186	696,049	100,900	729,611	2,004,126
1952	506,566	10,161	1,101,301		244,926	294,414	109,000	527,932	201,238	1,141,417	712,616	113,200	755,897	2,378,607
1953	356,189	50,803	937,455		259,587	298,000	119,947	529,983	225,134	1,225,368	740,000	132,394	651,136	1,786,548
1954	624,049	119,945	923,544		252,504	299,326	130,995	565,384	209,807	1,250,892	794,880	153,293	652,072	1,894,061
1955	796,880	129,537	1,023,054		302,833	305,341	142,993	589,073	232,793	1,316,951	843,740	156,593	736,288	2,326,240
1956	949,541	66,274	1,087,022	59,998	294,071	303,839	154,026	644,389	235,990	1,370,974	840,564	170,688	669,747	2,295,523
1957	1,124,498	36,208	1,084,474	49,998	297,141	323,602	149,962	601,702	229,616	1,468,028	831,269	169,672	667,279	2,216,834

XV. WORLD PYRITES PRODUCTION (Continued)

(Gross Weight in Metric Tons)

| | EUROPE—CONTINUED | | | | ASIA | | | | | | UNION | | WORLD TOTAL* | |
	SWEDEN	UNITED KING-DOM	YUGO-SLAVIA	CYPRUS	JAPAN	PHILIP-PINES	TAIWAN	TURKEY	ALGERIA	RHO-DESIA	OF S. AFRICA	AUS-TRALIA	GROSS WEIGHT	SULPHUR CONTENT
1900	179	12,476			16,166								1,729,418	
1905	20,763	12,362			25,569								1,761,782	
1910	25,446	9,531	36,837		79,680							2,963	2,146,141	
1915	76,324	10,711			67,536						554	19,706	5,259,174	
1920	107,336	6,766	3,682	1,422	138,409				18,891		3,217	10,628	3,682,597	
1925	69,873	5,373	38,988	176,036	312,627				11,000		5,373		6,199,570	
1930	60,441	5,585	50,345	242,316	561,400				16,627		3,603		7,563,925	
1935	106,815	4,261	83,648	211,124	1,311,468				12,350	12,232	25,068	25,965	7,994,741	3,500,000
1940	194,000	5,400	135,000	253,000	1,859,000				40,500	34,440	36,701	50,500	8,400,000	3,700,000
1941	227,000	6,500		9,000	1,946,000				46,000	42,600	32,000	56,000	8,500,000	3,900,000
1942	303,000	17,500		5,051	1,778,000				35,820	39,941	40,467	69,000	9,000,000	3,600,000
1943	325,023	9,759		13,195	1,167,710				25,590	35,065	37,030	78,860	8,500,000	3,000,000
1944	317,455	10,935		11,451	716,188				32,905	34,177	36,155	109,290	7,000,000	3,000,000
1945	261,984	11,468		101,681	118,750				30,132	33,465	38,556	108,384	5,500,000	2,300,000
1946	280,208	20,959	49,000	294,052	474,842			300	40,360	25,413	38,044	131,364	7,000,000	3,000,000
1947	310,571	10,106	76,000	611,800	832,845			5,000	35,295	17,144	34,820	110,410	8,700,000	3,700,000
1948	399,033	11,800	300,006	589,772	1,138,782				35,900	13,224	35,992	90,848	9,700,000	4,000,000
1949	424,007	17,191	244,775	942,848	1,535,082				32,705	16,968	35,527	87,923	11,100,000	4,600,000
1950	406,809	13,501	117,167	829,889	1,926,750				25,075	13,810	36,026	113,973	11,800,000	5,000,000
1951	466,934	13,501	153,779	959,838	2,250,784		6,728	19,350	31,450	28,269	33,378	153,818	13,200,000	5,500,000
1952	411,276	15,896	188,129	1,072,968	2,628,357		33,232	23,091	24,010	19,053	31,141	201,902	15,000,000	6,300,000
1953	388,974	10,408	173,003	1,001,572	2,343,260	1,976	25,291	34,478	29,760	36,665	93,844	169,687	14,000,000	5,900,000
1954	399,182	7,123	162,273	1,121,021	2,677,733	5,285	24,239	16,395	33,540	36,969	229,143	210,088	14,900,000	6,300,000
1955	394,058	5,602	226,581	1,339,457	2,736,026	30,781	29,016	19,994	21,667	21,608	357,276	227,053	16,600,000	6,900,000
1956	493,443	4,274	255,936	1,628,993	3,097,353		29,661	48,531	6,093	18,973	436,843	190,392	17,600,000	7,400,000
1957	499,872	3,655	312,987	1,097,369	3,041,600	17,847	33,270		18,799	20,305	394,427	242,858	17,200,000	7,200,000

Source: United States Bureau of Mines *Minerals Yearbook* and *Statistical Yearbook*, United Nations for 1940-1942 period.

* In addition to countries listed Austria, Brazil, China, Czechoslovakia, Kenya, Korea, Morocco, Romania, Tunisia and U.S.S.R. produce or have produced pyrites but production figures are not available; estimates by senior author of Sulphur Chapter included in total.

XVI. U. S. ANNUAL AVERAGE PRICE OF DOMESTIC CRUDE BRIMSTONE (F.O.B. Mine)

YEAR	PRICE PER LONG TON	YEAR	PRICE PER LONG TON	YEAR	PRICE PER LONG TON
1913	$22.00	1928	$18.00	1943	$16.00
1914	22.00	1929	18.00	1944	16.00
1915	22.00	1930	18.00	1945	16.00
1916	31.33	1931	18.00	1946	16.00
1917	43.33	1932	18.00	1947	16.50
1918	32.29	1933	18.00	1948	18.00
1919	28.00	1934	18.00	1949	18.00
1920	23.85	1935	18.00	1950	18.90
1921	15.91	1936	18.00	1951	21.00
1922	14.08	1937	18.00	1952	21.00
1923	14.00	1938	17.51	1953	24.38
1924	14.10	1939	16.00	1954	26.50
1925	14.67	1940	16.00	1955	26.50
1926	18.21	1941	16.00	1956	26.50
1927	18.00	1942	16.00	1957[a]	25.50

Source: Bureau of Labor Statistics.

[a] Effective September 1957, $23.50.

XVII. COMMERCIAL GRADES OF SULPHURIC ACID[1]

TECHNICAL NAME	° BÉ.	SPECIFIC GRAVITY ($15.56°C.$ or $60°F.$)	PERCENTAGE OF H_2SO_4	PERCENTAGE OF SO_3	M.P. OR FREEZING POINT
Battery acid	42	1.4	50.87	41.53	$-31°F.$
Chamber acid	50	1.5263	62.18	50.76	-27
Glover or tower acid	60	1.7059	77.67	63.40	$+12.6$
Oil of vitriol (O.V.)	66	1.8354	93.19	76.07	-29
Monohydrate	..	1.8391	100.00	81.63	$+10$
Oleum, 20% anhydride	..	1.916	104.49	85.30	-12
Oleum, 40% anhydride	..	....	109.00	88.98	$+35$

[1] Adapted from Andrew M. Fairlie, *Sulfuric Acid Manufacture* N. Y., 1936.

XVIII. U. S. PRODUCTION OF SULPHURIC ACID

(Thousands of Short Tons—100% H_2SO_4 Basis)[1]

YEAR	GROSS PRODUC-TION	NUMBER OF ESTABLISH-MENTS[2]	PRODUCTION OF NEW ACID		CONTACT—FORTIFIED
			CHAMBER	CONTACT	
1880	264	49			
1889	487	105			
1899	963	127			
1909	1,710	183			
1919	3,454[a]	216	2,337	710	
1921	2,718	197	2,037	686	
1923	4,078	185	2,949	1,126	
1925	4,357	177	3,080	1,275	
1927	4,563	181	3,179	1,382	
1929	5,282	170	3,367	1,913	
1931	3,785	175	2,262	1,522	
1933	3,406	112	—	—	
1935	4,000	155	1,866	2,133	
1937	4,941	157	2,577	2,365	
1939	4,795	183	2,121	2,674	
1941	6,770		3,012	3,758	
1943	8,442		3,148	4,703	591
1945	9,522	174	3,169	5,518	835
1947	10,780	180	3,275	6,829	677
1949	11,432	191	2,745	7,982	705
1950	13,029	209	2,956	9,187	887
1951	13,372		2,886	9,503	983
1952	13,310	191	2,711	9,635	965
1953	14,003	194	2,736	10,291	976
1954	14,376		2,512	11,045	820
1955	16,255	203	2,321	12,998	936
1956	16,495	211	2,234	13,504	757
1957	16,388	217	1,988	13,708	691

[a] Includes 407,000 tons of acid output for plants producing both chamber and contact acid.

[1] Includes spent acid either fortified in contact units or decomposed into SO_2 and made into new acid. Production data prior to 1954 exclude production of government-owned, privately operated plants.

[2] Excludes plants fortifying spent acid only.

Source: *Census of Manufacturers* and *Facts for Industry M-19A*, Bureau of Census.

XIX. PERCENTAGE OF U. S. SULPHURIC ACID
MADE FROM PRIMARY RAW MATERIALS

YEAR	ELEMENTAL	PYRITES	BY-PRODUCT SMELTER GASES	H₂S GAS	SLUDGE	FORTI- FIED ACID
1885	85	14	1	—	—	—
1895	75	24	1	—	—	—
1905	10	79	11	—	—	—
1910	3	79	18	—	—	—
1915	9	64	27	—	—	—
1920	52	23	25	—	—	—
1925	68	14	18	—	—	—
1930	66	19	15	—	—	—
1935	59	29	12	—	—	—
1940	64	24	11	1	—	—
1945	69	12	9	1	—	9
1950	74	11	6	1	1	7
1951	70	13	6	2	2	7
1952	70	13	7	1	2	7
1953	72	11	6	1	2	7
1954	71	12	6	2	3	6
1955	72	10	7	1	4	6
1956	72	11	7	1	4	5
1957	70	11	8	2	5	4

Source: 1885-1895 from Theodore J. Kreps, *The Economics of the Sulphuric Acid Industry*, page 105.
Other years estimated.

XX. DISTRIBUTION OF SULPHURIC ACID CONSUMED IN U. S.

(Thousands of Short Tons 100% H_2SO_4 Basis)

CONSUMING INDUSTRIES	1925 TONS	1925 %	1930 TONS	1930 %	1935 TONS	1935 %	1940 TONS	1940 %	1945 TONS	1945 %	1950 TONS	1950 %
Fertilizers	1,228	28	1,540	32	1,076	26	1,406	25	2,850	31	—	—
Superphosphate	[a]		[a]		[a]		[a]		[a]		3,790	27
Ammonium Sulphate	[a]		[a]		[a]		[a]		[a]		1,508	11
Coal Products	[a]		498	10	389	9	560	10	600	7	—	
Chemicals	682	16	510	11	585	14	697	12	2,220	24	3,226	23
Petroleum Refining	904	21	883	19	610	14	784	14	1,020	11	1,422	10
Iron and Steel	453	10	411	9	392	9	746	13	570	6	1,027	7
Other Metals	437	10	348	7	323	8	398	7	330	4	211	2
Paints and Pigments	196	4	124	3	249	6	361	6	520	6	1,322	9
Explosives	115	3	110	2	109	3	106	2	100	1	375	3
Rayon and Cellulose Film	[b]		90	2	192	5	292	5	495	5	670	5
Textiles	[b]		49	1	56	1	78	1	70	1	37	
Miscellaneous	346	8	205	4	203	5	286	5	400	4	399	3
Total	4,361	100	4,768	100	4,184	100	5,714	100	9,175	100	13,987	100

CONSUMING INDUSTRIES	1951 TONS	1951 %	1952 TONS	1952 %	1953 TONS	1953 %	1954 TONS	1954 %	1955 TONS	1955 %	1956 TONS	1956 %	1957 TONS	1957 %
Fertilizer														
Superphosphate	3,944	27	4,053	28	4,050	26	4,060	27	4,650	27	4,650	27	4,700	27
Ammonium Sulphate	1,161	8	1,236	8	1,150	8	1,320	9	1,650	10	1,600	9	1,600	9
Total	5,105	35	5,289	36	5,200	34	5,380	36	6,300	37	6,250	36	6,300	36
Chemicals	3,814	26	3,718	25	4,000	26	3,880	26	4,195	25	4,350	25	4,400	26
Petroleum Refining	1,573	11	1,663	12	1,780	12	1,770	12	1,800	11	1,900	11	1,900	11
Iron and Steel	954	6	838	6	1,010	7	850	5	1,160	7	1,265	7	1,100	6
Other Metals	241	2	218	1	220	1	220	1	248	1	265	1	250	1
Paints and Pigments	1,331	9	1,249	9	1,300	9	1,300	9	1,400	8	1,450	8	1,400	8
Explosives	403	3	375	3	420	3	400	3	450	3	475	3	470	3
Rayon and Cellulose Film	687	5	634	4	670	4	620	4	750	4	850	5	850	5
Textile Finishing	31		28		30		30		30		30		30	
Miscellaneous	514	3	632	4	670	4	650	4	675	4	675	4	600	4
Total	14,653	100	14,644	100	15,300	100	15,100	100	17,008	100	17,510	100	17,300	100

[a] Not listed separately.
[b] Included in paint and pigments.
Source: Years 1925-1945, 1953-1956 as estimated in Annual Review issues of *Chemical Engineering*. Data for years 1925-1945 probably do not include spent acid used as such. Year 1957, industry estimate.

XXI. ESTIMATED U. S. GROSS SULPHURIC ACID CONSUMPTION BY USE: 1950-1952
(Thousands of Short Tons)

Use	Total	1950	1951	1952
		13,987	14,653	14,644
Alcohols		516	648	650
Aluminum sulfate (for public water treatment and sewage)		83	95	85
Aluminum sulfate (for other purposes)		280	298	275
Ammonium sulfate (coke oven)		639	678	608
Ammonium sulfate (synthetic)		869	483	628
Aviation gasoline		824	981	1,181
Chemicals not elsewhere classified		984	1,197	1,245
Chlorine drying		32	39	40
Chromium chemicals incl. chromic acid		64	86	60
Copper sulfate		20	31	27
Dyes		196	202	150
Fat splitting		18	16	15
Hydrochloric acid		129	137	128
Hydrofluoric acid		114	137	135
Industrial explosives		375	403	375
Industrial water treatment		30	35	30
Inorganic pigments		1,322	1,331	1,249
Insecticides		99	125	130
Iron and steel (pickling)		1,027	954	838
Light oil refining (coke oven)		62	71	64
Medicinals		28	37	33
Nonferrous metal pickling		22	18	18
Other nonferrous metallurgical purposes		189	223	200
Other petroleum products (except sulfonated hydrocarbons)		598	592	482
Petroleum catalysts		123	143	155
Petroleum sulfonates (lube oil additives)		128	151	150
Phosphatic fertilizers		3,790	3,944	4,053
Rayon (high tenacity yarn)		192	197	274
Rayon (other)		354	359	255
Regenerated cellulose film, sheet or products		124	131	105
Rubber (including synthetic)		103	135	110
Storage batteries		78	74	60
Sulfonated oils		6	5	5
Synthetic detergents		202	217	225
Tall oil		37	46	39
Textile finishing		37	31	28
Miscellaneous		293	403	539

Based on reports to the former National Production Authority (forms NPAF-74, 159, and 161), and a special survey covering the recovery of spent acid during 1950 and 1951. Data for 1952 were partially estimated.

XXII. ESTIMATED U. S. SULPHUR CONSUMPTION BY USE: 1950-1952 (1)
(Thousands of Long Tons)

	1950	1951	1952
Chemicals			
Sulphuric Acid...............	3,077	3,074	2,925
Carbon Bisulphide............	183	214	186
Other Chemicals.............	94	103	92
Pulp and Paper................	418	391	371
Ground Crude and Refined for Agricultural Use (2).........	274	248	198
Rubber......................	46	42	39
Miscellaneous.................	44	40	28
TOTAL DOMESTIC USE.	4,136	4,112	3,839
Exports (crude sulphur) (3)..	1,441	1,283	1,304
TOTAL USE..........	5,577	5,395	5,143

Notes: (1) Based on Consumers' reports on Forms NPAF-98, 157 and 158 to National Production Authority as published in *Chemical and Public Division Report on Sulphur*, BDSA, Department of Commerce, June 25, 1954.
(2) Excludes industrial uses but includes exports of ground crude and refined.
(3) As reported by Bureau of Census.

XXIII. WORLD SULPHURIC ACID PRODUCTION
(Thousands of Metric Tons, 100% H_2SO_4)

	1938	1950	1956
Total World[a]	15,100	25,700	37,000
North America	4,042	12,506	15,914
United States	3,799	11,820	14,960
Canada	243	686	954
South America	40	77	78
Argentina	40	77	78
Europe	8,062	9,513	14,204
Austria	32	9	74
Belgium	749	880	1,116
Czechoslovakia	165	252	422
Denmark	140	162	170
Finland	27	88	143
France	1,272	1,215	1,534
Germany, East	} 2,272	300	611
Germany, West		1,446	2,530
Greece	52	41	87
Hungary	40	62	102
Ireland	55	62	57
Italy	1,076	1,276	2,054
Netherlands	525	438	709
Norway	40	69	80
Poland	180	285	481
Portugal	78	148	254
Spain	87	456	859
Sweden	167	333	399
Switzerland	120	119	128
United Kingdom	960	1,832	2,287
Yugoslavia	25	40	107
Africa	96	327	1,073
Algeria	NA	35	26
Belgian Congo	13	39	117
Egypt	8	38	80
South Africa	75	215	850
Asia	2,165	2,161	4,053
India	26	104	168
Israel	0	10	72
Japan	2,139	2,030	3,695
Korea	0	2	55
Philippines	0	0	22
Taiwan	0	15	41
Oceania	668	842	1,236
Australia	503	622	911
New Zealand	165	220	325

From United Nations *Statistical Yearbook* for 1956 and 1957 and from estimates based on pyrites and sulphur shipments and superphosphate production.
[a] Includes estimated tonnages for countries not listed in the table.

XXIV. BRITISH SULPHURIC ACID PRODUCTION AND RAW MATERIALS

YEAR	ACID PRODUCTION 100% H_2SO_4 LONG TONS	PYRITES	SPENT OXIDE	SULPHUR[1]	ZINC CONCEN-TRATES	ANHY-DRITE
			PERCENTAGE MADE FROM			
1938	994,000	40.4	20.3	21.3	11.6	6.4
1939	1,068,500	38.0	19.1	24.3	12.3	6.3
1940	1,180,700	35.6	18.0	29.4	10.4	6.6
1941	1,152,700	32.2	17.1	33.8	10.1	6.7
1942	1,204,000	29.5	16.8	33.8	13.3	6.6
1943	1,181,000	26.5	21.5	32.4	13.3	6.3
1944	1,197,100	24.9	21.0	34.5	12.5	7.0
1945	1,167,500	22.5	21.2	38.0	10.4	7.8
1946	1,328,100	20.0	19.1	43.1	10.1	7.6
1947	1,332,800	18.8	18.0	46.6	10.1	6.5
1948	1,552,300	19.3	17.0	49.1	7.9	6.6
1949	1,660,267	17.9	15.5	52.7	7.8	6.1
1950	1,802,699	14.8	14.5	57.2	8.0	5.5
1951	1,606,078	16.7	19.9	49.1	8.3	6.0
1952	1,505,473	20.0	22.0	43.0	9.0	6.0
1953	1,875,177	26.8	20.9	39.1	7.7	5.5
1954	2,042,492	31.8	18.9	36.2	8.0	5.1
1955	2,097,146	28.5	16.5	35.8	7.7	11.5
1956	2,251,180	23.2	15.0	36.5	7.0	18.3
1957	2,335,891	20.8	15.2	39.7	5.8	18.5

[1] Includes H_2S and Filter Cake (sulphur). Use of Filter Cake started in 1955.

Index

Page numbers in *italics* refer to quotations or to citations in "Notes and References" or in the "Appendix."

295